Books are to be returned on or before
the last date below.

Guide to Biochemistry

D1556556

Marjalle

Guide to Biochemistry

James C. Blackstock
Department of Biological Sciences
Glasgow Polytechnic
Cowcaddens Road,
Glasgow,
UK

Butterworth-Heinemann Ltd
Linacre House, Jordan Hill, Oxford OX2 8DP

 PART OF REED INTERNATIONAL BOOKS

OXFORD   LONDON   BOSTON
MUNICH   NEW DELHI   SINGAPORE   SYDNEY
TOKYO   TORONTO   WELLINGTON

First published 1989
Reprinted 1991

British Library Cataloguing in Publication Data
Blackstock, James C.
   Guide to biochemistry
   1. Biochemistry
   I. Title
   574.19′2

ISBN 0 7506 0484 0

Library of Congress Cataloguing in Publication Data
Blackstock, James C.
   Guide to biochemistry/James C. Blackstock
   p.   cm.
   Bibliography: p
   Includes index.
   ISBN 0 7506 0484 0

Printed and bound in Great Britain by
Hartnolls Ltd, Bodmin, Cornwall

Preface

Biochemistry has achieved the status of being considered as an essential subject for students participating in a wide variety of biological science courses. Ongoing research activities continue to generate a wealth of information which should develop our understanding of the chemical systems of living organisms. The vast amount of accessible information however presents particular difficulties for new entrants into the discipline. Although excellent textbooks are available, the presentation of a rapidly expanding subject has resulted in extensive documentations of material considered to be elementary. These treatises represent daunting challenges to the uninitiated who have no longer a simple task in abstracting accepted fundamental knowledge from detailed treatments. This *Guide to Biochemistry* seeks to present students with a concise account of the essentials of the subject. In the consideration of numerous complexities, I have attempted to encourage the understanding of the principles without deceiving the reader as to the inherent uncertainties.

It is essential for students to appreciate the broad spectrum of basic concepts before embarking upon more ambitious courses of study.

Although this book is directed toward the ancillary course in biochemistry, it is nevertheless hoped that the text provides a core of biochemical knowledge which adequately underpins a range of advanced studies. Summaries, bibliographies, exercises and the historical perspective have been deliberately omitted to retain the essence of the concept of the book as a 'first contact' guide.

I am exceedingly grateful to John Blackstock of the Scottish Marine Biological Association, Ian M. Packer and John Porter both of Glasgow College of Technology for their valuable advice and critical review of the original manuscript. The responsibility for any undetected embarrassments resides, of course, entirely with myself. I apologize in advance for any remaining errors. I wish to express my gratitude to all authors and publishers who kindly granted their permission for the reproduction of copyright material. Finally, I acknowledge the moral support and assistance of my wife, Marja, to whom this book is dedicated.

Jim Blackstock
Glasgow College of Technology
January 1988

Acknowledgements

I acknowledge with pleasure the source of the following illustrations and data for tables:

Table 2.2 — After Weast, R. C. (ed.) (1983) *Handbook of Chemistry and Physics*, 64th edn, CRC, Boca Raton.

Table 4.11 — From Kimball, J. W. (1984) *Cell Biology*, 3rd edn, Addison-Wesley, Reading, p. 44, by kind permission of Author and Publisher.

Figure 4.13a — From Prockop, D. J., Kivirikko, K. I., Tuderman, L. and Guzman, N. A. (1979) The biosynthesis of collagen and its disorders. *New England Journal of Medicine* **301**, 16, reprinted by kind permission of Authors and The New England Journal of Medicine.

Figure 4.14 — From Dickerson, R. E. (1964) in *The Proteins*, 2nd edn (ed. H. Neurath), Academic Press, New York, Vol. 2, p. 634, by kind permission of Author and Publisher.

Figure 4.17 — From Gordon-Smith, E. C. (1983) Biochemical aspects of haematology, in *Biochemical Aspects of Human Disease* (eds R. S. Elkeles and A. S. Tavill), Blackwell, Oxford, p. 409, by kind permission of Author and Publisher.

Table 4.2 — After Kyte, J. and Doolittle, R. F. (1982) *Journal of Molecular Biology*, **157**, 105–132.

Tables 4.4, 5.2, 5.3, 16.2 — After International Union of Biochemistry (1984) *Enzyme Nomenclature*, Academic Press, London.

Figure 7.6 — From Freifelder, D. (1985) *Essentials of Molecular Biology*, Jones and Bartlett, Boston, p. 41, by kind permission of Author and Publisher.

Figure 7.9 — From Lake, J. A. (1985) *Annual Reviews of Biochemistry*, **54**, 509, by kind permission of Author and Annual Reviews Inc.

Figure 7.10 — From Brimacombe, R. (1984) *Trends in Biochemical Sciences*, **9**, 274, by kind permission of Author and Elsevier Publishers.

Table 7.2	After Szekely, M. (1980) *From DNA to Protein the Transfer of Genetic Information*, Macmillan, London, p. 13.
Table 7.4	After Kozak, M. (1983) *Microbiological Reviews*, **47**, 1–45.
Figures 9.1, 9.2	From Berns, M. W. (1983) *Cells*, 2nd edn, Saunders, Philadelphia, p. 3 and p. 6, by kind permission of Author and Publisher.
Tables 13.1, 13.2	After Hafeti, Y. (1985) *Annual Reviews of Biochemistry*, **54**, 1015–1069.
Figure 14.2	From Foyer, C. (1984) *Photosynthesis*, Wiley, New York, p. 6, by kind permission of Author and Publisher.
Table 14.1	After Hoober, J. K. (1984) *Chloroplasts*, Plenum, New York, pp. 79–109.
Figure 17.1	From Freifelder, D. (1985) *Essentials of Molecular Biology*, Jones and Bartlett, Boston, p. 135, by kind permission of Author and Publisher.
Table 17.2	After Moldave, K. (1985) *Annual Reviews of Biochemistry*, **54**, 1109–1149.
Table 18.1	After Hübscher, U. (1984) *Trends in Biochemical Sciences*, **9**, 391.

Contents

CHAPTER 1

Biological molecules

1.1 Cell theory

The word cell was introduced to biology in 1665 by Robert Hooke in his collection of microscopic drawings, called *Micrographia*, which included one of a thin slice of cork. He recorded the honeycomb structure of cork and referred to the compartments as cells by analogy to the cell of a prisoner or monk. The term, however, has been retained not to describe the voids remaining after the disintegration of cell cytoplasm (observed by Hooke) but the living contents normally resident between these plant cell walls. Today, the cell may be defined as the simplest integrated unit in living systems capable of independent survival.

By the early nineteenth century, recognition was given to cells as life forms and their organization into more complex multicellular organisms. In 1839, Theodor Schwann, a zoologist, published *Mikroskopische Untersuchungen*, which also contained figures supplied by Mathias Schleiden, a botanist, to record that plants and animals are composed of similar cells. Twenty years later, Rudolf Virchow announced 'omnis cellula e cellula', i.e. all cells arise from pre-existing cells.

Despite the wide variety of cell types, most cells can be classified according to their size and complexity into one of two categories: prokaryotes or eukaryotes. These terms are derived from Greek, karyon meaning kernel as in a nut, pro- meaning before and eu- meaning well. The eukaryotes therefore contain a well-formed nucleus (Latin for nut) whereas the prokaryotes are devoid of a discrete nucleus since their genetic material is not enclosed by an intracellular membrane.

A definitive feature of prokaryotic cells is their lack of membrane-bound structures although layers of internal membranes may arise from the plasma membrane. In contrast, eukaryotic cells contain numerous membrane-bound organelles, e.g. mitochondria, chloroplasts, endoplasmic reticulum, Golgi apparatus and microbodies. Although the size of cells of both categories are variable, in general, prokaryotic cells range from 0.1 to 3 µm whereas the dimensions of most eukaryotic cells are 10 to 20 µm. Prokaryotic organisms may be subdivided into three groups: bacteria, mycoplasmas and cyanobacteria which differ morphologically.

During the 1970s, the dichotomy of cells into prokaryotic and eukaryotic began to be challenged by the discovery of a few classes of bacteria, called archaebacteria, which, although possessing the general structural features of prokaryotic cells, exhibit distinctive biochemical characteristics.

1.2 The role of carbon

There are 92 natural chemical elements of which living cells contain only approximately 27. The actual number depends on the type of cell and species of the organism. Over 99% of the mass of most cells is composed of only six elements which are called the major elements. The other constituent elements are the minor elements (Table 1.1).

Water (H_2O) accounts for about 70% of the weight of cells and provides a medium for most intracellular chemical reactions. The vast majority of other cellular molecules contain carbon. Carbon (atomic number 6, atomic weight 12) is a small atom which has four electrons in its outer electronic orbital enabling it to participate in electron-sharing with up to four other atoms. The outer electrons of carbon are arranged around the carbon nucleus as in a tetrahedron, a pyramid with triangular faces (Figure 1.1a). A bond formed by the sharing of electrons is a covalent bond (Figure 1.1b).

Carbon can share each electron with a hydrogen atom to form single bonds or it may share multiple electrons, e.g. two electrons shared with oxygen to form a double bond. It is possible for carbon to share three electrons with certain atoms, e.g. nitrogen but this is rare in biological systems. One of the most important properties of carbon is its ability to form covalent bonds with other carbon atoms to form chains or rings which are the basis of large and complex molecules (Figure 1.2).

Carbon atoms when bonded to each other by single bonds have the ability to rotate unless they are restricted by the attachment of large or

TABLE 1.1   The elements found in living cells

Major elements		Minor elements	
Element	Symbol	Element	Symbol
Carbon	C	Arsenic	As
Hydrogen	H	Boron	B
Nitrogen	N	Calcium	Ca
Oxygen	O	Chlorine	Cl
Phosphorus	P	Chromium	Cr
Sulphur	S	Cobalt	Co
		Copper	Cu
		Fluorine	F
		Iodine	I
		Iron	Fe
		Magnesium	Mg
		Manganese	Mn
		Molybdenum	Mo
		Nickel	Ni
		Potassium	K
		Selenium	Se
		Silicon	Si
		Sodium	Na
		Tin	Sn
		Vanadium	V
		Zinc	Zn

TABLE 1.2   Some biologically important functional groups

Structure	Functional group
$R — CH_3$	Methyl
(benzene ring structure) $R — C$	Phenyl
$R — OH$	Hydroxyl (alcohol)
(benzene ring structure) $R — C \cdots C — OH$	Hydroxyl (phenol)
$R — C(=O) — H$	Aldehyde
$R — C(=O) — OH$	Carboxyl
$R — C(=O) — R$	Carbonyl (keto)
$R — C(=O) — O — R$	Ester
$R — O — R$	Ether
$R — O — P(=O)(OH) — OH$	Phospho
$R — NH_2$	Amino
$R — C(=O) — NH_2$	Amido
$R — NH — C(=NH) — NH_2$	Guanido
$R — S(=O)(=O) — OH$	Sulpho
$R — SH$	Thiol (sulphydryl)

R = A hydrocarbon chain

FIGURE 1.1   The electrons of carbon and covalent bonding. (a) The tetrahedral arrangement in carbon: ●, outer electron; - - - -, outline of tetrahedron; ——, distance from nucleus to electron, 0.154 nm; ⌒, angle between two electrons, 109.5°. (b) Covalent bonding between carbon, hydrogen, nitrogen and oxygen

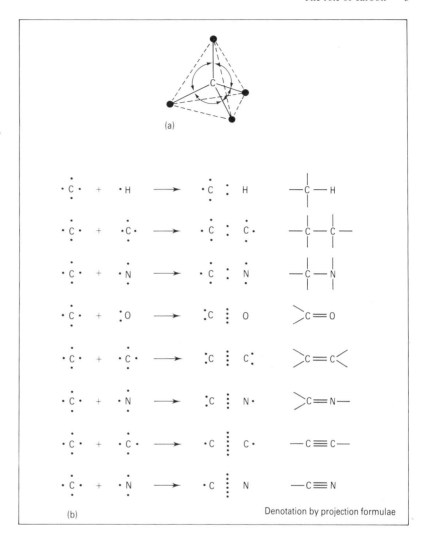

charged groups. Rotation enables an organic molecule to assume different shapes called conformations. Carbon–carbon double bonds are shorter than single bonds, limit rotation and make large organic molecules more rigid. Double bonding also causes the angle between any two electrons to change affecting the conformation of the molecule. This has a major impact on the biological activity of the molecule since its activity often involves a shape-dependent interaction with another molecule. The chains and rings may have bonding arrangements in which single and double bonds alternate giving rise to a conjugated bond system. In this system, the bonding electrons move within the molecule increasing the stability of the structure. This phenomenon is called resonance stabili-

zation and the actual structure is constantly shifting between the two representations shown in Figure 1.2.

Functional biological molecules are derived from the ability of carbon to bond covalently to nitrogen, hydrogen, oxygen and sulphur. For convenience, most molecules may be considered initially as derivatives of long, branched or unbranched chains or rings of carbon atoms. Hydrogen atoms which are bonded to these carbon atoms may be replaced by N, O and S atoms to constitute functional groups (Table 1.2). This results in the great chemical variation found in biological molecules. Functional groups can alter the electron distribution and bond angles, and contribute considerably to chemical reactivity. Biological molecules often

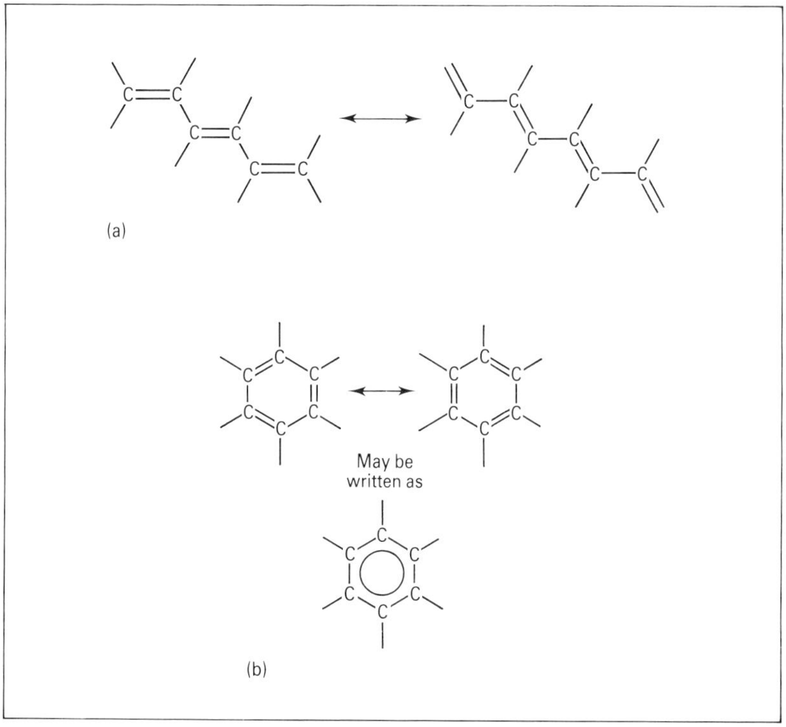

FIGURE 1.2 Resonance stabilization of conjugated bond systems. (a) Chains; (b) rings

contain more than one functional group, frequently of different kinds. Such molecules are said to be polyfunctional with each type of group displaying its own chemical characteristics and contributing to the overall chemical properties of the molecule. For example, amino acids contain at least one amino group and one carboxyl group which determine a number of the chemical properties of the amino acid.

1.3 Stereochemistry

The bonding of four different groups to a carbon atom results in two possible tetrahedral structures (Figure 1.3a). These are best viewed using chemical models. Since the molecules have identical composition but different structures, they are called isomers. Isomers which differ in the spatial arrangement of the atoms in the molecules are called stereoisomers. Neither of the structures have a plane or centre of symmetry and the term, asymmetric, was applied. This term has been superseded by chirality, indicating that the stereoisomers can be considered as right or left handed. Consider your two hands. Your hands cannot be exactly superimposed on each other or on their mirror images, e.g. your thumbs will be on opposite sides. A molecule that cannot be superimposed on its mirror image is called a chiral molecule (Figure 1.3b). When a carbon atom has up to three different groups attached to it, the spatial arrangement permits the molecular structures to be superimposed on its mirror image and the molecule is said to be achiral (Figure 1.3c).

With chiral molecules, if the reflection of one of them in a mirror was viewed, the reflection would show the other stereoisomer. These stereoisomers are called mirror images or enantiomers. Enantiomers are optically active; one rotates the plane of polarized light to the right (clockwise) and is called the dextrorotatory stereoisomer, whilst the other rotates the plane of polarized light to the left (anticlockwise) to the same extent and is called the laevorotatory stereoisomer. A mixture of each

FIGURE 1.3 Stereochemistry. (a) The tetrahedral structures formed by the bonding of four different groups to carbon. (b) A chiral molecule. (c) An achiral molecule

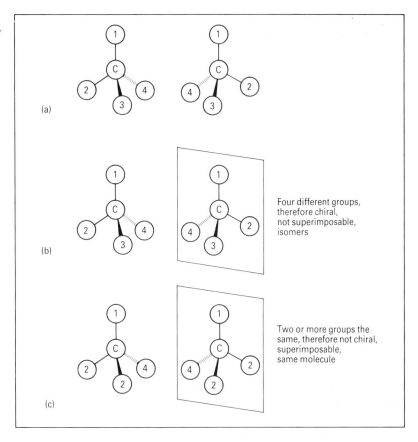

(a)

(b)   Four different groups, therefore chiral, not superimposable, isomers

(c)   Two or more groups the same, therefore not chiral, superimposable, same molecule

enantiomer in equal proportions is optically inactive or racemic. The positions of atoms and groups around a chiral carbon atom are not however related to the direction of the rotation of the plane of polarized light in a simple manner. The direction can change by varying the wavelength of the light. Until the 1940s when specialized techniques based on X-ray diffraction studies were introduced, there was no means of accurately relating structure to optical activity. Nevertheless, a German chemist, Emil Fischer, in 1891, arbitrarily and correctly assigned a molecular structure to the dextrorotatory form of glyceraldehyde and called it D-glyceraldehyde. The laevorotatory isomer was called L-glyceraldehyde (Figure 1.4). Today, glyceraldehyde remains the basis of the stereochemical configuration of biological molecules (Sections 3.2 and 4.1). Stereoisomers of all chiral compounds have structural configurations related to one form of glyceraldehyde and are designated D or L irrespective of their optical activity which is denoted by (+) for dextrorotatory and (−) for laevorotatory.

Some molecules with two or more chiral centres can be assigned to either the D series or L series depending on the manner of their consideration. Because of this ambiguity, and other reasons, an alternative system was invented called the *R, S* system (from the Latin words rectus (*R*) meaning right and sinister (*S*) meaning left. Among biochemists, this system has still to gain universal utilization.

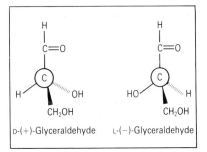

D-(+)-Glyceraldehyde   L-(−)-Glyceraldehyde

FIGURE 1.4 The stereochemistry of glyceraldehyde

Chirality is of biological importance since many biomolecules contain chiral centres. Nature appears selective in that virtually all proteins and polysaccharides of higher organisms are composed of L-amino acids and D-monosaccharides respectively (Section 1.4). This selectivity is due to the additional stability these configurations confer on the polymeric molecules.

1.4 The nature of macromolecules

Large numbers of small molecules may interact chemically to form macromolecules (derived from the Greek makros meaning long) which in turn constitute larger structures. The sizes of molecules are compared by the consideration of their molecular weight or mass. The unit of mass employed is the dalton (Da) or kilodalton (1000 Da, kDa) where one dalton equals the weight of one hydrogen atom, i.e. 1.66×10^{-24} g. There are four major classes of biological macromolecules: the polysaccharides, proteins, nucleic acids and lipids. The nucleic acids are the largest macromolecules with molecular masses extending to the billion dalton range (Table 7.2) with those of polysaccharides and proteins reaching into the million range. However, lipid molecules are very much smaller and range in their molecular masses from about 300 to 1500 daltons. However, large numbers of certain lipid molecules frequently associate to form very large structures such as the basic structure of cell membranes and so these lipids are considered to be a class of macromolecules. Macromolecules, other than lipids, are constructed by the chemical linkage of small building-block molecules to form chains. Individual building blocks are called monomers and the linkage, unique to each type of macromolecule, is formed by a condensation reaction, an energy-requiring process (Figure 1.5).

Table 1.3 highlights the salient features of macromolecule construction. Polymeric carbohydrates are composed of monosaccharides linked by glycosidic bonds to form multiple units which, if relatively small, are called oligosaccharides, and, if larger, are called polysaccharides. Oligosaccharides may be described as disaccharide, trisaccharide, tetrasaccharide etc. according to their number of monomeric units. Similar nomenclature is employed for proteins and nucleic acids. The numbers of different monomeric units found in their respective macromolecules is low and variable. For example, there are over 300 amino acids known to man but only 20 plus a few of their derivatives are found in proteins. Also, many proteins exist which lack some of the 20 amino acids.

The precise shape of the polymeric structure is conferred by the nature of the covalent bond and additional bonds such as hydrogen bonds (Section 2.2). Additional bonding may occur between certain atoms or functional groups of the same polymeric chain called intramolecular bonds or

FIGURE 1.5   Construction of macromolecules from building-block molecules

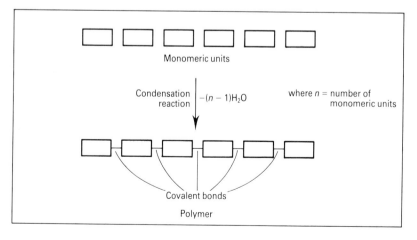

Monomeric units

Condensation reaction $-(n-1)H_2O$ where n = number of monomeric units

Covalent bonds

Polymer

Feature	Carbohydrate	Protein	Nucleic acids
Monomeric units	Monosaccharides	Amino acids	Nucleotides
Covalent bond formed by condensation reaction	Glycosidic	Peptide	Phosphodiester
Number of major monomeric units	6	20	8
Nomenclature of multiple units			
2–10 units	Oligosaccharide	Oligopeptide	Oligonucleotide
>10 units	Polysaccharide	Polypeptide	Polynucleotide
Occurrence of hydrogen bonds	Intra- and inter-molecular	Intra- and inter-molecular	Intra- and inter-molecular
Hydrolytic enzyme	Glycosidases	Peptidases	Nucleases

TABLE 1.3   Comparison of classes of macromolecules

between adjacent chains called intermolecular bonds. The polymeric structure can be degraded back to its monomeric units by hydrolysis, the addition of elements of water to the groups which are involved in the covalent linkages. In biological systems, this is achieved by the action of enzymes.

A more detailed discussion of these compounds is available in Chapter 3 (carbohydrates), Chapter 4 (amino acids and proteins), Chapter 7 (nucleic acids) and Chapter 8 (lipids).

1.5 Hybrid molecules

The classes of biological macromolecules are not mutually exclusive and may interact to produce hybrid or conjugate molecules (Table 1.4). Proteoglycans are complex structures which are primarily carbohydrate in nature but contain protein linked to the linear carbohydrate by both covalent and non-covalent bonding. Glycoproteins contain a much lower percentage of carbohydrate which is branched and linked to the polypeptide chain by covalent bonds only. Certain amino acids play important roles in these covalent linkages; serine, threonine and hydroxylysine provide hydroxyl groups for *O*-glycosidic linkages whilst asparagine provides amino groups for *N*-glycosidic linkages (Figure 1.6). Proteins which function either on the surface of the cell membrane or extracellularly tend to be glycosylated whereas intracellular proteins tend to be devoid of carbohydrate. Carbohydrates may also interact with lipids to form glycolipids which are also constituents of cell membranes.

Some lipids including phospholipids, triacylglycerols and cholesterol may associate with proteins to form lipoproteins. These lipoproteins serve as a convenient form of lipid transport in the blood circulation because of the solubility characteristics of lipids (Section 8.1).

Nucleic acids in all cells are found complexed with proteins to form nucleoproteins. The ribosome, the protein-manufacturing organelle, can be considered as a ribonucleoprotein complex in which ribosomal RNA interacts with more than 50 different proteins to form a complex responsible

TABLE 1.4   Composition of hybrid molecules

Hybrid molecule	Major component	Minor component
Proteoglycan	Carbohydrate	Protein
Glycoprotein	Protein	Carbohydrate
Glycolipid	Lipid	Carbohydrate
Lipoprotein	Protein	Lipid
Nucleoprotein	Protein	Nucleic acid

FIGURE 1.6   Some protein–carbohydrate linkages in glycoproteins. (a) *O*-Glycosidic linkage; (b) *N*-glycosidic linkage

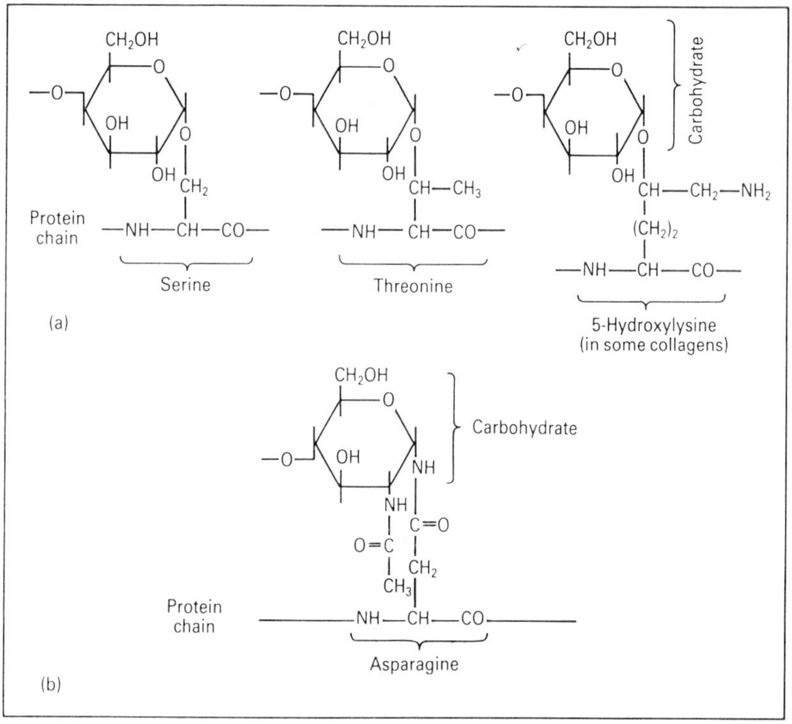

for the architecture of the ribosome (Section 7.4). Infective structures called viruses are nucleoprotein assemblies composed of genetic material in the form of either DNA or RNA enclosed in a protective sheath of protein which, in turn, may be enveloped by a layer of lipoprotein.

1.6 The functions of macromolecules

The functions of the macromolecules are listed in Table 1.5 and brief descriptions follow. Carbohydrates are the major source of energy in most cells. In addition, they have important structural functions, which include protection of cells, e.g. the polysaccharide capsule of some bacteria. The carbohydrate moieties of complex molecules on the surface of cells have an important role in confer-

TABLE 1.5   Functions of macromolecules

Carbohydrates	Proteins	Nucleic acids	Lipids
Energy-yielding fuel	Enzymes	Genetic material	Structural components
Structural	Structural	Transmission of genetic	of membranes
Protection	Transport	information	Energy-yielding fuel
Components of	Hormones	Protein synthesis	Steroid hormones
proteoglycans,	Gene regulation	Components of	Insulation
glycoproteins and	Protection	cell organelles	Protection
glycolipids	Toxins		Vitamins
Adherence			
Turnover of glycoproteins			

ring specificity to the processes of binding biologically active agents to the cell, e.g. the binding of protein hormones to receptors. Cell surface saccharides are also involved in the adherence of viruses or bacteria such as *Escherichia coli* to tissue cells during an early stage of infection by a microorganism.

Proteins may have a catalytic function in which case the protein is called an enzyme, e.g. hexokinase catalyses the phosphorylation of (addition of a phosphate group to) glucose. Some proteins have a structural function, e.g. the proteins which form the microtubules (Section 9.8) contribute to the maintenance of the shape of the cell. Transport proteins carry specific molecules or ions from one organ to another, e.g. haemoglobin (Section 4.7) carries oxygen from the lungs to the peripheral tissues where intracellularly it is employed in oxidative processes. Other transport proteins may function in the transport of substances across cell membranes. Hormones are substances which act as chemical messengers between cells in different parts of the body with the result that the activity of the recipient cell is in some way modified. Some hormones are lipid in nature, whilst others are proteins. Repressor proteins regulate the expression of genes contained within the chromosomes (Section 17.8). Some proteins, e.g. immunoglobulins (Section 4.7), have the role of affording protection to higher animals against invading bacteria or viruses and foreign proteins. Some plants, animals and bacteria defend themselves against other species by the production of proteinaceous toxic substances.

The important cellular functions of nucleic acids can be summarized by reference to the central dogma of molecular biology (Figure 1.7). Nucleic acids exist as two different types: deoxyribonucleic acid (DNA) and ribonucleic acid (RNA) of which there are three main forms. In all living organisms, DNA is the reservoir of genetic information. DNA therefore contains the instructions for all chemical processes within the organism. The information is held in the sequence of nucleotides contained within its structure in the same way as the sequence of the letters in a written word imparts certain information to the reader. DNA is the only biological molecule capable of direct self-replication so that, during the process of cell division, each daughter cell will receive deoxyribonucleotide sequences containing identical information.

The manifestation of this information is the proteins manufactured by the cell. In prokaryotic cells, the information for protein synthesis must be transported from the DNA to the ribosomes. This is the function of messenger RNA (mRNA) whose synthesis is called transcription. The ribonucleotide sequence of the mRNA is complementary to the deoxyribonucleotide sequence of the DNA and is translated into the amino acid sequence of the protein, a process involving the ribosomes. Translation involves numerous molecules of transfer RNA (tRNA) which deliver and insert the amino acids according to the instructions into growing polypeptide chains. Ribosomal RNAs also play an important role in protein synthesis (Section 17.6). In eukaryotic cells, the mRNA conveys the

FIGURE 1.7   The central dogma of molecular biology in eukaryotic and prokaryotic cells

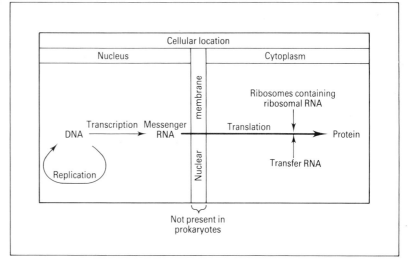

instructions from the nucleus to the ribosomes through the nuclear membrane. The flow of genetic information in cells is therefore DNA→RNA→ protein.

Lipids are essentially non-polar organic molecules which are grouped together because of solubility characteristics rather than structural similarities. Phospholipids, sphingolipids and steroids are major constituents of membranes. Fatty acids and their storage form, triacylglycerols, function as metabolic energy sources. In some animals, e.g. seal and walrus, triacylglycerols stored beneath the skin serve as an insulation barrier against subzero temperatures. Some steroids are hormones which regulate aspects of the development of certain cells. Other lipids which have a regulatory function are prostaglandins, thromboxanes and leukotrienes. Bile salts are steroids which emulsify dietary lipids to aid their absorption from the intestine. Waxes serve as protective coatings on feathers, fur, skin, leaves and fruit. Some vitamins are lipids. A vitamin is any organic compound required in minute quantities for normal growth and the maintenance of the life of animals and man who cannot synthesize these compounds. Some are required for the normal functioning of the mechanisms by which energy is produced.

1.7 Other functions of monomeric units

In addition to their important roles as the building blocks of macromolecules, the monomers perform other important functions. Certain coenzymes, e.g. NAD^+, FAD, coenzyme A (Section 5.2), contain nucleotide structures. The chemical form in which energy is carried and from which it is released in the cell is ATP, a nucleotide. Some nucleotides are involved in carbohydrate biosynthesis as glycosyl carriers, e.g. UDP-glucose in glycogen biosynthesis. Glucose and fatty acids serve as major sources of energy in many cells. Individual amino acids may perform different biological roles, e.g. glutamate serves as a transmitter of intercellular messages in the nervous tissue of the human brain.

Biological activity is not confined to monomeric units or large polymeric chains. Examples of biologically active oligopeptides and polypeptides may be found with any number of amino acid residues. Glutathione, a tripeptide, functions in the maintenance of membrane integrity. Glucagon, a single 29-amino acid polypeptide chain, acts to increase blood sugar levels.

Suggested further reading

Molecules of Life – Readings from Scientific American, Freeman, New York, 1986

DAWBER, J. G. and MOORE, A. T. (1980) *Chemistry for the Life Sciences*, 2nd edn, Macmillan, London

FRUTON, J. S. (1972) *Molecules and Life: Historical Essays on the Interplay of Chemistry and Biology*, Wiley, New York

CHAPTER 2

The physical chemistry of aqueous systems

2.1 Ionization and macromolecules

Water is a vital substance. A 70 kg man contains approximately 45 dm³ (litres) of water and his death will ensue when about 20% of the body water is lost. Varying quantities of water are stored in different body tissues where it is not slopping about as in a bucket but is compartmentalized by cell membranes so that it is a major constituent of the cytosol (Section 9.1). Water comes into contact with and bonds to cellular components, e.g. proteins, nucleic acids and lipids, and in this way, cellular water can and does affect the properties of biological compounds.

Most macromolecules exist within the cell in a charged state, i.e. they are ionized. An ion is an atom or group of atoms which has lost or gained one or more orbital electrons. The ionic state is determined by the concentration of hydrogen ions, written as [H^+], in the aqueous medium. Any alteration in the [H^+] of this environment may affect the state of ionization of these molecules and thus result in a change in their structural shape which may lead to a modification in their biological activity, e.g. effect of [H^+] on enzymes (Section 6.1).

2.2 Hydrogen bonding in water

The physical properties of water are markedly different from those of other commonly used solvents. Water has a higher melting point, boiling point, heat of vaporization (the amount of heat energy required to change 1 g of water from its liquid state into the gaseous state, expressed in $J\,g^{-1}$) and dielectric constant (the capacity to store

electrical potential energy in an electric field). These higher values are due to the structure of water (Figure 2.1). Each O–H bond is formed by a sharing of electrons and is therefore a covalent bond. However, the more electropositive oxygen nucleus attracts the electrons more strongly than the hydrogen atom which results in a slight

FIGURE 2.1   The ionization of water

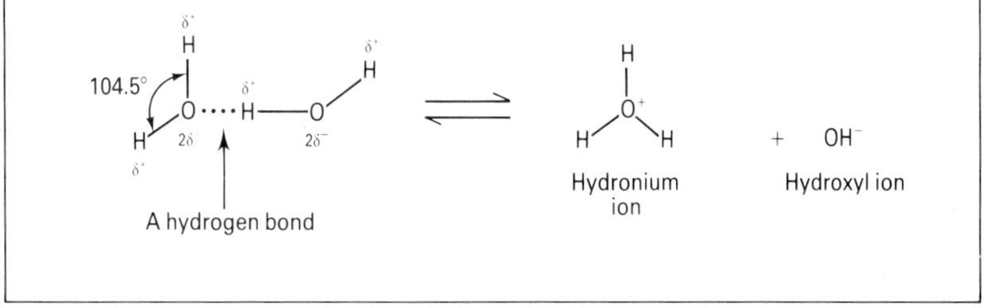

A hydrogen bond

Hydronium ion

Hydroxyl ion

negative charge (δ^-) in the region of the oxygen atom and a slight positive charge (δ^+) in the region of the hydrogen atom. This means that the water molecule, although it has no net charge, has two regions of partial positivity and one region of partial negativity which results in the molecule being an electric dipole, i.e. polar.

When two molecules of water are in close proximity, electrostatic attraction occurs between the partial negative charge on the oxygen atom of one water molecule and a partial positive charge on a hydrogen atom of its neighbour. This is accompanied by a redistribution of the electronic charges in both water molecules which enhances the attrac-

tion. This form of electrostatic attraction, called a hydrogen bond, is not unique to water and has an important role in determining the structures of macromolecules (Section 1.4). The arrangement of the electrons around the oxygen atom potentially allows the binding of four adjacent water molecules to any water molecule.

In liquid water, not all water molecules are fully hydrogen bonded; an average of 3.4 hydrogen bonds per molecule has been estimated. These bonds are constantly being formed and broken. The interlinking of the water molecules by hydrogen bonds is responsible for the internal cohesion of water resulting in its physical properties.

2.3 Ionization of water

The electron of the hydrogen atom is attracted to the nucleus of the oxygen atom and so there is a tendency for the hydrogen nucleus (a proton) to dissociate from this water molecule. This proton will be attracted to the oxygen of another water molecule to which it is hydrogen bonded forming a hydronium ion (H_3O^+) and a hydroxyl ion (Figure 2.1). The hydronium ion is usually considered to be a hydrated proton or hydrogen ion and is therefore designated by H^+.

Any reversible dissociation can be expressed in accordance with the Law of Mass Action which states 'at equilibrium, the mathematical product of the concentrations of the substances formed by a chemical reaction divided by the product of the concentrations of the reactants in that reaction is equal to a constant'. This constant is called the temperature-dependent equilibrium constant, K_{eq}. The equilibrium of a system is achieved when the rate of the reverse reaction equals the rate of the forward reaction. The dissociation of water may be written as:

$$H_2O \rightleftharpoons H^+ + OH^-$$

and $K_{eq} = \dfrac{[H^+][OH^-]}{[H_2O]}$

where [ ] denotes concentration. An accurate experimental value for this K_{eq} has been obtained at 25°C (298 K) by electrical conductivity measurements:

$$K_{eq} = 1.8 \times 10^{-16} \, mol \, dm^{-3}$$

Therefore, in pure water very little dissociation occurs so that the number of undissociated water molecules is very large and their concentration is essentially unchanged.

The above equation can also be written as:

$$K_{eq}[H_2O] = [H^+][OH^-]$$

in which $K_{eq}[H_2O]$ is a new constant, called K_w, the ionic product of water since it is equal to the mathematical product of the concentrations of the ions formed by the dissociation of water. The value of K_w is $1 \times 10^{-14} \, mol \, dm^{-3}$ from which the concentration of H^+ ions in pure water at 25°C may be calculated as $1.0 \times 10^{-7} \, mol \, dm^{-3}$.

2.4 pH scale

Hydrogen ion concentration values are complex figures to write and use in calculations since they contain negative powers of 10. In 1909, Sørensen introduced the term pH. pH expresses $[H^+]$ of an aqueous solution as a logarithmic function. The pH of a solution equals the negative of the logarithm to the base$_{10}$ of its hydrogen ion concentration, i.e. $pH = -\log_{10}[H^+]$. pH offers a convenient mechanism of expressing a wide range of $[H^+]$ in small positive numbers (Section 2.11). The letter, p, is used to denote the negative logarithm to the base$_{10}$ of.

The pH scale from 0 to 14 covers all the hydrogen ion concentrations (Table 2.1) found in dilute aqueous solutions and biological systems. Pure water has a pH of 7 which is considered to be neutrality. When pH < 7, the solution is acidic and when pH > 7, the solution is basic or alkaline. Because of the logarithmic function a change of one pH unit represents a tenfold difference in hydrogen ion concentration. Measurements of pH can be easily performed using a pH-meter.

TABLE 2.1   The pH scale

$[H^+]$ (mol dm^{-3})	pH	$[OH^-]$ (mol dm^{-3})	pOH	Acidity or basicity
$1.0\ (10^0)$	0	10^{-14}	14	
$0.1\ (10^{-1})$	1	10^{-13}	13	
10^{-4}	4	10^{-10}	10	Increasing acidity
10^{-7}	7	10^{-7}	7	Neutral
10^{-10}	10	10^{-4}	4	Increasing basicity
10^{-13}	13	10^{-1}	1	
10^{-14}	14	10^0	0	

2.5 Theories of acids and bases

There are three theories, named after their proposers, employed to explain the behaviour of the substances called acids or bases.

1. Arrhenius acids and bases in which an acid may be defined as a substance which dissociates in water to yield H^+ ions whilst a base may be defined by the potential to dissociate in water yielding OH^- ions.
2. Brönsted and Lowry acids and bases in which an acid is defined as any substance that can donate a proton (H^+), i.e. a proton donor. Conversely, a base is defined as any substance that can accept a proton, i.e. a proton acceptor.
3. Lewis acids and bases in which a Lewis acid is defined as any substance which acts as an electron pair acceptor. Conversely, a Lewis base is any substance which acts as an electron pair donor.

The Lewis definitions are consistent with the Brönsted and Lowry view because a proton can be considered to be an electron pair acceptor and a substance which accepts a proton as an electron pair donor, e.g.

$$H^+ + \underset{\text{ammonia}}{\underset{\overset{|}{H}}{H-\ddot{N}-H}} \longrightarrow \underset{\text{ammonium ion}}{\underset{\overset{|}{H}}{\overset{\overset{H}{|}+}{H-N-H}}}$$

acid

Because of the aqueous environment of most biochemical reactions, the influence of ionization on the activity of biological compounds and the establishment of the pH scale, it is usual for the biochemist to consider acid and base behaviour in terms of the Brönsted and Lowry concept. According to the Brönsted–Lowry theory, an acid, HA, dissociates:

$$HA \rightleftharpoons H^+ + A^-$$

The dissociation is reversible and so A^- may interact with H^+ to re-form the acid. A^- is therefore acting as a proton acceptor and is, by definition, a base. The relationship of A^- to HA is denoted by the following terminology: HA and A^- are a conjugate acid–base pair, HA is the parent acid and A^- is the conjugate base of that acid.

2.6 The relative strengths of acids and bases

Acids and bases can be identified as monoprotic or polyprotic depending upon the numbers of dissociable protons the acid contains or the number of protons with which the base can combine. Irrespective of whether a substance is monoprotic or polyprotic, the strength of an acid or base refers to the efficiency with which the substance demonstrates the properties of an acid or a base. For an acid, this means the ease with which it donates protons; for a base, this means the ease with which it accepts protons. These properties of a substance will be affected by its environment; it is easier for an acid to donate protons in a proton-accepting medium. In biological systems, non-membranous environments are essentially aqueous.

With respect to strength, there are two general classes, strong and weak. Strong acids and bases are ones which are almost completely dissociated in dilute aqueous media. Weak acids and bases are ones which are only partially dissociated in dilute aqueous media. The strength of an acid or a base is most frequently determined by the dissociation constant, K (Figure 2.2). If B is a strong base, it will have a high affinity for H^+ and hence BH^+ is a weak acid. Conversely, if B is a weak base, it will have a low affinity for H^+ and so BH^+ is a strong conjugate acid. For this reason, the strength of a base is frequently expressed in terms of the acid dissociation constant of its conjugate acid, BH^+, i.e.

$$K_a = \frac{[B][H^+]}{[BH^+]}$$

Therefore the strength of an acid is given by K_a and the strength of a base by K_b or K_a of its conjugate acid.

For weak acids and bases, there is a gradation of strength, i.e. some are weaker than others as shown by K_a (or pK_a) or K_b (or pK_b) values in Table 2.2. Biochemical interest in these substances lies in their potential impact on biomolecules.

FIGURE 2.2 Dissociation constants. (a) Acid dissociation constant; (b) base dissociation constant

(a) For an acid, HA:

$$HA + H_2O \rightleftharpoons H^+ + A^-$$

$$\therefore K_{eq} = \frac{[H^+][A^-]}{[HA][H_2O]}$$

$$\therefore K_{eq}[H_2O] = \frac{[H^+][A^-]}{[HA]}$$

$K_{eq}[H_2O]$ equals a new constant called K_a, the acid dissociation constant,

$$\therefore K_a = \frac{[H^+][A^-]}{[HA]}$$

(b) For a base, B:

$$B + H_2O \rightleftharpoons BH^+ + OH^-$$

$$\therefore K_{eq} = \frac{[BH^+][OH^-]}{[B][H_2O]}$$

$$\therefore K_{eq}[H_2O] = \frac{[BH^+][OH^-]}{[B]}$$

$K_{eq}[H_2O]$ equals a new constant called K_b, the base dissociation constant,

$$\therefore K_b = \frac{[BH^+][OH^-]}{[B]}$$

TABLE 2.2 The strengths of some monoprotic weak acids and bases

Substance	Formula	K_a	pk_a	K_b	pK_b	Acidity or basicity
Formic acid	HCOOH	1.77×10^{-4}	3.75	—	—	↑
Acetic acid	CH_3COOH	1.76×10^{-5}	4.75	—	—	Increasing
Trimethylacetic						acidity
acid	$(CH_3)_3CCOOH$	9.4×10^{-6}	5.03	—	—	⋮
Ammonia	NH_3	5.62×10^{-10}	9.25	1.77×10^{-5}	4.75	Increasing
Trimethylamine	$(CH_3)_3N$	1.55×10^{-10}	9.81	8.32×10^{-5}	4.19	basicity
Dimethylamine	$(CH_3)_2NH$	1.85×10^{-11}	10.73	5.25×10^{-4}	3.28	↓

These data were obtained at 298 K except for formic acid at 293 K and trimethyl-acetic acid at 291 K.

2.7 The interaction of aqueous solutions of monoprotic acids and bases

The interaction of acids and bases according to Brönsted and Lowry involves the transfer of a proton from an acid to a base:

$$HA + B \rightleftharpoons BH^+ + A^-$$

Acid   Base   Conjugate acid   Conjugate base

The events occurring during this interaction can be followed on a plot of the change in pH during the dropwise addition of one component to a fixed volume of the other component. The plot is called a titration curve. The events which occur during the interaction depend upon the nature of the components, i.e. whether both the acid and base are strong or one component is strong and the other weak, or both weak.

Many biological compounds behave as weak acids, e.g. carboxylic groups, or weak bases, e.g. amino groups, and so the appreciation of their interactions is of more concern. During the titration of a weak acid, HA, with a strong base (OH$^-$), the interaction can be represented as:

$$HA + OH^- \rightleftharpoons H_2O + A^-$$

Weak acid Strong base   Conjugate base

However, in this case, the product of the interaction is the relatively stronger conjugate base of the weak acid which can accept protons from the water and thereby effect the reverse reaction. During the initial stages of this titration, weak acid is being removed to produce its conjugate base which is actively reconstituting the weak acid and thereby depressing the dissociation of the weak acid. The effect of this process on the pH of any mixture of solutions of weak acid and its conjugate base can be calculated using the Henderson–Hasselbalch equation:

$$pH = pK_a + \log \frac{[\text{base}]}{[\text{acid}]}$$

This allows the pH to be calculated for any mixture in which both weak acid and its conjugate base are present using pK_a values. The interaction of a weak base (B) and a strong acid (HCl) can be represented as:

$$B + HCl \rightleftharpoons BH^+ + Cl^-$$

Weak base   Conjugate acid

The relatively stronger conjugate acid formed can release H$^+$ and thereby reverse the reaction. So during the initial stages of this titration, the process of removing the weak base is being hampered by the dissociation of the BH$^+$. The effect of this process on the pH of any mixture of weak base and its conjugate acid can be calculated from the Henderson–Hasselbalch equation. Examples of the titration curve obtained when a weak acid is titrated with strong base and a weak base is titrated with strong acid are given in Figure 2.3. Because of the gradation of strength found in weak acids and weak bases, Figure 2.3(a) represents the actual plot of the titration of only one weak acid (0.1 mol dm^{-3} acetic acid with 0.1 mol dm^{-3} NaOH) although the shape is characteristic of weak acid–strong base titrations in general. Similarly, Figure 2.3(b) represents the plot of one weak base (NH_3) with equimolar HCl.

The points to note from these titrations are:

1. The equivalence points differ from pH 7 due to the basicity of the conjugate base ion or the acidity of the conjugate acid ion.
2. The zones of rapid pH change are smaller than in strong acid–strong base titrations.
3. A most important feature of these titration curves is their sigmoidal shapes in their first parts. When half an equivalent quantity of titrant (strong base or acid) has been added, there is a point of inflection. Here, one half of the weak acid (or weak base) will have interacted with the strong base (or strong acid) whilst the other half has not. From the Henderson–Hasselbalch equation:

$$pH = pK_a + \log \frac{[\text{base}]}{[\text{acid}]}$$

at half-equivalence point,

$$[\text{acid}] = [\text{conjugate base}] = X$$
$$(\text{or } [\text{base}] = [\text{conjugate acid}] = X),$$

therefore

$$pH = pK_a + \log \frac{X}{X} = pK_a + \log 1 = pK_a + 0 = pK_a$$

Therefore, at half-equivalence point, $pH = pK_a$

and hence the pK_a value of the weak acid or conjugate acid of the weak base can be obtained from the appropriate titration curve.

4. The point of inflection per titration curve centres on a region in which the addition of strong base or strong acid results in a small change in pH. A solution which resists a change in pH on the addition of strong acid or base is called a buffer solution. If acid or base is added in drops of uniform volume, the further from the half-equivalence point in the titration curve, the greater the effect of the addition, i.e. less buffering (Figure 2.3). The limits of the buffer zone correspond to weak acid–conjugate base or weak base–conjugate acid mixtures in which the [acid] is ten times that of the [base], i.e. [acid]/[base] = 10:1 or in which [base]/[acid] = 10:1.

Applying these values to the Henderson–Hasselbalch equation:

$$pH = pK_a + \log \frac{[\text{base}]}{[\text{acid}]} \qquad pH = pK_a + \log \frac{[\text{base}]}{[\text{acid}]}$$
$$= pK_a + \log \frac{1}{10} \qquad\qquad = pK_a + \log \frac{10}{1}$$
$$= pK_a - 1 \qquad\qquad\qquad = pK_a + 1$$

The buffer zone is defined by $pK_a - 1$ to $pK_a + 1$.

FIGURE 2.3 Interaction of aqueous solutions of monoprotic acids and bases. (a) Titration of a weak acid with a strong base. (b) Titration of a weak base with a strong acid

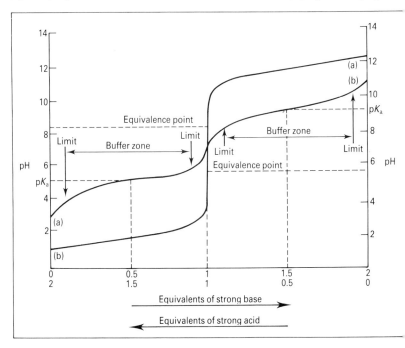

5. For other reasons of physical chemistry, the Henderson–Hasselbalch equation should not be used when [base]/[acid] is very large or very small or when the pH of the aqueous solution is below 4 or above 10.

2.8 The interaction of polyprotic weak acids and strong bases

Biological media contain many components which have more than one exchangeable proton, i.e. they are polyprotic. At physiological pH, many substances exist as ionic species, e.g. sugar derivatives, amino acids, nucleotides, triacylglycerols and phosphoacylglycerols. It is therefore important to consider the changes in polyprotic substances. Figure 2.4 shows the characteristic titration curve of a triprotic weak acid with a strong base. Again, because of the gradation of strength, the plot represents only one triprotic weak acid (0.1 mol dm^{-3} phosphoric acid) titrated with equimolar NaOH. The points to note from this titration are:

1. A number of steps are observed, the number being equal to the number of dissociable protons. Each step terminates in an equivalence point.

2. The pH at half-equivalence represents a pK_a value but since there is a half-equivalence point per step, each pK_a is identified by a subscript, e.g. pK_{a_1}, pK_{a_2} etc. pK_{a_1} represents the most acidic pK_a value, and pK_{a_2} etc. are in order of decreasing acidity.

3. The progressive dissociation of H$_3$A by titration with base is given by:

$$H_3A \underset{+H^+}{\overset{-H^+}{\rightleftharpoons}} H_2A^- \underset{+H^+}{\overset{-H^+}{\rightleftharpoons}} HA^{2-} \underset{+H^+}{\overset{-H^+}{\rightleftharpoons}} A^{3-}$$

| | Amphiprotic conjugate base | Amphiprotic conjugate base | Conjugate base |

This indicates that H$_2$A$^-$ and HA^{2-} are both the conjugate base formed by dissociation of weak acid but are also able to act as acids,

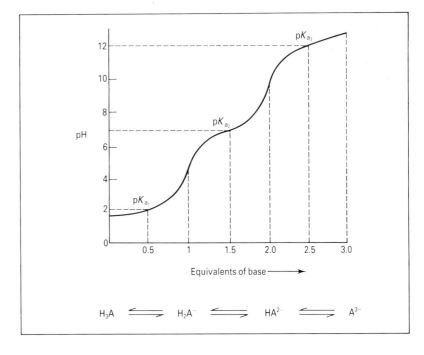

FIGURE 2.4 Titration of a polyprotic weak acid with a strong base

i.e. they display amphoteric behaviour. H_2A^- and HA^{2-} are amphiprotic conjugate bases. The interaction sequence can be reversed by the titration of A^{3-} with acid.
4. The dissociation of one acidic species is completed before any appreciable

dissociation of its amphiprotic conjugate base.
5. Each equivalence point is the mid-point between the previous and subsequent half-equivalence points.

2.9 Buffer systems

Cells and body fluids of living organisms employ buffer systems to regulate the free $[H^+]$ within the limits which allow normal function. In man, the main buffer system is the diprotic bicarbonate (HCO_3^-)–carbonic acid (H_2CO_3) system although other systems, e.g. monohydrogen phosphate (HPO_4^{2-})–dihydrogen phosphate ($H_2PO_4^-$), make important contributions to safeguard the organism from the adverse effects of acids produced during cellular metabolism.

In the laboratory, buffer systems are employed to enable:
1. the preparation of biological materials which retain their biological activity *in vitro* for further investigation;
2. the investigation of biochemical reactions which often involve proton transfer;
3. the control of pH in microbiological, cell and tissue culture media.

Tables of buffer mixtures are available.

2.10 Summary of useful equations in pH calculations

The reader is advised to refer to physical chemical textbooks for the derivation of the formulae.

1. $pH = -\log_{10}[H^+]$
2. $pOH = -\log_{10}[OH^-]$
3. $pK_w = pH + pOH = 14$
4. $pK_a = -\log_{10} K_a$
5. $pK_b = -\log_{10} K_b$
6. $pK_w = pK_a + pK_b$
7. pH of a solution of strong monoprotic acid is given by: $pH = -\log_{10}[H^+]$ where $[H^+] =$ initial concentration of the acid.
8. pH of a solution of a strong monoprotic base is given by: $pOH = -\log_{10}[OH^-]$ where $[OH^-] =$ initial concentration of the base, then $pH = 14 - pOH$.

9. pH of a solution of a weak monoprotic acid is given by: $pH = -\log_{10}[H^+]$ where $[H^+] = \alpha c$. α is the degree of dissociation, i.e. the percentage of molecules dissociated at equilibrium and c is the initial concentration of the acid.
10. pH of a solution of a very weak monoprotic acid ($K_a = n \times 10^{-5}$ or 10^{-6} or 10^{-7}) is given by: $pH = \frac{1}{2}pK_a - \frac{1}{2}\log c$ where $c =$ concentration of the acid.
11. pH of a solution of weak monoprotic base is given by: $pH = pK_w - \frac{1}{2}pK_b + \frac{1}{2}\log c$ where $pK_w = 14$.
12. The Henderson–Hasselbalch equation:
$$pH = pK_a + \log \frac{[base]}{[acid]}$$

2.11 Example calculations

No. 1

Calculate the pH of a solution in which the hydrogen ion concentration is $4.2 \times 10^{-4}\,\text{mol}\,\text{dm}^{-3}$.

$[H^+] = 4.2 \times 10^{-4}\,\text{mol}\,\text{dm}^{-3}$ and
$pH = -\log_{10}[H^+]$
$pH = -\log(4.2 \times 10^{-4})$

Take log by pocket calculator:

$pH = -(-3.38)$
$pH = \underline{3.38}$

pH is normally quoted to two decimal places and so the logarithm used is to two figures.

No. 2

Calculate the hydrogen ion concentration in a solution of pH 8.32.

$pH\ 8.32;\ pH = -\log[H^+]$
$8.32 = -\log[H^+]$
$\log[H^+] = -8.32$

Take antilog: $[H^+] = 4.79 \times 10^{-9}\,\text{mol}\,\text{dm}^{-3}$
i.e. the $[H^+]$ in a solution of
$pH\ 8.32 = \underline{4.79 \times 10^{-9}\,\text{mol}\,\text{dm}^{-3}}$

Suggested further reading

MORRIS, J. G. (1974) *A Biologist's Physical Chemistry*, 2nd edn, Arnold, London
MONTGOMERY, R. and SWENSON, C. A. (1976) *Quantitative Problems in the Biochemical Sciences*, Freeman, San Francisco

CHAPTER 3

Carbohydrates

3.1 The definition of carbohydrate

Carbohydrates are substances containing carbon, hydrogen and oxygen which conform to the empirical formula, $C_x(H_2O)_y$ where x and $y = 3$ or more. Since hydrogen and oxygen are present in the same proportions as in water, it was believed that this group of compounds could be chemically described as hydrates of carbon. With the passage of time, it became clear that this representation did not adequately fit the facts. For example, $C_3H_6O_3$ is also the formula of lactic acid which has a different chemistry to that of a carbohydrate whilst $C_5H_{10}O_4$, 2-deoxyribose, is without doubt a carbohydrate. Some carbohydrates contain the elements, nitrogen and sulphur. One of the carbon atoms forms a carbonyl (aldehyde or ketone) group whilst the other carbon atoms exhibit hydroxyl groups. Today, the term, carbohydrate is retained to describe those substances which are more accurately defined as polyhydroxyaldehydes or polyhydroxyketones with the definition extended to include their derivatives and the products of their polymerization by condensation reactions.

Carbohydrates may be divided into monosaccharides, oligosaccharides and polysaccharides (Section 1.4). Polysaccharides may be subdivided into various homopolysaccharides and heteropolysaccharides on the basis of whether their structure yields one or more type(s) of monosaccharide(s) on hydrolysis.

3.2 The monosaccharides

Monosaccharides are the simplest carbohydrates; they conform to the general chemical formula $(CH_2O)_x$ and are termed simple sugars. The most commonly occurring monosaccharides contain three to six carbon atoms in an unbranched single-bonded chain. Monosaccharides are signified by the suffix -ose. Further classification utilizes the number of carbon atoms and the functional carbonyl group. A monosaccharide containing an aldehyde group is therefore referred to as an aldose; those which contain a ketone group are ketoses. A three-carbon sugar is called a triose (an aldotriose or ketotriose). Sugars with four, five or six carbon atoms are termed tetroses, pentoses or hexoses respectively. The monosaccharides are water soluble but are insoluble in non-polar solvents.

Glyceraldehyde and glycerone are considered to be the simplest aldose and ketose respectively (Figure 3.1). From these trioses, the homologous series of the monosaccharides can be constructed. Glyceraldehyde exists in two stereoisomeric forms, D and L (Section 1.3), which serve as the precursors from which the D- and L-series of aldoses arise. Each aldose series can be constructed by the stepwise introduction of a chiral carbon (H–C–OH or HO–C–H) at position 2 in the carbon chain as demonstrable by the Kiliani–Fischer nitrile synthesis, or dismantled systematically by the Wohl degradation. Since in biological systems, the D-forms of the sugars predominate, the D-series of

FIGURE 3.1 The trioses from which the monosaccharide series can be constructed. Optical activity is indicated

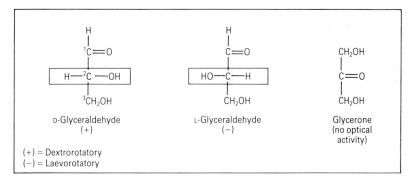

the aldoses is shown in Figure 3.2. The configuration of the penultimate carbon from the carbonyl carbon atom determines the series to which the sugar belongs.

L-Monosaccharides are the mirror image (i.e. enantiomers) of the corresponding D-sugar. The term diastereoisomer is used to refer to sugars of the same series and containing the same number of

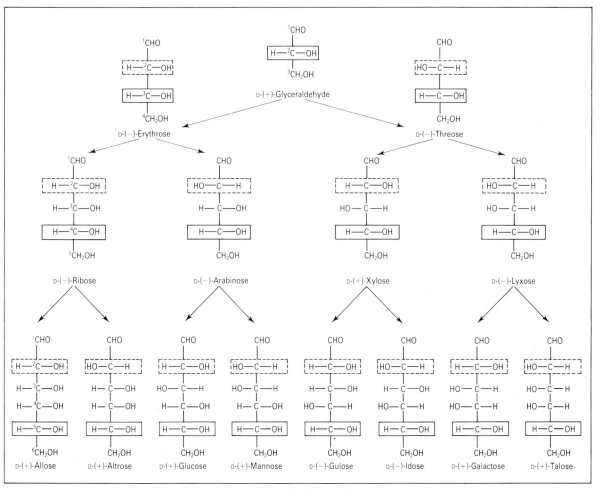

FIGURE 3.2   Relationships in the D-series of aldoses indicating optical activity

carbon atoms. Diastereoisomers that differ in the configuration of the OH group on one specific chiral carbon atom are referred to as epimers. D-Glucose is an epimer of both D-galactose (different only at C-4) and D-mannose (different only at C-2) but D-galactose and D-mannose are not epimers.

Glucose is the most abundant monosaccharide. Galactose, mannose, fructose and ribose are also of major biological importance. The syllable, -ul-, in the names of some ketoses allows distinction from the corresponding aldose, e.g. ribulose–ribose.

3.3 The ring structures of monosaccharides

The monosaccharides have been presented as open-chain compounds using the projection formulae (Figure 1.1) of Fischer. However, in solution, only the trioses and tetroses exist in appreciable quantities in this form. Pentoses and hexoses undergo cyclization, i.e. they form ring structures. The projection formulae disregard the possible rotation around carbon–carbon single bonds and their bond angles of 109.5°. Certain hydroxyl groups and the carbonyl carbon may lie close together enabling electrons of the oxygen atom of the hydroxyl group to subject the electron-deficient carbonyl group to nucleophilic attack. Nucleophilic groups or reagents seek to replenish the electronic complement of atomic orbitals. When one aldehyde molecule reacts with one alcohol molecule in the presence of acid, the product is a hemiacetal since the reaction of one aldehyde and alcohol molecule yields an acetal (Figure 3.3a). Similarly, ketones may form hemiketals and ketals. Therefore, if the carbonyl carbon atom and a hydroxyl group are positioned in the same monosaccharide molecule so as to permit their interaction to form a five- or six-membered ring, a cyclic hemiacetal or hemiketal will be produced.

The hydroxyl substituent on C-5 may attack an aldehyde group at C-1 to create a six-membered ring structure (Figure 3.3b). Depending on the orientation of the C-1 group, two hemiacetal products are possible. These products differ only in the configuration of the hydroxyl group on C-1 and so they are epimers. To signify the positional importance, they are referred to as anomers with C-1 being termed the anomeric carbon atom. When the OH group of the anomeric carbon atom of a D-monosaccharide is below the plane of the ring, the compound is termed the α-anomer. If the OH group is above the plane of the ring, the anomer is β. In the L-series, however, the OH group of the α-anomer points upwards whilst that of the β-anomer points downwards, i.e. the termi-

nology is reversed. Ring structures may similarly be formed by the interaction of the hydroxyl group at C-4 with the carbonyl carbon atom. This type of reaction produces a five-membered ring structure again based upon hemiacetal formation (Figure 3.3c).

The conformation adopted by the newly formed ring will be its most stable conformation. For six-membered rings, there are two conformations: the boat and chair forms based upon the conformations of the cyclohexane ring (Figure 3.4a). The position of the substituent groups either in axial or equatorial bonds determines the stability and form of the structure. The preferred form will be the form in which most of the bulky groups are equatorial. Large axial substituents, e.g CH_2OH, tend to reduce the stability of the ring because of steric interactions. In most sugars, e.g. glucose, the chair conformation is preferred although in some sugars the most stable form is the boat conformation. Upon examination of models, it can be discovered that glucose may exist in two chair conformations (Figure 3.4b). The most stable chair conformation is that in which most of the bulky substituents are in the equatorial position.

The stable ring systems which can be formed when monosaccharides are placed in an aqueous environment are five- or six-membered rings which contain four or five carbon atoms respectively and one oxygen atom (Figure 3.3b,c). Because of their resemblance to furan and pyran, the ring structures of the monosaccharides are named as their derivatives, e.g. α-D-glucofuranose , α-D-glucopyranose and β-D-glucopyranose. Structures are frequently represented by Haworth projection formulae (Figure 3.5). Ketoses similarly form pyranose and furanose ring structures of varying stability. Since the hemiacetal (and hemiketal) reaction is reversible, the ring structures may revert to their open-chain structure. An aqueous solution of glucose therefore contains both glucopyranose anomers

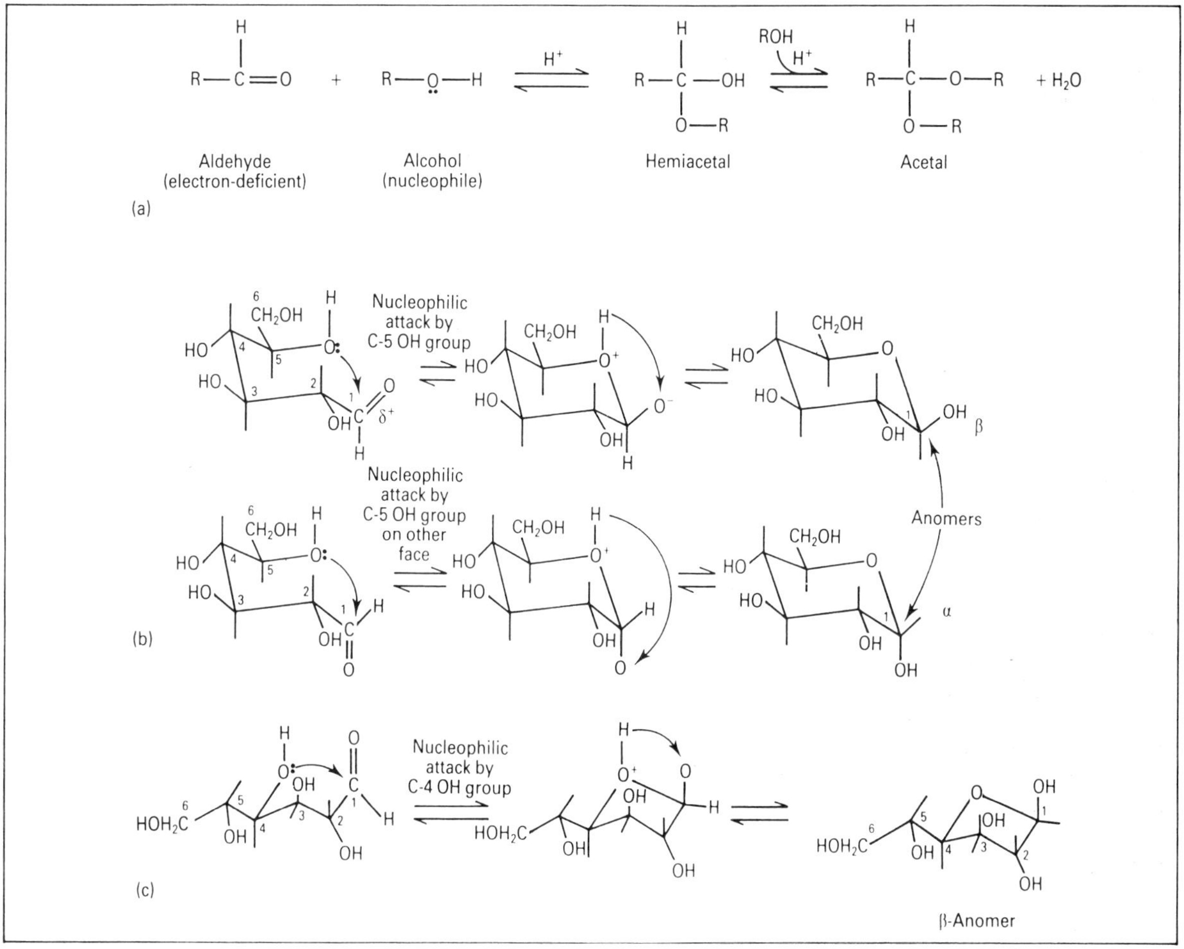

FIGURE 3.3 The ring structures of monosaccharides. (a) The formation of a hemiacetal and acetal. (b) The formation of ring structures through nucleophilic attack by the electrons of an alcoholic hydroxyl group at position C-5. (c) The formation of ring structures through nucleophilic attack by the electrons of an alcoholic hydroxyl group at position C-4

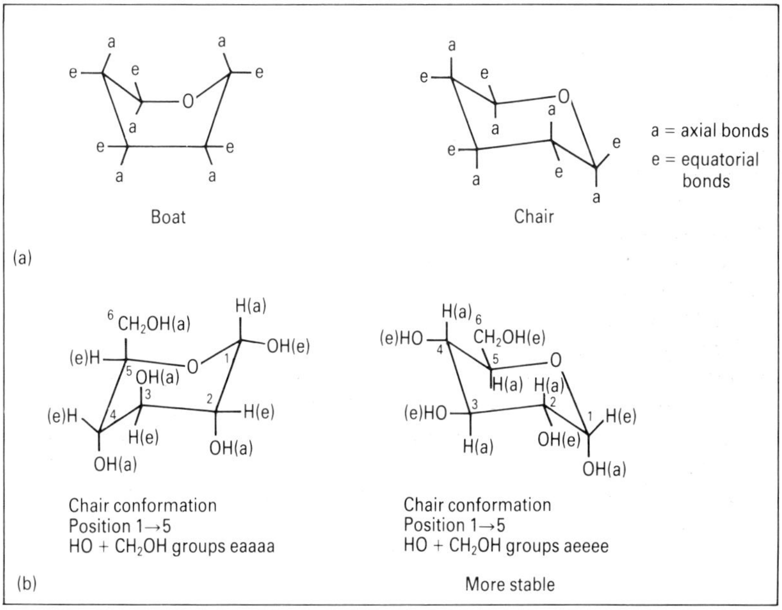

FIGURE 3.4 Conformations of ring structures. (a) Boat and chair conformation. (b) Stability of chair form of D-glucose

FIGURE 3.5 Structures of glucosamine and *N*-acetylneuraminic acid

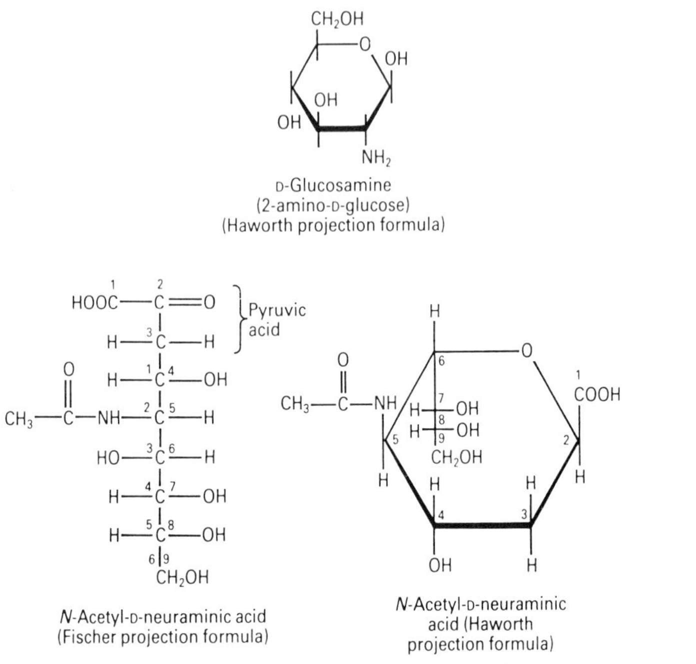

D-Glucosamine
(2-amino-D-glucose)
(Haworth projection formula)

N-Acetyl-D-neuraminic acid
(Fischer projection formula)

N-Acetyl-D-neuraminic acid (Haworth projection formula)

and both glucofuranose anomers in equilibrium with a small percentage of the open-chain form. Whilst in this form, the carbonyl oxygen can donate one or more electrons to a number of substances, thereby effecting their reduction. Sugars which can open their ring structure are therefore referred to as reducing sugars. Glucose can reduce cupric ions (Cu^{2+}) to cuprous ions (Cu^{+}) and is a reducing sugar.

Intracellular environments are essentially aqueous and so pentoses and hexoses in metabolic pathways are usually denoted by the major ring form. Also, condensation of monosaccharides into oligosaccharides and polysaccharides involves the development of chains comprising the major ring conformation of the monosaccharides.

3.4 Derivatives of monosaccharides

The monosaccharides may be oxidized to yield different sugar acids depending upon the oxidation conditions. Mild chemical oxidation converts the aldehyde group into a carboxylic acid group at C-1 of aldoses, thereby yielding aldonic acids, e.g. gluconic acid. Oxidation at C-6 yields an alduronic (uronic) acid, e.g. glucuronic acid, while oxidation at both C-1 and C-6 generates the dibasic aldaric acids, e.g. glucaric acid.

Phosphorylated monosaccharides play important roles in cellular metabolism, e.g. glucose 6-phosphate (Chapters 10 and 11) and ribulose 5-phosphate (Chapters 11 and 14). 6-Phosphogluconate, a derivative of gluconic acid, is an intermediate in the pentose phosphate pathway (Chapter 11). Phosphorylation involves the interaction of an alcoholic hydroxyl group and phosphoric acid to form an ester linkage. Substitution of monosaccharides at the anomeric carbon atom, e.g. glucose 1-phosphate, prevents reversion to an open-chain structure and so such derivatives are non-reducing.

Deoxy sugars are monosaccharides in which one (or more) hydroxyl group has been replaced by hydrogen atom(s) (Figure 7.1). The most abundant of these derivatives found in nature is 2-deoxy-D-ribose which is found in the furanose form in DNA. Other important deoxy sugars include L-rhamnose and L-fucose. L-Fucose appears in the oligosaccharide moieties of some animal and human glycoproteins and glycolipids.

The hydroxyl group on C-2 of some monosaccharides can be substituted by an amino group to produce amino sugars (Figure 3.5). Amino derivatives of hexoses, e.g. D-glucosamine or D-galactosamine, are most common. This amino group may be acetylated (or sulphonated) to form N-acetyl (or N-sulphate) derivatives, e.g. N-acetylglucosamine. These derivatives are abundant in polysaccharides and proteoglycans (Section 3.6). In addition, these amino sugars are constituents of more complex structures. N-Acetylneuraminic acid, a major component of the oligosaccharide chains of the glycoproteins and glycolipids found on the membrane surfaces of animal and human cells, may be considered as a derivative of N-acetylmannosamine in which the carbonyl carbon atom bonds to pyruvic acid (Figure 3.5). Neuraminic acid derivatives are known as sialic acids.

Glycosides are the acetal or ketal product of the reaction of the hemiacetal or hemiketal form of the monosaccharide with an alcohol (Section 3.3). The reaction involves the most reactive hydroxyl group of the monosaccharide, i.e. the one attached to the anomeric carbon atom in the formation of an ether linkage called a glycosidic bond. The non-carbohydrate moiety of a glycoside is termed the aglycone. Glycosides derived from pyranose ring structures are termed pyranosides whilst furanoses yield furanosides. The reacting alcohol forms an α-glycosidic bond with an α-pyranose or α-furanose and a β-glycosidic bond with a β-pyranose or β-furanose (Figure 3.6).

A variety of glycosides are found in nature. Some pigmentation in plant leaves is due to the presence of complex glycosides. Several glycosides serve as therapeutic agents, e.g. digitoxin which strengthens the action of cardiac muscle. Several antibiotics, e.g. streptomycin and neomycin, are glycosides.

FIGURE 3.6   Formation of glycosides

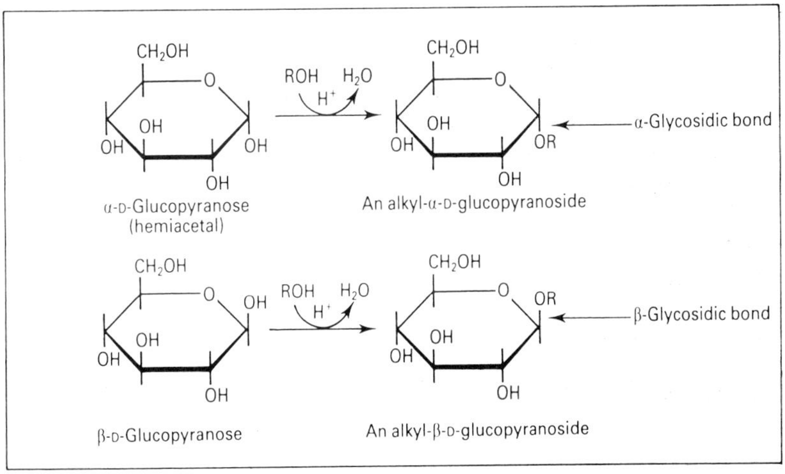

α-D-Glucopyranose (hemiacetal) → An alkyl-α-D-glucopyranoside — α-Glycosidic bond

β-D-Glucopyranose → An alkyl-β-D-glucopyranoside — β-Glycosidic bond

3.5 Oligosaccharides

The term oligosaccharide describes short polymeric glycosides that contain up to 10 monosaccharide units. Since the monosaccharide may be either in a pyranose or furanose form, α or β-anomeric form and the glycosidic bond may involve the hemi-acetal hydroxyl group of one unit with any stereochemically permissible hydroxyl group on the other unit, numerous permutations are possible. Biological processes, e.g. enzyme activity, limit the variety of oligosaccharides of natural occurrence.

Oligosaccharides containing only one type of monosaccharide unit may be termed homo-oligosaccharides (Figure 3.7a) whilst those consisting of more than one monosaccharide are termed hetero-oligosaccharides (Figure 3.7b). Maltose, isomaltose, cellobiose and trehalose are glucose-containing homodisaccharides which contain an α-(1→4), and α-(1→6), a β-(1→4) and α-(1→1) glycosidic bond respectively. Lactose and sucrose are glucose-containing heterodisaccharides. The glycosidic linkage prevents reversion to the open-chain structure of the unit which has donated the hydroxyl group of its anomeric carbon atom. This moiety is no longer able to reduce substances

(Section 3.3) and is termed the non-reducing end. Disaccharides that have a free anomeric carbon atom may act as reducing sugars because they retain the ring-opening potential whereas disaccharides such as trehalose and sucrose are non-reducing. Glycosidic bond position is determined from the non-reducing end of the oligosaccharide to its reducing end. This is why maltose contains an α-(1→4) bond [and not an α-(4→1) bond]. In trehalose, the anomeric carbon atoms of both units are involved in the linkage. Since trehalose contains the same monomeric units, there is no problem. However, in sucrose the anomeric carbon atoms of different monomeric units are involved in the linkage. Thus,

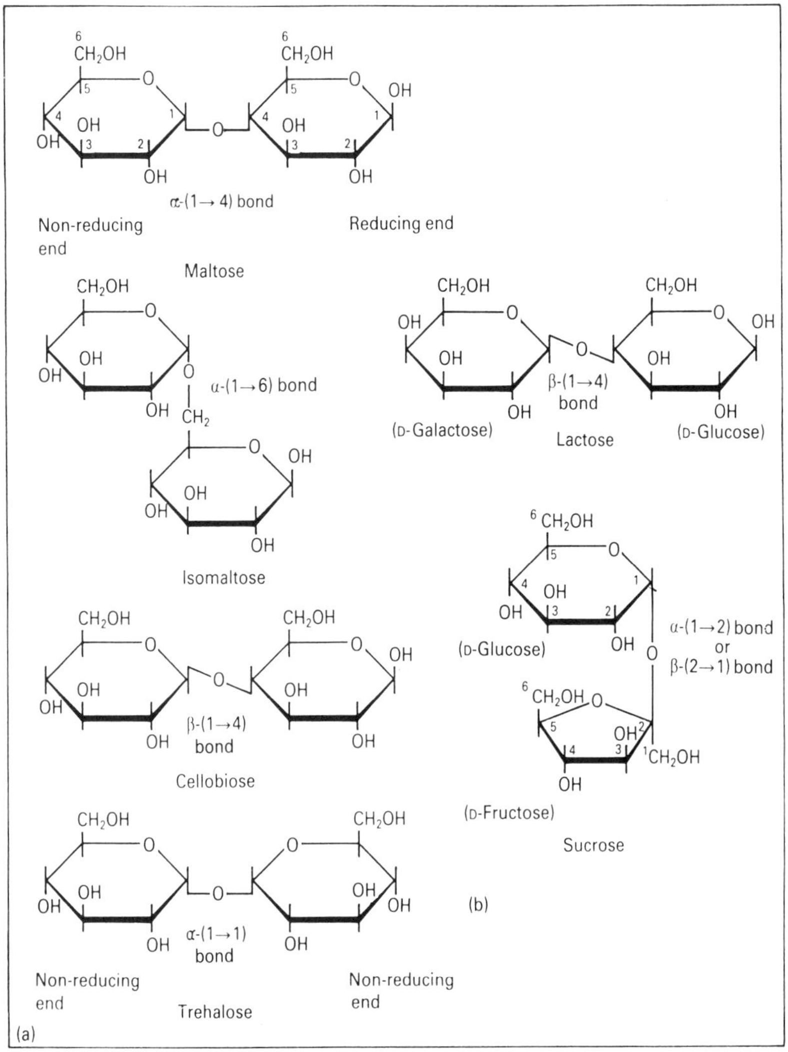

FIGURE 3.7 Structures of some glucose-containing disaccharides. (a) Homodisaccharides. (b) Heterodisaccharides

the glycosidic bond of sucrose is α-(1→2) when considered from glucose but β-(2→1) when considered from fructose. The position and nature of the glycosidic linkage in carbohydrate may be enzymically determined. In addition to their trivial names, systematic nomenclature may be employed. For example, maltose is O-α-D-glucopyranosyl-(1→4)-β-D-glucopyranoside and sucrose may be O-α-D-glucopyranosyl-(1→2)-β-D-fructofuranoside or O-β-D-fructofuranosyl-(2→1)-α-D-glucopyranoside.

3.6 Polysaccharides: homoglycans

Polysaccharides, like oligosaccharides, are long polymers of monosaccharides held together by glycosidic linkages. The polysaccharides may be subdivided into homoglycans and heteroglycans. The homoglycans contain a single type of monosaccharide monomer in a ring structure whereas the heteroglycans contain more than one type of monosaccharide unit. Homoglycans frequently contain a low percentage of other monosaccharides. Homoglycans can be subdivided on the basis of the nature of the monosaccharide unit (Table 3.1).

Glucans have both structural and nutritional functions. Cellulose, the most abundant of the naturally occurring macromolecular compounds, constitutes 20–30% of the primary cell walls of plants. It is therefore the main structural component of plant cell walls and cotton fibres are almost pure cellulose. Cellulose is composed of up to 14 000 D-glucose residues joined only by β-(1→4) glycosidic linkages which are responsible for cellulose being a long straight unbranched polymer (Figure 3.8a) which has the strength to support large trees. Cellulose contains intramolecular hydrogen bonds between the hydroxyl at C-3 and the ring oxygen of the adjacent monosaccharide. Intermolecular hydrogen bonds crosslink individual chains to adjacent chains to form a fibrous and insoluble structure (Figure 3.8b).

Starch, unlike cellulose, can be readily hydrolysed to its monosaccharide units and is therefore utilized as an energy reserve by plants. Starch consists of two components, amylose and amylopectin, which are complexed together approximately in a 1:3 ratio to form discrete starch granules. Both molecules contain only α-glycosidic linkages. Amylose contains only α-(1→4) glycosidic linkages but amylopectin contains additional α-(1→6) glycosidic linkages which gives rise to its branched structure (Figure 3.9a). The nature of the α-glycosidic linkage confers a helical conformation to the molecule (Figure 3.9b) in contrast to cellulose. Glycogen, the animal storage glucan (Section 11.4) which is equivalent to the starch of plants, has a similar structure to amylopectin but is more highly branched (Figure 3.9c). Table 3.2 outlines the major features of these glucans.

Medically and industrially important glucans include the dextrans which differ in chain length and the degree of branching. Their backbones have α-(1→6) linkages with branching via α-(1→3) or α-(1→4) bonds. Biochemists employ dextrans in certain column chromatographic procedures, e.g. gel filtration chromatography.

Fructans, which also function as energy reserve carbohydrates, are widely distributed in plants. Most fructans contain a small amount of glucose, often as a terminal residue which is probably

TABLE 3.1 Homoglycan subgroups

Nomenclature	Major monomeric unit
Glucans	Glucose
Fructans	Fructose
Mannans	Mannose
Xylans	Xylose
Arabans	Arabinose
Galactans	Galactose
Chitin	N-Acetylglucosamine
Glycuronans	Glycuronic acids

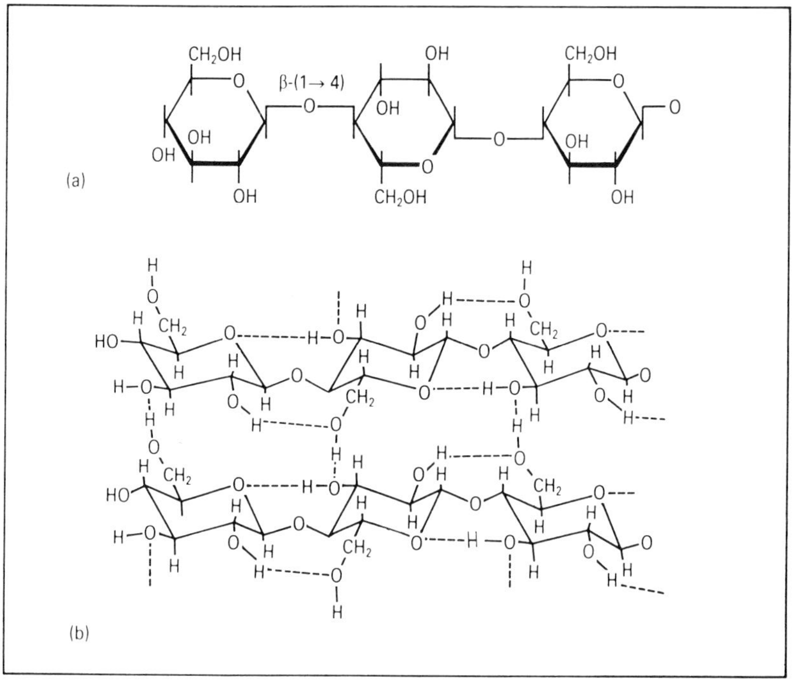

FIGURE 3.8   Structures of
cellulose. (a) Representation by
Haworth projection formula. (b)
Intramolecular and intermolecular
hydrogen bonding in cellulose

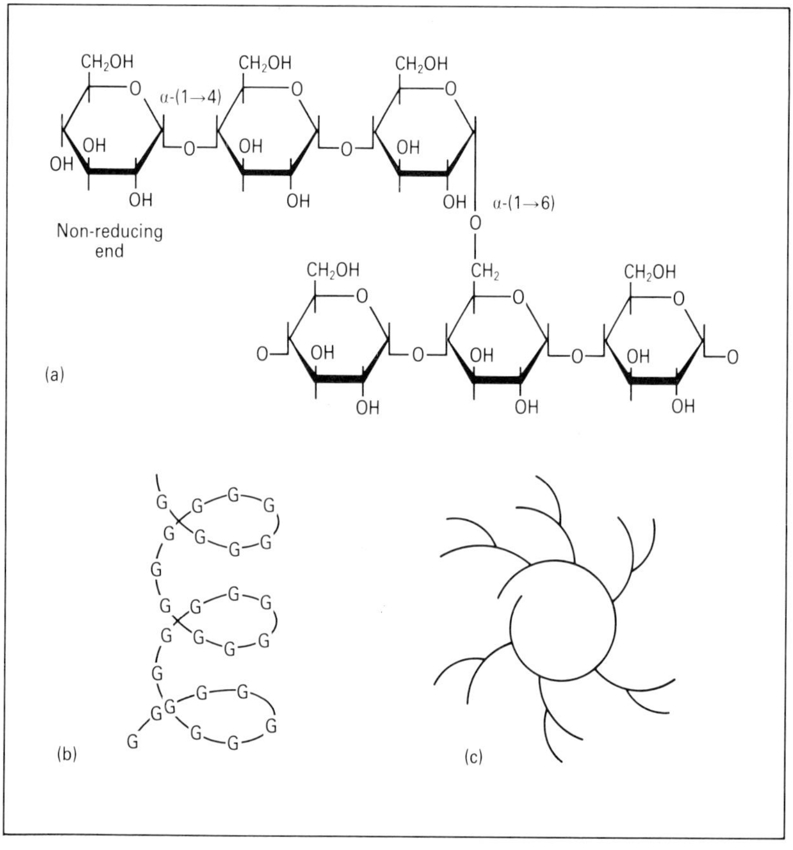

FIGURE 3.9   Part structures of
some glucans. (a) A branch point in
amylopectin or glycogen. (b) Helical
conformation of amylose. (c) A
segment of glycogen

TABLE 3.2 Comparison of amylose, amylopectin and glycogen

	Amylose	Amylopectin	Glycogen
Monomeric unit	D-Glucose	D-Glucose	D-Glucose
Molecular weight	4000–500 000	50 000–16 × 10^6	50 000–n × 10^6
Type of polymer	Linear	Branched	Branched
Distance between branches	—	20–25 Glucose units	8–12 Glucose units
Glycosidic bonds	α-(1→4)	α-(1→4), α-(1→6)	α-(1→4), α-(1→6)

resultant from sucrose being their biosynthetic precursor. The best known fructan is inulin which consists of a linear chain of about 30–35 β-(2→1)-linked fructose residues. The other major group of fructans, called levans, contain β-(2→6) glycosidic bonds.

Plants, seaweeds, invertebrates and microorganisms are sources of the other types of homoglycans. Chitin, found in most fungi, numerous algae and some yeasts as a cell wall component and in the exoskeleton of crustacea and insects, can be considered as a structural variation of cellulose since its chains consist of N-acetyl-D-glucosamine residues linked by β-(1→4) linkages and are hydrogen-bonded to form fibrils. The major polysaccharide of agar, employed by microbiologists as a gel medium for the culture of microorganisms, is agarose which consists of D-galactose and a modification of L-galactose called anhydro-L-galactose. Two types of glycosidic linkages, α-(1→3) and α-(1→4), create a helical structure in which the anhydromonosaccharide enhances stability.

3.7 Polysaccharides: heteroglycans

Heteroglycans can be considered structurally as polysaccharides composed of repeating disaccharide units in which the constituent monosaccharides are different. The glycosidic linkage forming the disaccharide units frequently differs from the linkages comprising the disaccharide. Often one

TABLE 3.3 The structure of the repeating disaccharides of some important heteroglycans of connective tissue

Heteroglycan	Repeating disaccharide			Glycosidic bond between adjacent dimers
	Component 1	Glycosidic bond	Component 2	
Hyaluronate	D-Glucuronate	β-(1→3)	N-Acetyl-glucosamine	β-(1→4)
Chondroitin 4-sulphate	D-Glucuronate	β-(1→3)	N-Acetyl-galactosamine 4-sulphate	β-(1→4)
Chondroitin 6-sulphate	D-Glucuronate	β-(1→3)	N-Acetyl-galactosamine 6-sulphate	β-(1→4)
Dermatan sulphate	L-Iduronate	α-(1→3)	N-Acetyl-galactosamine 4-sulphate	β-(1→4)
Keratan sulphate	D-Galactose	β-(1→4)	N-Acetyl-glucosamine 6-sulphate	β-(1→3)
Heparin	D-Glucuronate	α-(1→4)	N-Sulphate glucosamine 6-sulphate	α-(1→4)
Heparan sulphate	L-Iduronate 2-sulphate	α-(1→4)	N-Acetyl-glucosamine 3,6-bis-sulphate	α-(1→4)

of the monosaccharide units is an amino sugar or contains one or more acidic groups, e.g. carboxyl (uronic acid) or sulphate. Heteroglycans usually associate with protein utilizing the negative charge at physiological pH of its acidic groups to form ionic bonds (Section 4.3). Covalent bonds are also formed. The quantity of protein found in association with these molecules is usually less than 5% of their total weight so that the hybrid molecule is a proteoglycan (Section 1.5). Because of their content of amino sugars, these molecules are often called glycosaminoglycans. Table 3.3 indicates the variety of structures found in

connective tissue heteroglycans. Proteoglycans are important constituents of connective tissue, i.e. the tissue which supports cells in a jelly-like matrix, reinforced by various fibrils or fibres, called the ground substance or intercellular cement.

The cell walls (Section 9.1) of bacteria contain substances called mureins or peptidoglycans, the latter being the preferred name. The polymeric backbone of peptidoglycans is structurally close to chitin (Section 3.6), being composed of N-acetyl-D-glucosamine and its 3-lactyl derivative, N-acetyl-muramic acid which are linked together by β-(1→4) bonds (Figure 3.10a). Chains of this struc-

FIGURE 3.10 Bacterial cell wall. (a) Repeating disaccharide of peptidoglycan. (b) Structure of the peptidoglycan of *Staphylococcus aureus.* ○, L-alanine; ●, D-alanine; ▲, D-glutamine; □, L-lysine; ▽, L-glycine

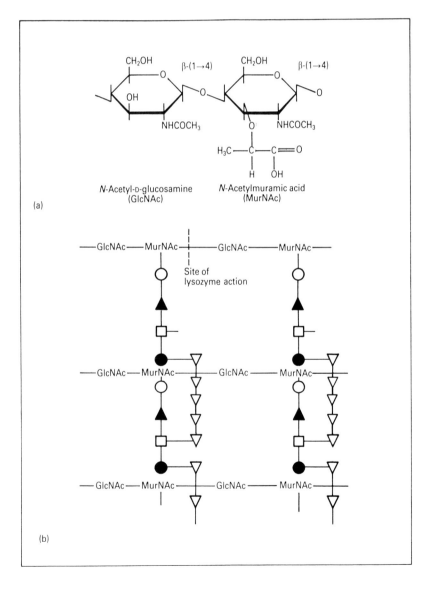

ture are covalently crosslinked to each other through a tetrapeptide side chain composed of alternating D- and L-amino acids, the terminal D-alanine of which is connected to a pentaglycine bridge which has its terminal glycyl residue attached to the penultimate amino acid of the tetrapeptide of another chain (Figure 3.10b). Within this framework, which is responsible for the rigidity of the bacterial cell wall, variations in the second and third amino acid of the tetrapeptide, in the structure of the crosslinking bridge and in the frequency of crosslinks occur. The enzyme lysozyme (Section 5.4) may weaken the cell wall by the hydrolysis of the glycosidic bonds between the repeating disaccharides.

Suggested further reading

BARTON, D. and OLLIS, W. D. (1979) *Comprehensive Organic Chemistry: The Synthesis and Reactions of Organic Compounds*, Vol. 5, *Biological Compounds*, E. Haslam (ed.), Pergamon, Oxford

DUFFUS, C. M. and DUFFUS, J. H. (1984) *Carbohydrate Metabolism in Plants*, Longman, London

CHAPTER 4

Amino acids and proteins

4.1 The classification of amino acids

Protein was the name given by Mulder, in 1838, to a substance which he considered as of primary importance to all living organisms (proteios in Greek means 'of the first quality'). Today the immense variety of protein molecules is recognized. Proteins are the most abundant macromolecules found within cells and perform a wide variety of functions (Section 1.6). A protein can be considered as a unique polymer of amino acids (Section 1.4) which determine its chemical and structural properties. It is therefore imperative to consider the amino acids before embarkation upon a discussion of protein structure.

Of the 308 catalogued natural amino acids, only 20 (plus a few derivatives) occur in proteins in which all are α-amino acids of the L-series (Section 1.3). They conform (except proline) to a general formula (Figure 4.1) in which an amino group and a carboxylic acid group are attached to the α-carbon (C^{α}) atom. Proline, an imino acid, is normally included because of its occurrence in proteins. The properties of individual amino acids vary according to the nature of the R group called the side chain (Table 4.1). Asparagine and glutamine are considered as amide derivatives of aspartic acid and glutamic acid respectively. Tyrosine may be classified either by its hydroxy or aromatic group. To refer to amino acids in polypeptide sequences, three- or one-letter codes are frequently employed. L-α-Amino acids, with the exception of glycine, contain a chiral α-carbon atom (Section 1.3). These amino acids exhibit optical activity; in some cases, dextrorotatory, e.g. alanine, in other cases laevorotatory, e.g. phenylalanine. Because of the conjugated double-bond system of their aromatic rings, tyrosine, tryptophan and phenylalanine absorb light in the ultraviolet region. The absorp-

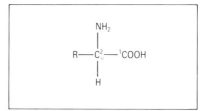

FIGURE 4.1 General formula of L-α-amino acids (nature of R groups given in Table 4.1)

tion coefficient of tryptophan and tyrosine at 280 nm is large enough to allow the exploitation of this property in their estimation either free or as residues in polypeptide chains.

The amino acids may be classified into four main categories according to the tendency of their R groups to interact with water at pH 7.0 (Table 4.2). Non-polar amino acids do not interact with or bind water and are called hydrophobic (water-hating). Polar R groups may bind water through hydrogen-bond formation (Section 2.2) and comprise hydrophilic (water-loving) amino acids. Certain hydrophilic amino acids carry a negative charge on their R groups at pH 7.0 and are called acidic amino acids. Similarly, basic amino acids are hydrophilic amino acids, the R groups of which may accept protons to become positively charged.

Some proteins may contain derivatives of common amino acids, e.g. collagen contains 5-hydroxylysine (Figure 1.6). Some amino acids which do not occur in proteins may function in cellular metabolism, e.g. citrulline and ornithine (Section 16.5). D-Amino acids occur alongside L-amino acids in some peptide antibiotics, e.g. valinomycin and actinomycin D, and in the peptidoglycan of the bacterial cell wall (Figure 3.10b).

Table 4.1 The R groups of the amino acids found in proteins

Aliphatic	Hydroxy	Acidic, neutral amides	Basic	Sulphur	Aromatic	Imino
Glycine (Gly, G)	Serine (Ser, S)	Aspartic acid (Asp, D)	Arginine (Arg, R)	Cysteine (CySH, C)	Phenylalanine (Phe, F)	Proline (Pro, P)
$H-$	$HO-CH_2-$	$HO-\overset{O}{\overset{\|}{C}}-CH_2-$	$H_2N-\overset{\|}{\underset{NH}{C}}-NH-CH_2-CH_2-CH_2-$	$HS-CH_2-$	(aromatic ring) CH_2-	(pyrrolidine ring) $CH-COOH$

Alanine (Ala, A)	Threonine (Thr, T)	Asparagine (Asn, N)	Histidine (His, H)	Methionine (Met, M)	Tryptophan (Trp, W)	
CH_3-	$CH_3-\overset{\|}{\underset{OH}{CH}}-$	$H_2N-\overset{O}{\overset{\|}{C}}-CH_2-$	(imidazole ring) $CH=C-CH_2-$	$CH_3-S-CH_2-CH_2-$	(indole ring)	

Valine (Val, V)	Tyrosine (Tyr, Y)	Glutamic acid (Glu, E)	Lysine (Lys, K)			
$CH_3-\overset{\|}{\underset{CH_3}{CH}}-$	$HO-$ (aromatic ring) $-C-CH_2-$	$HO-\overset{O}{\overset{\|}{C}}-CH_2-CH_2-$	$H_2N-CH_2-CH_2-CH_2-CH_2-CH_2-$			

Leucine (Leu, L)		Glutamine (Gln, Q)				
$CH_3-\overset{\|}{\underset{CH_3}{CH}}-CH_2-$		$H_2N-\overset{O}{\overset{\|}{C}}-CH_2-CH_2-$				

Isoleucine (Ile, I)						
$CH_3-CH_2-\overset{\|}{\underset{CH_3}{CH}}-$						

TABLE 4.2   Classification of amino acids according to R group properties at pH 7.0

R groups of amino acids			
		Polar (hydrophilic)	
Non-polar (hydrophobic)	Uncharged	Acidic	Basic
Alanine	Asparagine	Aspartic acid	Arginine
Cysteine	Glutamine	Glutamic acid	Histidine
Isoleucine	Glycine		Lysine
Leucine	Serine		
Methionine	Threonine		
Proline	Tyrosine		
Phenvlalanine	Tryptophan		
Valine			

4.2 Ionic properties of amino acids

The ionization characteristics of the amino acids in aqueous media are denoted by their pK_a values (Table 4.3). Note the similar values observed for pK_{a1} and the pK_a of the α-NH_2 group of different amino acids. Amino acids respond to changes in their aqueous environment in accordance with acid–base principles (Sections 2.7 and 2.8). In aqueous solutions at pH 1 (Figure 4.2), the amino acid is fully protonated. Titration of this amino acid by equimolar base will on the addition of one

TABLE 4.3   The pK values of groups occurring in the common amino acids

Amino acid	pK_{a_1} α-COOH	pK_{a_2} R-COOH	α-NH_2	Other R	pK_{a_3} α-NH_2	R-NH_2	Other R
Glycine	2.34	—	9.60	—	—	—	—
Alanine	2.34	—	9.69	—	—	—	—
Valine	2.32	—	9.62	—	—	—	—
Leucine	2.36	—	9.60	—	—	—	—
Isoleucine	2.36	—	9.60	—	—	—	—
Serine	2.21	—	9.15	—	—	—	—
Threonine	2.09	—	9.10	—	—	—	—
Tyrosine	2.20	—	9.11	—	—	—	10.07
Aspartic acid	1.88	3.65	—	—	9.60	—	—
Asparagine	2.02	—	8.80	—	—	—	—
Glutamic acid	2.19	4.25	—	—	9.67	—	—
Glutamine	2.17	—	9.13	—	—	—	—
Arginine	2.17	—	9.04	—	—	12.48	—
Histidine	1.82	—	—	6.00	9.17	—	—
Lysine	2.18	—	8.95	—	—	10.53	—
Cysteine	1.96	—	—	8.18	10.28	—	—
Methionine	2.28	—	9.21	—	—	—	—
Phenylalanine	1.83	—	9.13	—	—	—	—
Tryptophan	2.83	—	9.39	—	—	—	—
Proline	1.99	—	10.60	—	—	—	—

FIGURE 4.2 Titration of the monoamino-monocarboxylic amino acid alanine with equimolar base

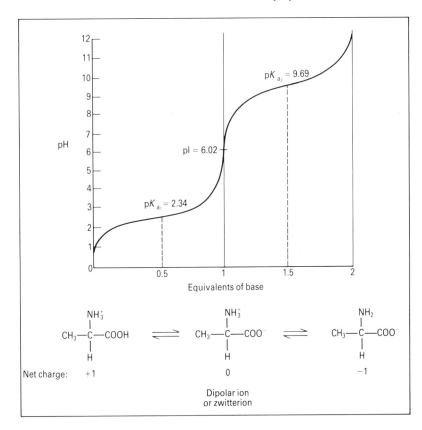

equivalent of base release a proton from the carboxylic acid group. Addition of a second equivalent of base deprotonates the amino group. At low pH, fully protonated alanine carries a net charge of +1. Increasing pH results firstly in the complete ionization of the carboxyl group (no net charge) and secondly in the removal of the proton from the NH_3^+ group of alanine which now has a net charge of −1. Thus the amino acids display amphoteric behaviour, i.e. are capable of acting as an acid or base. pK_{a1} and pK_{a2} can be determined at the appropriate half-equivalence point.

With neutral and monoamino-dicarboxylic acids, at the first equivalence point, the positive charge balances the negative charge and so the molecule is in its dipolar ionic state and is called a zwitterion

(German meaning 'hybrid ion'). Since the net charge is 0, the zwitterion cannot migrate in an electric field, e.g. during the technique of electrophoresis. This pH is termed the isoelectric point (pI).

The titration of amino acids with the dissociable R groups conforms to the same principles but requires three equivalents of bases. The general shape of the titration curve resembles that for the titration of a polyprotic weak acid with strong base (Figure 2.4). The pI of any amino acid can be calculated according to the following formulae:

1. for all amino acids except basic amino acids: $pI = \frac{1}{2}(pK_{a1} + pK_{a2})$
2. for basic amino acids: $pI = \frac{1}{2}(pK_{a2} + pK_{a3})$

4.3 The major bonds between amino acids in polypeptide chains

Chemical bonding between amino acids is responsible firstly for the construction of (Section 1.4) and secondly for the conformations adopted by the polypeptide chain. The linear sequence of amino acids linked by peptide bonds along a polypeptide chain is the first level of the structural organization of proteins and is referred to as the primary structure (Figure 4.3). Hydrogen bonds involving peptide bond atoms although individually weak are responsible for the fundamental ordered shapes of the second level of protein structure described as secondary structure. Hydrogen bonds between R-group atoms along with ionic bonds, hydrophobic interactions and disulphide bonds within a polypeptide chain, i.e. intramolecular bonds, contribute to the stability of the protein structure at the third level described as tertiary structure. The types of bonds which maintain the tertiary structures of proteins excluding disulphide bonds are also responsible for the spatial arrangement of protein subunits through intermolecular bonding. This is the fourth level of protein structure described as quaternary structure.

Two amino acids may link together by a

FIGURE 4.3 Hierarchy of protein structure indicating the forms of bonding found at each level

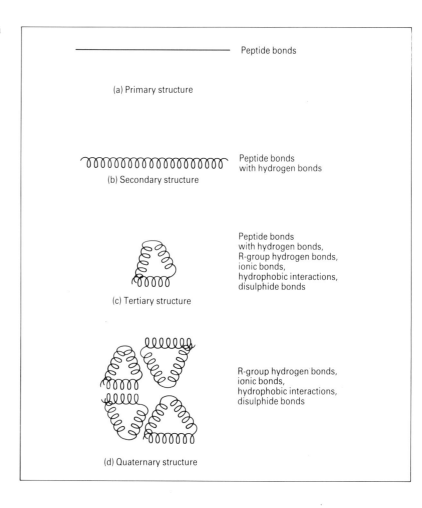

Peptide bonds

(a) Primary structure

Peptide bonds
with hydrogen bonds

(b) Secondary structure

Peptide bonds
with hydrogen bonds,
R-group hydrogen bonds,
ionic bonds,
hydrophobic interactions,
disulphide bonds

(c) Tertiary structure

R-group hydrogen bonds,
ionic bonds,
hydrophobic interactions,
disulphide bonds

(d) Quaternary structure

condensation reaction in which one donates its carbonyl group and the other an amino group to form a peptide bond. One end of the dipeptide exhibits a free amino group and is called the *N*-terminus. The other end exhibits a free carboxyl group and is called the *C*-terminus.

The geometry of the peptide bond (Figure 4.4a) is important. The C–N bond length in the peptide bond is shorter than the 0.145 nm recorded for a single covalent C–N bond. This is a result of the propensity of the oxygen atom to withdraw electrons. The electrons associated with the C–N bond and the C=O group resonate between two struc-

tures (Figure 4.4b) to create a partial double bond character (about 40%) for the C–N single bond and an equal partial single bond character for the C=O double bond. As a result of resonance stabilization, the rotation of the C–N single bond is restricted so that six atoms are rigidly positioned in the same plane (i.e. are coplanar) and the bond has a *trans* configuration. Because proteins are composed of only L-amino acids, the R group on each of the C$^\alpha$ atoms are arranged on opposite sides of the backbone. This arrangement minimizes steric interaction of bulky R groups (Figure 4.4c, d). Since the imino group (N–H) of the peptide

FIGURE 4.4 Architecture of the peptide bond. (a) Geometry. (b) Resonance structures. (c) *Trans* configuration. (d) *Cis* configuration

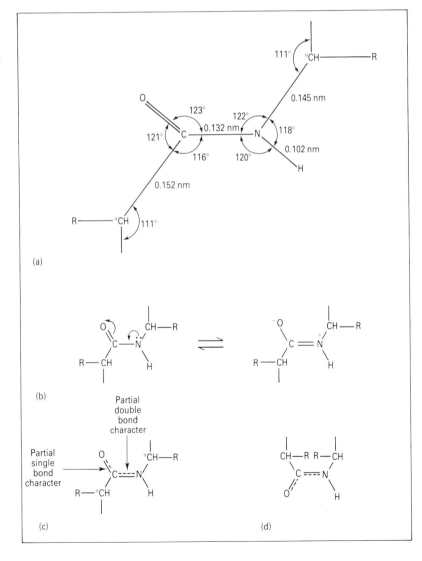

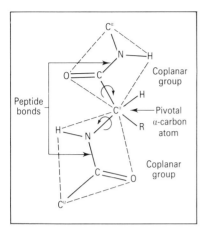

FIGURE 4.5   Rotation around
C$^\alpha$–C and C$^\alpha$–N bonds

bond has no significant tendency to protonate at
physiological pH. The ionic properties of a protein
are the result of only R group ionizations and
those of the *N*-terminal amino and *C*-terminal carboxyl groups. Although the peptide bond cannot
rotate freely, the C$^\alpha$ atom serves as a pivot on
which the coplanar groups may rotate (Figure 4.5).

In proteins, hydrogen bonding (Section 2.2) can
occur between groups associated with different
peptide bonds (Figure 4.6a) or between appropriate amino acid R groups. The nitrogen atom
tends to draw the electron away from its hydrogen
atom so that the hydrogen atom has a slight posi-

tive charge (δ^+). The oxygen atom has a tendency
to attract electrons from the carbon atom so that
the oxygen atom is slightly electronegative (δ^-).
Hydrogen bonding results from electron sharing
between the oxygen and hydrogen atoms which
produces a further redistribution of the electronic
arrangement within the C=O and N–H groups
thereby enhancing the attraction (Figure 4.6b). In
addition, the electron-withdrawing properties of
oxygen and nitrogen may render a hydrogen electropositive (δ^+) so that it may interact with an
appositely positioned δ^- oxygen or nitrogen atom
on another R group.

At physiological pH, the R groups of aspartate
and glutamate carry a negative charge due to
deprotonation but the R groups of arginine and
lysine are protonated and bear a positive charge.
Oppositely charged amino acids may attract each
other to bring regions of the polypeptide chain(s)
into adjacency with attendant stability. These electrostatic attractions are called ionic bonds or salt
bonds or salt bridges (Figure 4.7a).

The R groups of hydrophobic amino acid residues (Table 4.2) do not permit hydrogen bonding
with water but weakly associate by their mutual
hydrophobic properties to provide a sanctuary
from an aqueous environment (Figure 4.7b).

The strongest of the bonds which contribute to
the conformation of the protein is the covalent
disulphide bond or bridge. The R group of cysteine terminates in a free sulphydryl group. Perti-
nently positioned cysteine residues of proteins may

FIGURE 4.6   (a) Hydrogen
bonding in proteins involving
peptide bonds. (b) Electron
distribution in hydrogen bonding

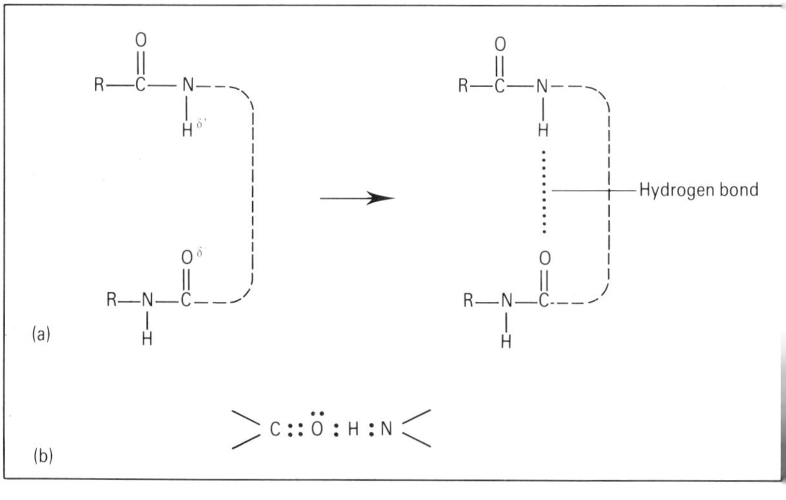

FIGURE 4.7 Some bonds occurring in proteins. (a) Ionic bonds. (b) Hydrophobic interactions. (c) Disulphide bond

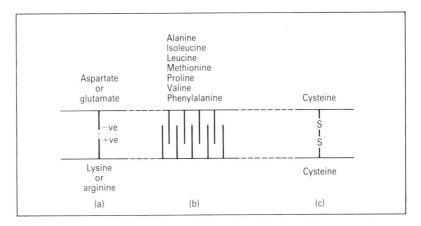

dimerize on enzymic or chemical oxidation to form a disulphide bond (Figure 4.7c).

A number of physical agents, e.g. heat and ultraviolet radiation, disrupt hydrogen and ionic bonds because of increased molecular vibration. These bonds may also be affected by chemical agents, e.g. ionic reagents. The destruction of the molecular conformation of the protein is termed denaturation and results in loss of biological activity.

4.4 The primary structure of proteins

The determination of the amino acid sequence of a protein is important for the understanding of the way(s) in which a protein achieves its biological function. Knowledge of these sequences together with detailed conformational information of numerous proteins enhance the deduction of the rules governing the folding of proteins. Investigations into altered protein functioning have, on sequence analysis, been correlated with either single or multiple amino acid substitutions (Section 17.7).

The strategy for the determination of the amino acid sequence of any protein is given in Figure 4.8. It is based upon the pioneer work of Frederick Sanger, who, in 1953, successfully elucidated the primary structure of the 51-residue polypeptide hormone, insulin. A prerequisite of any sequence analysis is that a pure sample of protein has been prepared.

The determination of the number of polypeptide chains may be achieved in an aliquot of the sample by various techniques including the disruption of quaternary bonds followed by gel electrophoresis. Guanidinium chloride, urea or ionic detergents, e.g. sodium dodecyl sulphate (SDS), disrupt hydrogen and ionic bonding. Disulphide bonds may be cleaved by either reduction, e.g. by 2-mercapto-ethanol followed by –SH group stabilization by an alkylating agent, e.g. iodoacetamide to prevent recombination of chains or oxidation by performic acid. Comparison of pre- and post-treatment protein samples by gel electrophoresis or isoelectric focusing enables the elucidation of the number of chains. If necessary, polypeptide chains may be separated by ion-exchange chromatography, gel filtration chromatography, preparative polyacrylamide gel electrophoresis, fast protein liquid chromatography (FPLC) etc.

Knowledge of the amino acids present in each chain (i.e. amino acid composition) may be acquired by automated amino acid analysis or high-performance liquid chromatography (HPLC) to assist in the selection of techniques for the fragmentation of the polypeptide chains and the determination of the sequences of individual peptides. Sequence analysis requires the employment of at least two aliquots of each polypeptide chain.

Fragmentation of the polypeptide involves

FIGURE 4.8 Strategy for the elucidation of the primary structure of a protein

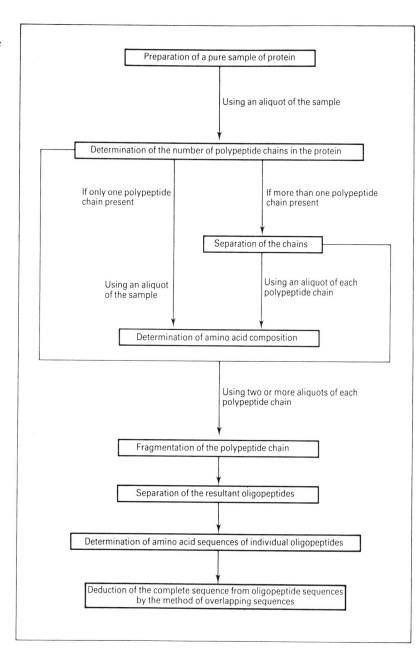

partial hydrolysis for which both selective chemical and enzymic means (Table 4.4) are available. Selection of at least two enzymes is based upon the amino acid composition of the polypeptide chain. For example, the presence of arginyl and lysyl residues may indicate that digestion by trypsin would yield workable oligopeptide fragments. The resultant oligopeptides may be separated (fractionated) by chromatographic or electrophoretic techniques. To obtain pure oligopeptides, several fractionation methods may be necessary.

The determination of amino acid sequences of individual oligopeptides is achieved by *N*- and *C*-terminal analyses for which a number of methods are available. The principle of chemical methods for *N*-terminal analysis is shown in Figure 4.9. A

TABLE 4.4   Sites of action of some endopeptidases

Enzyme	Preferential cleavage points (cleavage occurs at carbonyl end of the stated amino acid)	Source
Chymotrypsin	Tyr, Trp, Phe, Leu	Pancreas
Trypsin	Arg, Lys	Pancreas
Thermomycolin	Ala, Tyr, Phe	*Malbranchea pulchella* (fungus)
Staphylococcal serine protease	Glu, Asp	*Staphylococcus aureus* (microorganism)
Papain	Arg, Lys, Phe-AA (the CO side of an amino acid whose NH₂ group is linked to Phe)	*Carica papaya* (tree)
Clostripain	Arg (especially Arg-Pro bond)	*Clostridium histolyticum* (microorganism)
Pepsin A	Phe, Leu	Gastric mucosa

FIGURE 4.9   Identification of the *N*-terminal amino acid

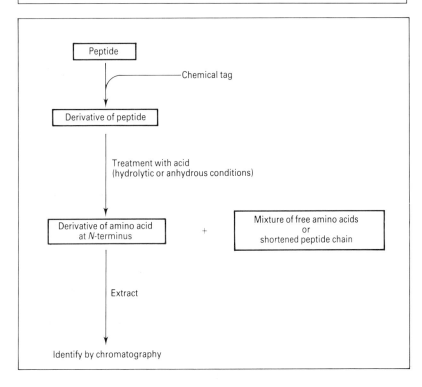

chemical tag is attached to the amino group of the *N*-terminal amino acid which is then removed from the peptide and identified by chromatographic methods. The Sanger method and dansylation require acid hydrolysis to release the *N*-terminal derivative degrading the remainder of the chain. The Edman method does not destroy the remainder of the chain which may be reprocessed. This method of derivatization is the basis of the auto-mated peptide sequencer which may sequence up to 60 residues.

The oligopeptide may also be sequenced from the *N*-terminus by an enzymic method using the cytosol aminopeptidase of pig kidney or cattle lens. This enzyme acts on all peptide bonds except arginyl or lysyl bonds. The concentrations of identified free amino acids are measured at given time intervals. The amino acid sequence of the oligopeptide can be determined from the concentration profiles. An analogous method for *C*-terminal sequences employs carboxypeptidase A which liberates *C*-terminal amino acids (except arginine, lysine and proline). Carboxypeptidase B, which preferentially cleaves lysine and arginine, may be used in conjunction with carboxypeptidase A, although complications due to the potential degradation of B by A must be overcome.

When the sequences of all oligopeptides are known, the primary structure of the polypeptide chain may be elucidated. The method of overlapping sequences (Figure 4.10) requires digestion by at least two enzymes since the sequences of the products of the action of one appropriate enzyme must overlap those from the other. A *C*-terminal peptide may be identified since it lacks a cleavage point residue, e.g. all other tryptic peptides will terminate in lysine and arginine. From the *C*-terminal peptide, the sequence of the whole chain may be established by careful selection and positioning of the peptides.

In recent years, it has become possible to predict the primary structure of a protein from sequence analysis of its gene (Section 19.7) by application of the genetic code (Section 17.5).

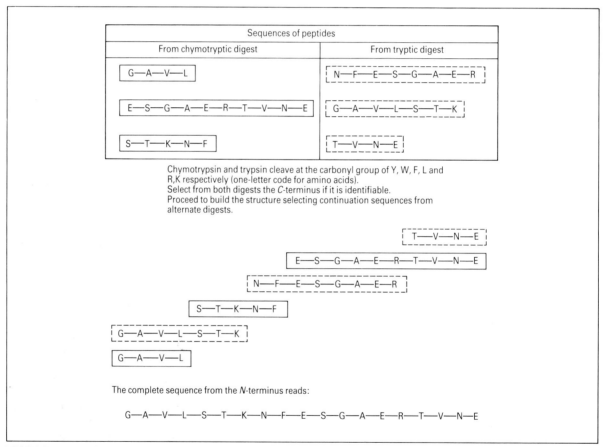

FIGURE 4.10   The method of overlapping sequences

4.5 The secondary structure of proteins

Protein conformation may be defined as the arrangement in space of its constituent atoms which determine the overall shape of the molecule. The conformation of the protein arises from the bonding arrangements within its structure (Figure 4.3). If the protein contained only peptide bonds, all proteins would be random in shape due to C^α–C and C^α–N bond rotations (Section 4.3). Investigations on a large number of proteins have indicated that proteins are highly organized structures with defined shapes. Although proton nuclear magnetic resonance (^{1}H-NMR) has been recently applied to the determination of protein conformation, the study of the conformation of a protein has been dominated by the technique of X-ray crystallography which offers a view of the relative positions of the atoms within a structure.

The X-ray diffraction studies of the 1940s highlighted general features regarding the shape of the protein. The distances between major recurrent features is termed major periodicity and between minor recurrent features is the minor periodicity. X-ray crystallography creates the impression that each atom in the protein molecule is firmly fixed in position. This view of a static structure is being replaced by an appreciation of the dynamic nature of the molecule in which the atoms of the protein are in a state of constant motion. Therefore, X-ray diffraction studies produce an average position around which each atom moves.

From the knowledge of the dimensions and characteristics of backbone bonds (Section 4.3), scale models were constructed in the 1940s to define the geometric relationship of neighbouring amino acid residues. In 1951, Pauling and Corey proposed the α-helical chain and β-conformation as fundamental structures of proteins (Figures 4.11 and 4.12).

The α-keratins (long thin water-insoluble fibrous proteins found in hair, wool, feathers and the outer layer of skin) serve as an example in which the backbone of the polypeptide chain is arranged in a helical coil of 3.6 amino acids per turn (Figure 4.11a). In the right-handed α-helix composed of L-amino acids, the degree of rotation for all C^α–C bonds is $-47°$ whilst that of all C–N bonds is $-57°$. This combination results in a very stable structure because the C=O group and the N–H group of the peptide bond are thereby in an orientation which promotes the formation of a network of intrachain hydrogen bonds between the carbonyl group of one peptide bond and the imino hydrogen atom of the third peptide bond along the chain (Figure 4.11b). Although individually weak, hydrogen bonds collectively reinforce each other directing this folding pattern. The R groups of the amino acids extend outwards from the helix to minimize their molecular interactions which would increase the molecular energy level and destabilize the structure.

The accuracy of this model was later confirmed by the X-ray crystallography of the protein from hair which demonstrated a major periodicity of 0.50–0.55 nm which closely corresponds to the length of one turn of the helix (Figure 4.11a). The minor periodicity of 0.15 nm from the diffraction studies corresponds to the distance per residue. The dimensions observed in some other proteins may vary from these although their structures are stable. Some amino acids (e.g. glycine, tyrosine, asparagine) tend to reduce the stability of an α-helix while other amino acids (e.g. alanine, leucine, methionine) tend to promote helix stability. Proline cannot be accommodated in the α-helix.

The β-conformation was based originally on an elongated α-helix. The α-keratin on treatment with steam at 100°C stretches due to disruption of the hydrogen bonds to almost twice its native length. This form is unstable due to R group steric interaction (Section 4.3). The major periodicity was estimated as 0.7 nm, the same value as that of fibroin, the major protein constituent of silk. Fibroin, however, is a stable structure because it contains very small R groups: alanine or serine alternating with glycine along the polypeptide chain (Figure 4.12a).

An essential difference however is that where the α-helix gives a long thin rod-like molecule, this extended structure is sheet-like and stabilized by hydrogen bonds perpendicular to the chains (Figure 4.12a). β-sheets may be parallel or antiparallel (as in fibroin) and are formed by appropriate folding of the polypeptide chain (Figure 4.12b). The change in the direction of the chain to produce an antiparallel conformation is commonly achieved by the formation of a tight loop called a

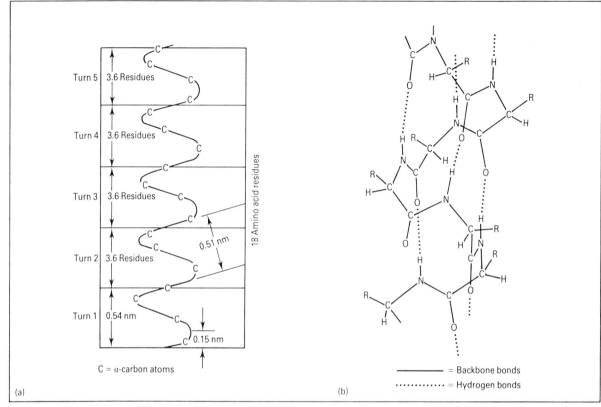

FIGURE 4.11   The α-helix of an α-keratin. (a) Dimensions of the α-helix. (b) Hydrogen bonding and R group positions

β-bend by hydrogen bonding between the C=O of one peptide bond and the N–H of the second peptide bond along the chain. Glycine, because of its small R group, and proline, whose geometry predetermines bending in a chain, frequently occur in β-bends. At the next level of organization, tertiary structure, the α-helix and β-sheet will be seen to occur within the same chain in some proteins.

One of the most abundant fibrous proteins in the animal body is collagen of which there are at least 11 types called type I, II etc. Collagen has a distinctive structure which occurs only in two other known proteins: complement subcomponent CIq and acetylcholinesterase of electric eels. Type I collagen, the most abundant, occurring in bone, tendon, skin, teeth and arteries, contains two identical polypeptide chains called α1(I) and a slightly different chain, α2(I). Individual chains form a left-handed helix which wind around each other to form a right-handed triple helix (Figure 4.13a).

Each α-chain is composed of about 1000 amino acid residues, which, except for both terminal sequences, conform to the general formula (Gly-X-Y)$_n$ where X and Y are other amino acids. Glycine occurs as every third residue because this position occupies a restricted space within the conformation of the chain. Prolyl residues, some of which may be converted into the 3-hydroxy derivative, occupy about 100 X positions; 4-hydroxyprolyl residues occupy about 100 Y positions. The pyrrolidine ring of proline residues cause individual collagen chains to assume an elongated helical conformation in which proline, 4-hydroxyproline and interchain but not intrachain hydrogen bonding promote stability. The 5-hydroxylysyl residues provide OH groups for glycosylation which involves the attachment of galactosyl residues. Some of the galactosyl residues are modified further into glucosylgalactosyl moieties.

The other amino acids in X and Y positions are clustered into regions of hydrophobicity and hydrophilicity which direct the assembly of individual collagen molecules into collagen fibrils with a characteristic longitudinal displacement called a quarter-stagger (Figure 4.13b). Condensation reac-

tions between lysyl or hydroxylysyl residues and their aldehyde derivatives create additional forms of stable interchain covalent bonding.

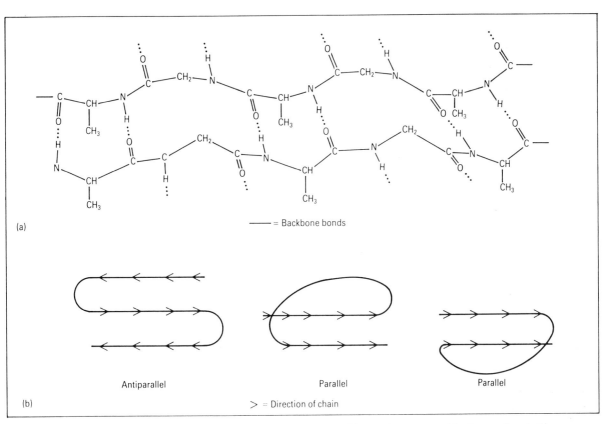

FIGURE 4.12   The β-conformation or β-pleated sheet. (a) The positions of groups and hydrogen bonds in an antiparallel β-conformation. (b) Formation of β-sheets

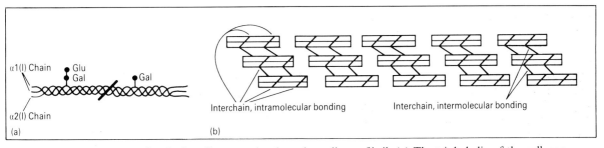

FIGURE 4.13   Structure of a single collagen molecule and a collagen fibril. (a) The triple helix of the collagen molecule. (b) The quarter-stagger arrangement of collagen molecules in a collagen fibril

4.6 The tertiary structure of proteins

The convolutions of most polypeptide chains produce compact molecules of maximum stability
approximating in shape to elongated or oblated
(orange-shaped) globes. The first of the globular
proteins to be analysed in detail by X-ray crystallography was sperm whale myoglobin. Myoglobin
(molecular weight, 17 500) functions as an oxygen-
carrying protein in mammalian muscle. Sperm
whale myoglobin was studied because of the large
quantity of the protein in the skeletal muscle of
diving mammals which have a requirement for
very large oxygen reserves.

Figure 4.14 shows two components: a single
polypeptide chain of 153 amino acid residues and a
haem group, the iron of which binds oxygen. The
noteworthy features of the molecule are:

1. Its dimensions are $4.5 \times 3.5 \times 2.5$ nm. The molecule is so compact that there is space only for
   four water molecules in the interior of the convoluted chain.
2. The interior of the molecule consists of a large
   proportion of hydrophobic residues and is
   devoid of acidic or basic amino acids (Table
   4.2).
3. Residues with a polar and non-polar part, e.g.
   threonine and tyrosine, are orientated to direct
   the non-polar part towards the interior of the
   molecule.
4. The only polar residues found in the interior
   of myoglobin are the two histidine residues
   which position the haem moiety.
5. Eight right-handed α-helical regions denoted

FIGURE 4.14   Tertiary structure of
the myoglobin chain

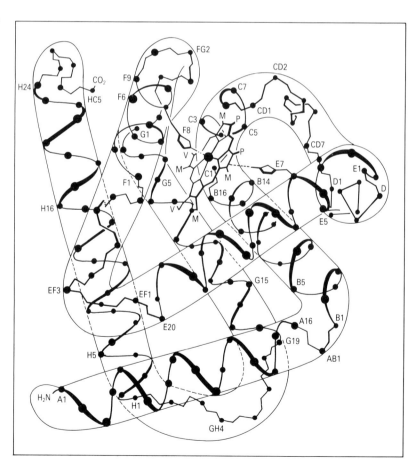

A–H constitute about 75% of the chain. Each amino acid residue within a helix is coded, e.g. C2 is the second residue of the third helix.

6. The chain contains a total of seven non-helical segments: five between helical regions denoted according to the helices they interrupt, e.g. CD, plus one at each N- and C-terminus.

7. The occurrence of proline terminates an α-helix. However, there are only four proline residues in myoglobin so that other factors such as the interference by the hydroxyl group of serine with secondary structure hydrogen bonding arrangements must be involved.

8. The haem group is located in a non-polar groove near the surface of the molecule. The hydrophobic environment of this groove does not impede the passage of the oxygen to the iron of the haem but prevents water from nullifying the oxygen-binding process.

9. The structure of the haem molecule is given in Figure 4.15a. The porphyrin nitrogen atoms bind iron through four of its six coordination positions (Figure 4.15b). The histidine at F8 is bound to the iron atom via its fifth coordination position. The sixth position of the iron atom is vacant and available for the binding of oxygen. Once bound, the oxygen is stabilized by hydrogen bonding to the imidazole ring of the E7 histidine.

10. Oxygenation can only occur with the iron atom in the ferrous state (Fe^{2+}) which is maintained by enzyme-catalysed redox reactions (Sections 11.8 and 13.3).

The structural information gained from the analysis of myoglobin served as the basis for hypotheses on tertiary structure. However, myoglobin is an atypical globular protein since it lacks cysteinyl residues (no disulphide bonds) and β-conformation, but contains a very large proportion of α-helical structure. Studies on over 200 globular proteins have demonstrated that polypeptide chains frequently contain both α-helical and β-sheet secondary structures (Figure 4.16).

Since proteins are composed of chiral L-amino

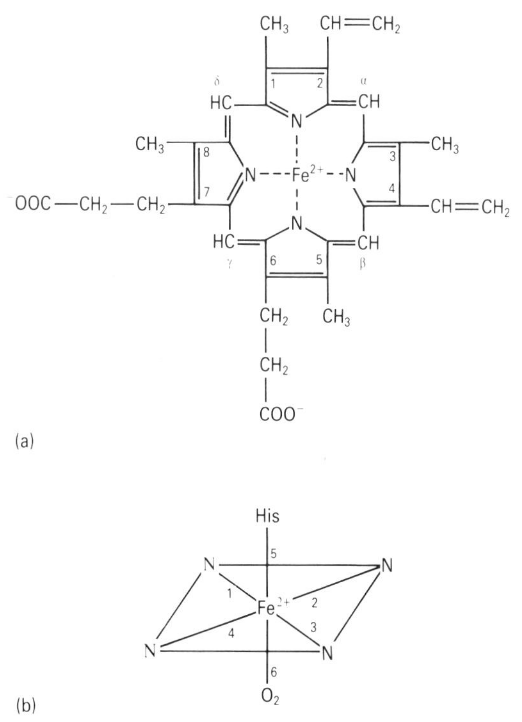

FIGURE 4.15 (a) Structure of haem. (b) Coordination positions of haem with position 5 bonded to F8 histidine of the globin molecule

FIGURE 4.16   Some α-helix and β-conformation arrangements in proteins. (a) β-barrel shape in pyruvate kinase. (b) Saddle shape in flavodoxin

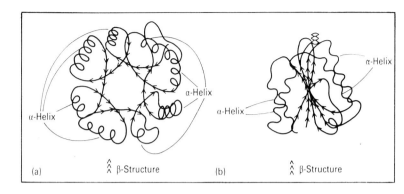

acids, the most stable β-conformations are not rectilinear but lightly twisted in a right-handed direction to form one or two major alignments:

1. the β-barrel, a cylindrical curvature promoted by a staggered hydrogen bond pattern with

α-helices or loops on the exterior of the molecule, or

2. the saddle conformation, a centrally constricted conformation in which the upper and lower hydrogen bonds are stretched.

4.7 The quaternary structure of proteins

The first oligomeric protein for which structural analysis was obtained by X-ray crystallography was the oxygen-transport protein of blood, haemoglobin. Haemoglobin (mol. wt $\simeq 64\ 500$) consists of four subunits. In human adult haemoglobin (Figure 4.17), the tetramer consists of two pairs of subunits: two α-chains (141 amino acid residues) and two β-chains of 146 residues each of which carries one haem group. The α- and β-chains share similar characteristics with each other and with myoglobin so that the conformational details given for myoglobin in Section 4.6 generally apply to each haemoglobin chain. A conformation–function relationship is thereby indicated.

Between each identical subunit, there are only a few electrostatic connections. Although there are two cysteinyl residues per α-chain and one per β-chain, no covalent bonding occurs between the

four subunits. Between one α- and one β-subunit, there are longer regions of electrostatic interactions which produce two identical dimers, $\alpha_1\beta_1$ and $\alpha_2\beta_2$ which are capable of integrated movement. Between the dimers exists a network of ionic and hydrogen bonds, which on reversible oxygenation of haemoglobin is disrupted and supplanted by the formation of new bonds. X-ray crystallography has shown that, on oxygenation, there is no change in the tertiary structure of each subunit but the α and β chains undergo opposite rotational and positional changes of different magnitude causing a repackaging of the subunits.

Myoglobin adsorbs oxygen whereas haemoglobin demonstrates a slow initial oxygen-binding which becomes progressively faster. This phenomenon is called positive cooperativity in which the binding of the first oxygen molecule to deoxyhaemoglobin facilitates the binding of subsequent

FIGURE 4.17 Tetrameric arrangement of α- and β-globin chains in haemoglobin A

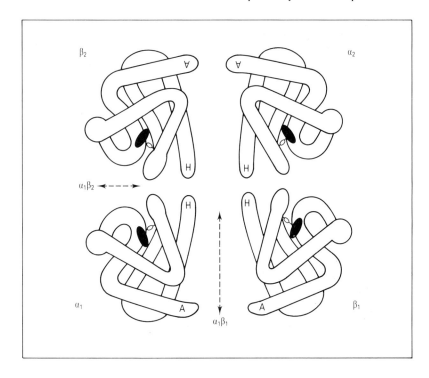

oxygens to the other subunits. Conversely during deoxygenation, the loss of the first oxygen molecule from oxygenated haemoglobin promotes the dissociation of oxygen from the other subunits. In addition to changes in quaternary structure due to oxygenation/deoxygenation, other factors including the concentrations of CO_2, 2,3-bisphosphoglycerate (2,3-BPG, an erythrocyte metabolite) and hydrogen ions also participate in the regulation of oxygen binding by haemoglobin. These substances bind to the protein (and are therefore called ligands) of haemoglobin and influence the uptake of O_2 by haem groups. This indicates that modifications at one site of the protein may vary the activity at another site. This phenomenon is called allostery. The allosteric behaviour of regulatory enzymes is considered to make a major contribution to the control of metabolic processes (Section 6.4).

Over 300 variations from the amino acid sequence of normal human adult haemoglobin (HbA) have been reported. These molecules often differ from HbA by the insertion of an incorrect amino acid into either the α- or β-chains during protein synthesis. Other variants may be due to deletion or frameshift mutations (Section 17.7). Haemoglobin variants may function normally or abnormally depending on the nature and position of the substitution (Table 4.5).

Some severe haemoglobinopathies have been reported, e.g. HbS which causes the disease sickle cell anaemia in negros. In sickle cell anaemia, the haemoglobin (called HbS) contains normal α-chains but its β-chains contain valine instead of glutamate at residue 6. Therefore a hydrophobic amino acid replaces an acidic one. This new arrangement allows hydrophobic interaction with the β^{85}-phenylalanine and β^{88}-leucine of an adjacent deoxyHbS. This modifies the Hb conformation so that the stacking arrangement of the 280 million Hb molecules within each erythrocyte is altered by the production of fibrous aggregates of the protein.

TABLE 4.5   Haemoglobin variants

Haemoglobin type	Substitution‡	Functional defect
HbS	β^6Glu→Val	Erythrocytes sickle, decreased O_2 affinity
Hb$_\text{Köln}$*	β^{98}Val→Met	Unstable, increased O_2 affinity
Hb$_\text{Torino}$	α^{43}Phe→Val	Decreased O_2 affinity
HbG†$_\text{Honolulu}$	α^{30}Glu→Gln	Normal oxygen affinity
Hb$_\text{Camden}$	β^{131}Gln→Glu	Normal oxygen affinity
Hb$_\text{Denmark Hill}$	α^{95}Pro→Ala	Decreased O_2 affinity

*Haemoglobins are frequently named after their place of identification
†Hb is an abbreviation for haemoglobin; G refers to electrophoretic mobility
‡α or β refer to normal haemoglobin chains; the superscript number refers to residue number at which substitution has occurred; the substitution is recorded by first indicating the normal amino acid followed by its replacement

This leads to a change in the shape of the erythrocyte from a biconcave disc to a crescent or sickle shape on deoxygenation. In individuals who have two copies of the altered gene (homozygotes), the erythrocytes interact and form clumps which may occlude the capillaries of vital organs and eventually produce their failure, e.g. renal failure. The life expectancy of a homozygote is less than 30 years.

The mutation however confers an important advantage on its carriers if they reside in a malaria-afflicted area of the world. *Plasmodium vivax* (one protozoon responsible for malaria) requires entry to the erythrocytes of its host during its life cycle. Sickle cells because of their fragility are rapidly degraded by the spleen. Any parasite contained within these cells will also be destroyed by splenic activity.

Another group of conditions worthy of brief mention are the thalassaemias which are diseases caused by decreased synthesis of either normal α- or β-chains. β-Thalassaemia, common in some Mediterranean countries and in malaria-infested regions of Asia, has two main varieties: β^+-thalassaemia, in which a partial loss of β-chain production occurs, and β^0-thalassaemia, characterized by a lack of β-chain synthesis.

Immunoglobulins or antibodies are a family of extracellular glycoproteins which function in the body's defence against invading organisms and foreign substances. Their salient structural features follow.

1. They are divided according to the primary structure of their respective heavy chains, called gamma, mu, alpha, delta and epsilon, into five classes: IgG, IgM, IgA, IgD and IgE. Human IgG can be subdivided into four subclasses, IgG$_1$ etc., whilst IgA has two subclasses.

2. Each immunoglobulin molecule (Figure 4.18) consists of two identical light chains (kappa or lambda) which are attached to two identical heavy chains by covalent bonds. The two heavy chains are also interlinked by disulphide bonds.

3. Each polypeptide chain of immunoglobulins consists of two well-defined regions, designated V for variable and C for constant amino acid sequence within each class of antibody. The V region of a light chain (V_L) is approximately 50% of chain length; the V region of a heavy chain (V_H) is approximately 25% of chain length.

4. The immunoglobulins are digested by papain into two major fragments: the Fab fragment which retains the *a*ntigen-*b*inding capacity of the intact molecule and the Fc fragment which is *c*rystallizable. Digestion by pepsin yields a fragment containing two-linked antigen-binding sites called F(ab')$_2$.

5. Within each chain of the molecule, intrachain disulphide bonds fold the molecule into compact globular domains denoted V_L, C_H1 etc. The C_H regions of γ and α chains contain three domains whilst IgM, IgD and IgE exhibit four C_H domains. Individual domains have been associated with certain biological activities.

6. The ability of an antibody molecule to combine specifically with a complementary antigen resides in the unique conformation and amino acid sequence of the antigen-binding cleft

formed by the V_H and V_L regions of the molecule.

7. Within V_H and V_L regions, irrespective of specificity, certain positions are always occupied by the same amino acid while certain other positions exhibit only a limited variation. However, some positions display large variations in amino acid occupancy to constitute hypervariable regions. Hypervariability occurs at positions 31–37, 51–68, 86–91 and 101–109 inclusive in the V_H regions and positions 24–34, 50–56 and 89–97 inclusive in the V_L region. These hypervariable regions are juxtaposed by the foldings of the V_H and V_L regions to frame the antigen-binding sites.

8. Blood plasma IgM is a pentamer composed of five such Y-shaped structures. IgA in external secretions is a dimer. Both contain an additional polypeptide chain, the J chain. Secretory IgA is associated with a secretory component.

The specific interaction between an antibody and an antigen has been exploited in the immunoassay of biomolecules. Traditionally, these antibodies were obtained by injection of laboratory animals with purified antigen. Since the antibodies raised had specificity for the antigen but were of various classes, this *in vivo* technique produced a polyclonal antiserum. Developments of the *in vitro* (Latin, in glass) hybridoma technique (Section 16.7) allows the production of identical antibody molecules with absolute specificity for one antigenic determinant by a single clone of immunoglobulin-producing lymphocytes, i.e. monoclonal antibodies.

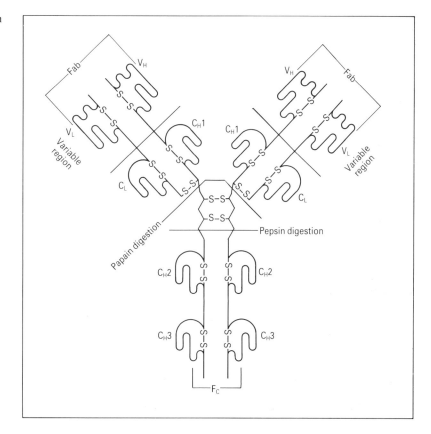

FIGURE 4.18 Schematic diagram of an IgG antibody molecule illustrating heavy and light chain domains and digest fragments

Suggested further reading

BELLANTI, J. A. (1985) *Immunology*, 3rd edn, Saunders, Philadelphia

CREIGHTON, T. E. (1985) *Proteins, Structures and Molecular Properties*, Freeman, New York

HUKINS, D. W. L. (1981) *X-Ray Diffraction by Disordered and Ordered Systems*, Pergamon, Oxford

CHAPTER 5

Enzymes

5.1 Comparison of chemical and enzymic reactions

Enzymes are proteins which accelerate the rates of the wide variety of chemical reactions which occur in biological systems under thermodynamically unfavourable conditions (Section 10.2). A catalyst is a substance which participates in a chemical reaction to enhance its rate without destruction or irreversible modification during the reaction. Enzymes are therefore considered as biological catalysts. The word enzyme (from Greek meaning in yeast) was introduced by Kühne in 1878 to refer to the occurrence in yeast of something responsible for its fermentative activity.

The effectiveness of enzymes can best be appreciated through the comparison of spontaneous chemical reactions and enzyme-catalysed reactions.

In the chemical reaction:

$$A + B \underset{v_2}{\overset{v_1}{\rightleftharpoons}} C + D$$

the rate or velocity, v, of the forward or reverse direction is proportional to the concentrations of the reactants, i.e.

$$v_1 = k_1 [A][B] \quad \text{or} \quad v_2 = k_2 [C][D]$$

where k_1 and k_2 are individual rate constants.

At equilibrium,

$$v_1 = v_2$$

Thus, $k_1 [A][B] = k_2 [C][D]$

Therefore $\dfrac{k_1}{k_2} = \dfrac{[C][D]}{[A][B]} = K_{eq}$, the equilibrium constant.

K_{eq} is a constant for the reaction, whether in the presence or absence of an enzyme. The presence of an enzyme, however, accelerates the attainment of the equilibrium state.

For the reaction to occur A and B must collide in the correct orientation so that orbital electrons can reposition to enable product formation. The closer the reactant molecules are the greater the chance of a collision, i.e. high concentrations of reactants augment the reaction. Enzymes promote the reaction by adsorbing the reactants on to a polypeptide chain in close proximity and proper orientation which results in an effective concentration of the reactants frequently present intracellularly in minute quantities.

For the reaction to occur A and B must collide with sufficient kinetic energy (energy of motion). In a solution of any molecular species, the molecules exhibit a range of kinetic energies due to fluctuations during random collisions. At a given time, only a small percentage of molecules will contain sufficient energy to result in the chemical reaction. The kinetic energy of the molecules can be increased by heating, which causes the molecule to hasten, collide more frequently and with greater impact during which some of the kinetic energy is converted into internal energy, causing the molecule to vibrate vigorously enhancing bond breakage. Enzymes, being proteins, cannot exploit this mechanism because of their potential denaturation by heat (Section 4.3). The rate of chemical reaction approximately doubles for every 10°C increase in temperature. This is only true for enzymic reactions within the temperature range in which the enzyme is stable. The proximity of the reactants to each other and the catalytic group on the surface of the enzyme is a positive advantage in the promotion of the reaction.

It is considered that, in energetic terms, the reactants do not directly yield products. According to the transition-state theory (based on the work of Eyring) the reaction proceeds through a high-energy state called the transition state (Figure 5.1). The kinetic energy of the reactants provides the energy for their delivery to the transition state. The energy required is called the activation energy (E_a) which may be evaluated from an Arrhenius plot (log reaction rate versus temperature^{-1}). The transition state is a state of maximum energy not an intermediate compound. At this point, the reaction may proceed to form products or revert to initial state reactants. The concentration of the 'activated complex' at the transition state determines the rate of the chemical reaction. Enzymes achieve their

reactions at relatively low temperatures by reducing the E_a required for the reaction because of the geometry of their reversible binding of the reactants. Although E_a is lowered, the net energetics of the reaction remains unaltered.

The stages of an enzyme-catalysed reaction involving only one reactant can be written as:

$$E + S \rightleftharpoons ES^* \rightleftharpoons ES \rightleftharpoons EX^* \rightleftharpoons EP \rightleftharpoons EP^* \rightleftharpoons P + E$$

where S = reactant called substrate, P = product, ES and EP = enzyme complexes and ES*, EX* and EP* = 'activated complexes' at transition states. For convenience, such reactions are frequently abbreviated to

$$E + S \rightleftharpoons ES \rightleftharpoons P + E$$

where ES = the enzyme–substrate complex.

FIGURE 5.1   Energy profile for uncatalysed and enzymic reactions

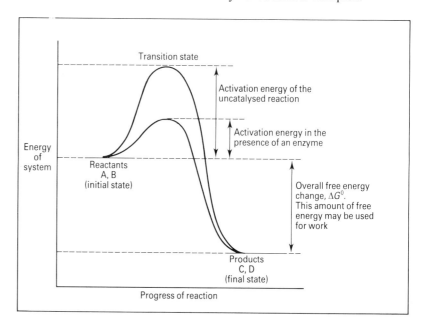

5.2 Enzyme architecture

As enzymes are globular proteins, their three-dimensional conformation is governed by the bonding arrangements (Section 4.3) which fold the protein in a specific manner and may cause distal amino acid R groups to be juxtaposed. The specific region of the convoluted polypeptide chain to which a substrate will bind is termed the active

site. Active sites are formed by a number of amino acid R groups as grooves or pockets resultant from the three-dimensional structure. Treatments which denature proteins will cause conformational changes in the active site with commensurate loss of catalytic activity. Amino acid residues within the active site called 'contact residues' function to attract and orientate the substrate and are responsible for the specificity of the enzyme. Substrates are bound to the active site by the chemical and physical properties of the amino acids, i.e. by hydrophobic interactions, ionic interactions between oppositely charged groups present on the enzyme and substrate, hydrogen bonding between hydrophilic amino acids (Table 4.2) and polar substrates. For example, chymotrypsin contains a hydrophobic pocket into which an aromatic residue may enter and bind to position the substrate's polypeptide chain for cleavage. Other amino acid functional groups called 'catalytic residues' form bonds with the substrate molecule and effect the catalytic change.

Because of the specific three-dimensional shape of the active site and the nature of the substrate-binding processes, the enzyme may only bind substrates with an appropriate structure. Enzymes exhibit substrate specificity of which there are four main classes:

1. Absolute specificity in which an enzyme binds only one biological substrate and catalyses only one of the reactions in which the substance may participate, e.g. glucose-6-phosphate dehydrogenase.

2. Relative (group) specificity in which certain enzymes can act on a group of structurally similar substrates, e.g. cytosol aminopeptidase (Section 4.4).

3. Linkage specificity in which certain enzymes are specific for a particular type of chemical linkage, e.g. esterases only cleave ester linkages.

4. Stereospecificity in which certain enzymes can differentiate between D- and L-stereoisomers, e.g. arginase only hydrolyses L-arginine (Section 16.5).

Stereospecificity led Fischer in 1894 to propose the lock-and-key hypothesis in which substrates were considered to have a structure complementary to a rigid active site, analogous to a key fitting a lock. Although adequate to explain stereo- and absolute specificity, this model cannot account for relative and linkage specificity. In 1958, Koshland propounded a modification called the induced-fit model in which the contact residues may interact with potential substrates. Following this initial binding, the substrate induces a conformational change in a flexible active site to improve the enzyme–substrate fit and locate the catalytic groups (Figure. 5.2).

To obtain information on the nature of the

FIGURE 5.2 Two proposed models for the binding of substrate to an enzyme. (a) Fischer's lock and key model. (b) Koshland's induced-fit model

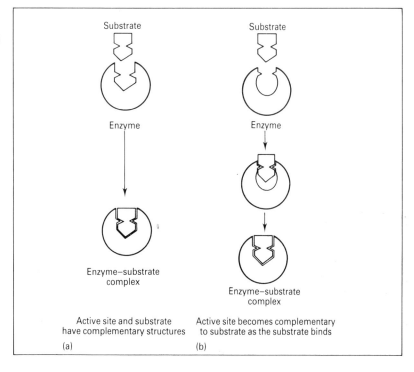

amino acid residues at the active site, a variety of methods have been employed, three of which are briefly described below.

1. Identification of the intermediate form of the enzyme: the enzyme phosphoglucomutase catalyses the conversion of glucose 1-phosphate to glucose 6-phosphate. Phosphoserine has been identified in this enzyme to demonstrate that serine participates as the intermediate phosphate acceptor.
2. Group-specific reagents: there are a variety of reagents which can specifically modify functional groups found in enzymes, e.g. iodoacetate at pH 5.5 was employed to identify specific histidine residues important in the catalytic activity of pancreatic ribonuclease. The other histidine residues in this enzyme molecule are less reactive with iodoacetate.
3. Affinity labels: these substances are complementary in structure to the substrate but incorporate one or more additional reactive groups. Once attached to the active site, the affinity label reacts to bond covalently to a near-by amino acid residue. These substances are designed on the consideration of the mechanism of binding and catalysis and are inactive outside the active site. For example, L-1-(p-toluenesulphonyl)-amido-2-phenylethylchloromethyl ketone (TPCK) was contrived as an affinity label for the peptidase, chymotrypsin (Table 4.4) with the benzyl group mimicking the aromatic group of substrate and stabilization of the enzyme–inhibitor complex by hydrogen bonding between the carbonyl group and a serine of the active site. TPCK irreversibly inactivated the enzyme and subsequent analysis demonstrated the modification of one histidine residue at position 57.

Sometimes enzyme activity results solely from the nature of the active site, e.g. pancreatic ribonuclease. Many enzymes also require an additional component called a cofactor for their activity. This type of enzyme is called a conjugated enzyme or holoenzyme, the protein component of which is

FIGURE 5.3 Structures and roles of some coenzymes. (a) Nicotinamide adenine dinucleotide (NAD) and nicotinamide adenine dinucleotide phosphate (NADP)

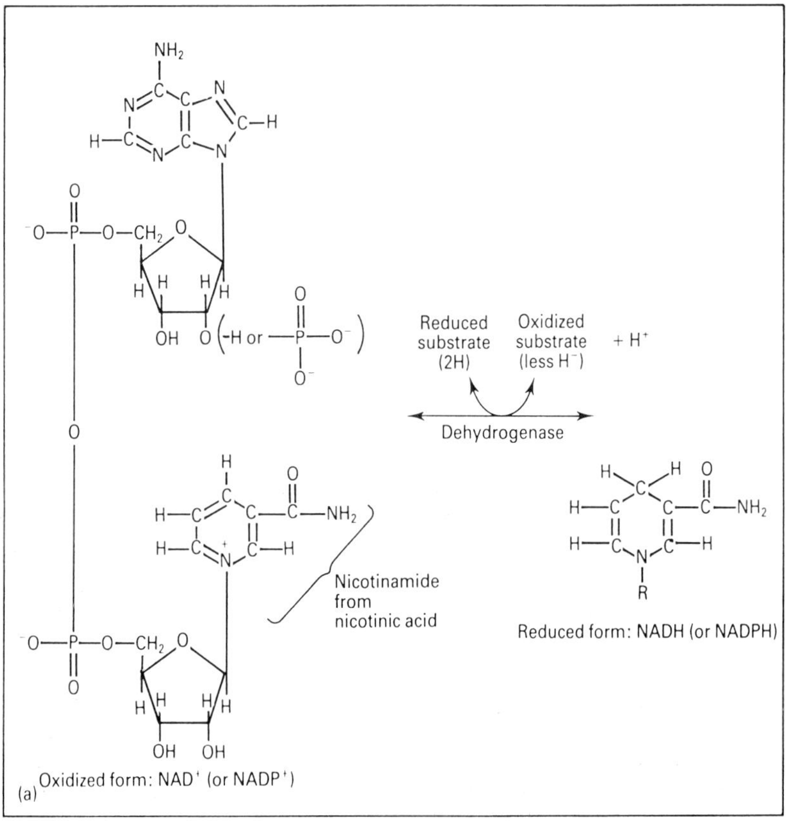

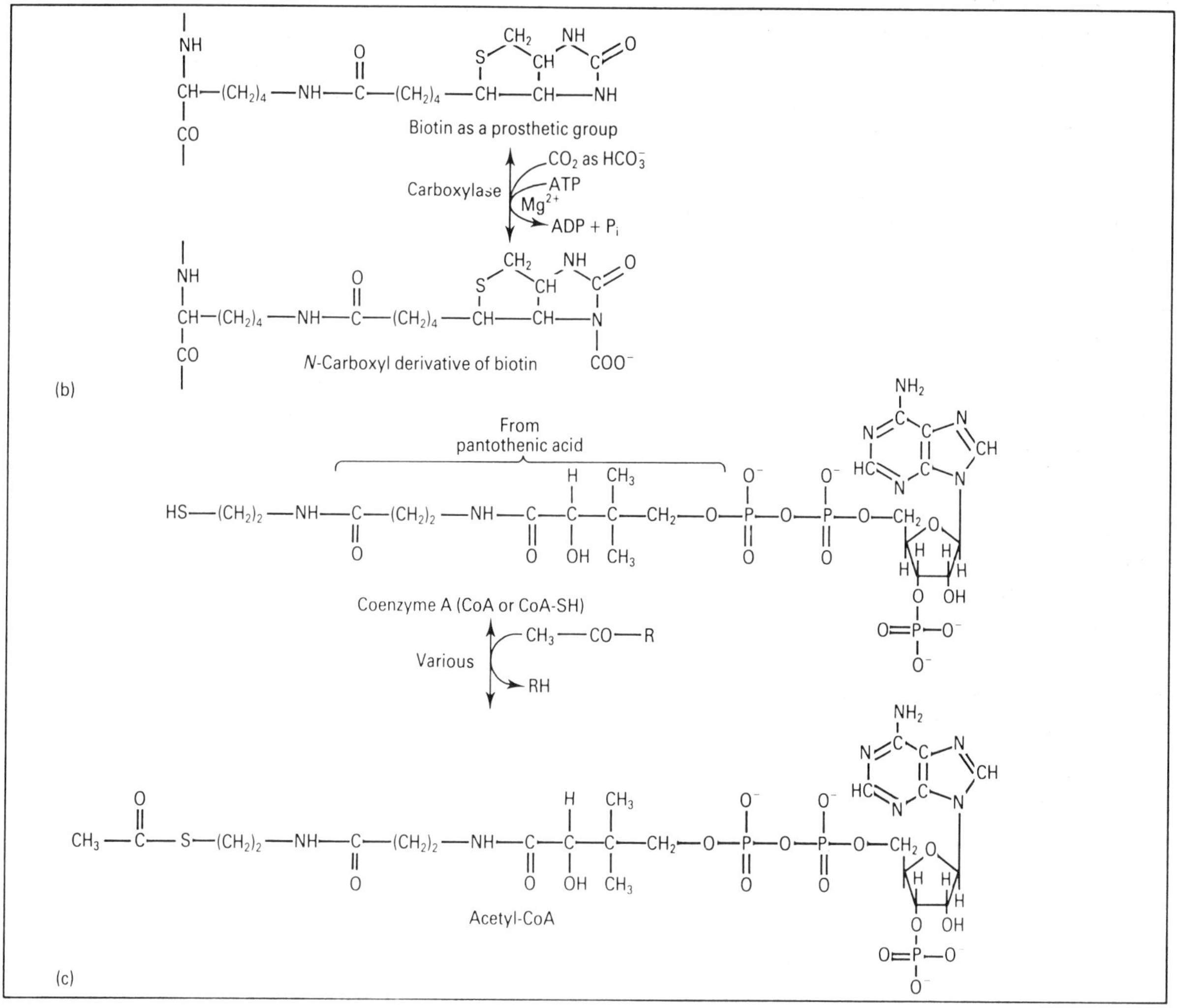

FIGURE 5.3 (*continued*)   (b) Biotin. (c) Coenzyme A

termed the apoenzyme. If the cofactor is tightly bound to the protein molecule by covalent bonds, it is called a prosthetic group. The cofactor may be inorganic ions, e.g. Fe^{2+}, Zn^{2+}, Mg^{2+}, Cu^{2+}, K^+, or a complex organic molecule called a coenzyme (Figure 5.3). Cofactors are bound into the active site together with the substrate and participate in the catalysis. Coenzymes generally act as acceptors or donors of a functional group or atoms which are removed from or contributed to the substrate. They are frequently large in size in comparison to their functional group. The remainder of the molecule is responsible for their enzyme-binding properties. All or component parts of some coenzyme molecules may not be synthesized *de novo* by the organism and are obtained from the diet or the external environment. The required precursors are called vitamins (Table 5.1). The vitamin concept does not apply to photosynthetic organisms (Section 14.1) which are capable of manufacturing all necessary organic substances from CO_2.

Many enzymes are organized into macromolecular complexes, found either free in the cytosol or within cellular membranes. These complexes facilitate the coordination and control of metabolic reactions.

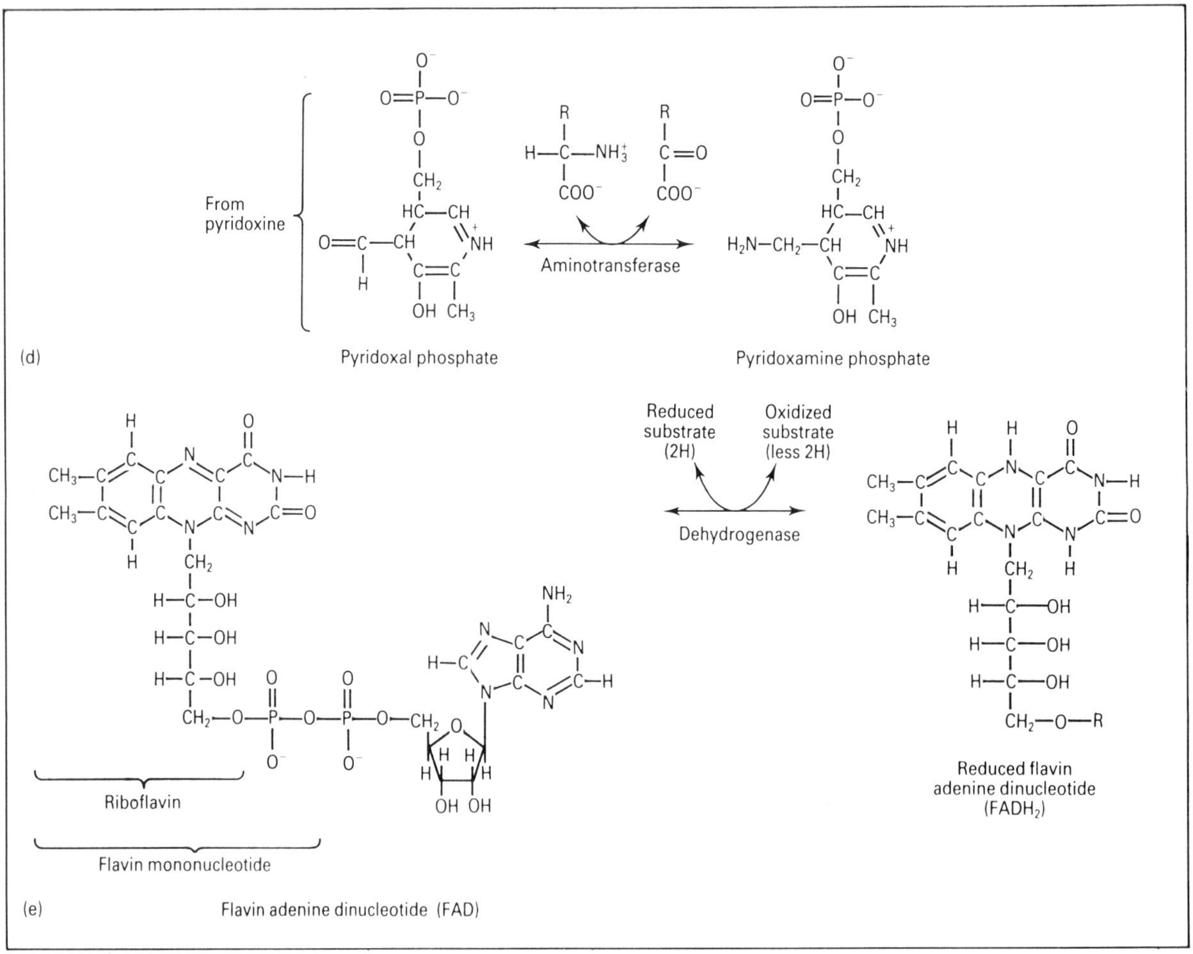

FIGURE 5.3 (*continued*)   (d) Pyridoxal phosphate. (e) Flavin adenine dinucleotide (FAD)

TABLE 5.1   Some coenzymes, their functions and precursor requirements

Coenzyme	Function-associated enzymes	Vitamin
Nicotinamide adenine dinucleotide (NAD$^+$)	Hydrogen transfer (as hydride ions) – dehydrogenase	Nicotinic acid
Nicotinamide adenine dinucleotide phosphate (NADP$^+$)	Hydrogen transfer (as hydride ions) – dehydrogenase	Nicotinic acid
Biotin	CO_2 transfer – carboxylase	Whole molecule
Coenzyme A	Acetyl group transfer – various	Pantothenic acid
Pyridoxal phosphate	Amino group transfer – aminotransferase	Pyridoxine
Flavin adenine dinucleotide (FAD)	Hydrogen transfer (as hydrogen atoms) – dehydrogenase	Riboflavin
Flavin mononucleotide (FMN)	Hydrogen transfer (as hydrogen atoms) – dehydrogenase	Riboflavin

5.3 Enzyme classification

By the late 1950s, enzyme nomenclature was in confusion. Without any guiding authority, the increase in known enzymes had led to the assignment of misleading or inappropriate names, and in many cases the same enzyme became known by several names while some catalytically different enzymes were identically named. In 1961, the first Enzyme Commission reported a system for enzyme classification and the assignment of code numbers.

The general principles of the current classification and nomenclature of enzymes are:

1. that enzyme names, especially those ending in -ase, should be used only for single enzymes. If the system features more than one catalytic entity, the word system should be included in the name;

TABLE 5.2   The six main divisions in enzyme classification

Number	Division	Catalytic activity
1	Oxidoreductases	Enzymes catalysing oxidoreduction reactions. The substrate is regarded as the hydrogen donor
2	Transferases	Enzymes transferring a group from one compound to another compound
3	Hydrolases	Enzymes catalysing the hydrolytic cleavage of C—O, C—N, C—C plus some other bonds
4	Lyases	Enzymes cleaving C—C, C—O, C—N and other bonds by elimination, leaving double bonds or rings, or conversely adding groups to double bonds
5	Isomerases	Enzymes catalysing geometric or structural changes within one molecule
6	Ligases	Enzymes catalysing the joining together of two molecules coupled with the hydrolysis of a pyrophosphate bond in ATP or a similar triphosphate

TABLE 5.3   Some examples of enzyme commission classification and coding

EC no. Explanation	Recommended name	Reaction	Basis for classification Systematic name
1.1.1.1 — With NAD^+ ($NADP^+$) as acceptor — Acting on CH—OH group of donors — Oxidoreductase	Alcohol dehydrogenase	Alcohol + NAD^+ = aldehyde ⎫ or ketone ⎭ + NADH	Alcohol: NAD^+ oxidoreductase
1.2.1.2 — With NAD^+ ($NADP^+$) as acceptor — Acting on the CHO or oxo group of donors — Oxidoreductase	Formate dehydrogenase	Formate + NAD^+ = CO_2 + NADH	Formate: NAD^+ oxidoreductase
2.1.3.3 — Carboxyl and carbamoyltransferases — Transfer of carbon groups — Transferase	Ornithine carbamoyltransferase	Carbamoyl phosphate + L-ornithine = orthophosphate + L-citrulline	Carbamoyl phosphate: L-ornithine carbamoyltransferase
3.1.3.9 — Phosphoric monoester hydrolase — Acting on ester bonds — Hydrolase	Glucose-6-phosphatase	D-Glucose 6-phosphate + H_2O = D-glucose + orthophosphate	D-Glucose-6-phosphate phosphohydrolase

2. that an enzyme is classified and named according to the specific reaction which it catalyses;
3. that enzymes be divided into groups on the basis of the type of chemical reaction catalysed.

Each enzyme is given a four-number code, e.g.

EC 3.1.3.9. The first number designates one of the six main divisions (Table 5.2), the second number indicates the subclass, the third number indicates the sub-subclass and the fourth number is the serial number of the enzyme in its sub-subclass (Table 5.3).

5.4 Enzymic catalysis

Although the enzymic reaction is denoted by

$$E + S \rightleftharpoons ES \rightleftharpoons P + E$$

the chemistry involved in substrate transformation varies among enzymes. In addition to catalytically reactive groups, other factors, not accessible to simple chemical catalysts, may conspire to promote such reactions (Section 5.1).

Four major factors have been advanced to account for the catalytic power of enzymes.

1. Proximity and orientation effects: substrates may interact with the enzyme and be positioned close to each other, close to the catalytic group and accurately oriented to minimize the activation energy requirement for entry into the transition state.
2. Distortion or strain effects: according to the induced-fit model (Section 5.2), the substrate may induce conformational changes in the active site of the enzyme. Positional movements in the polypeptide chain may distort or stretch pertinent bonds in the substrate contributing to the attainment of the transition state.
3. General acid–base catalysis: R groups of certain amino acids at the active site may donate or accept protons (Brönsted–Lowry acids or bases, Section 2.5) to or from bound substrates. Although such mechanisms are pH-dependent, they are augmented by the internal non-aqueous environment of many enzymes which influences the acidity or basicity of important amino, carboxylate, sulphydryl, imidazole and phenolic R groups. When protonated, they behave as acidic catalysts and their unprotonated forms act as basic catalysts.
4. Covalent catalysis: substrates may bind to the enzyme by temporary unstable covalent bonds which indicates a modulation of the electronic arrangement of both the substrate and the enzyme. The reactive groups involved are

described as electrophiles and nucleophiles. Enzymic electrophilic groups are electron deficient and attract electrons from the substrate. Conversely, nucleophilic groups are electron-rich and deliver electrons to electropositive substrates (Figure 5.4).

Potential nucleophilic groups are the hydroxyls of serine and tyrosine, the carboxylates of aspartate and glutamate, the imidazole of histidine and sulphydryl of cysteine. Although there are no strongly electrophilic amino acid R groups, cofactors (e.g. Mg^{2+}, Fe^{3+}) or coenzymes (e.g. NAD^+) may supply the electrophile.

The significance of these outlined principles may be perceived on the consideration of some enzymes whose primary structure, active-site structure and substrate-binding characteristics have been elucidated and for which rational mechanisms of action have been proffered. Two examples follow.

(i) The serine proteases are a group of enzymes which hydrolyse polypeptide chains. Their catalytic activity is dependent upon a seryl residue in the active site. All serine proteases, e.g. chymotrypsin, trypsin, elastase, thrombin, plasmin and subtilisin, function by a similar mechanism.

Chymotrypsin is synthesized as inactive chymotrypsinogen, a single polypeptide chain of 245 residues containing five intrachain disulphide bonds. Its activation by trypsin involves removal of two dipeptides, positions 14–15 and 147–148, to yield polypeptide chains, A, B and C conjoined by two disulphide bonds. Histidyl, aspartyl and seryl residues in positions 57, 102 and 195 respectively feature in the active site although the serine is present on a different chain. The polypeptide chain of the substrate is positioned antiparallel to the enzyme by hydrogen bonding to the peptide bonds of residues 215–219. The R group of the substrate prior to a cleavage point (Table 4.4) enters a hydrophobic pocket formed by residues 214–220,

FIGURE 5.4 Covalent catalysis.
(a) Nucleophilic attack by the
enzyme. (b) Electrophilic attack by
the enzyme

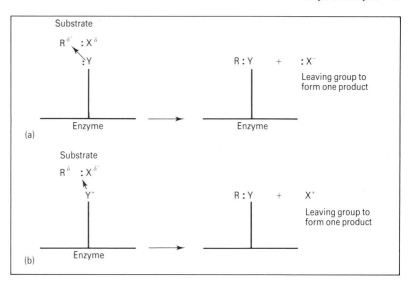

191–195 and a disulphide bond. The geometry and nature of this pocket provides an explanation for the specificity differences between chymotrypsin (Tyr-, Trp-, Phe-, Leu-), trypsin (Arg-, Lys-) and elastase (Glu-, Ala-, Val-, Leu-, Ile-), although each enzyme contains the same critical residues in identical positions. The pocket of chymotrypsin accommodates large aromatic groups whereas in trypsin a lysyl or arginyl group is permitted entry but the occluded entrance of the elastase pocket excludes bulky groups. When the R group is held in position, catalysis by the following mechanism (Figure 5.5) may proceed. In stage 1, histidine 57 acts as a base with the assistance of the electronegative carboxylate of aspartate-102 which forms transiently a hydrogen bond with the imidazole group proton, to draw the proton from the hydroxyl group of serine-195. This process is referred to as charge relay. Nucleophilic attack by the serine oxygen on the substrate carbonyl group results in covalent bonding. In stage 2, the histidine now acts as an acid and donates a proton to the imino group of the peptide bond. The N–C bond is thereby weakened, and in stage 3, the polypeptide chain with a free N-terminus departs from the active sites. The carbonyl group of the peptide bond remains attached to the seryl group as an acylated intermediate which is then deacylated by hydrolysis through the following stages. In stage 4, charge relay operates to enable a basic histidine-57 to deprotonate the water molecule, the oxygen of which acts as a nucleophile to form a covalent

bond through the carbonyl carbon of the substrate. Stage 5 involves electronic rearrangement and proton transfer by histidine-57 to re-form the serine hydroxyl group and terminate the covalent bonding. In stage 6, the C-terminus of a second polypeptide chain is released from the active site. Serine protease activity therefore utilizes both general acid–base and covalent catalysis in a sequential mechanism.

(ii) Lysozyme, a single polypeptide chain of 129 residues, may effect bacterial lysis through cleavage of the peptidoglycan of their cell wall (Section 3.7). The mechanism of action of lysozyme employs distortion of the polysaccharide chain and general acid catalysis. Investigations with N-acetylglucosamine oligomers have revealed that increasing the number of residues from four to five markedly increases the rate of catalysis with further enhancement on the addition of a sixth residue.

X-ray crystallography has shown that an N-acetylglucosamine trimer may occupy binding sites A, B and C but information with respect to longer oligomers has been derived from model building (Figure 5.6). The 3-lactyl groups of the natural substrate restricts its binding so that N-acetylglucosamine residues occupy sites A, C and E and N-acetylmuramic acids occupy sites B, D and F. However, the structure of site D causes distortion of the chair conformation (Section 3.3) of the respective residue. The binding of the other residues to their sites is energetically favourable and compensates for the unfavourable binding to site

62

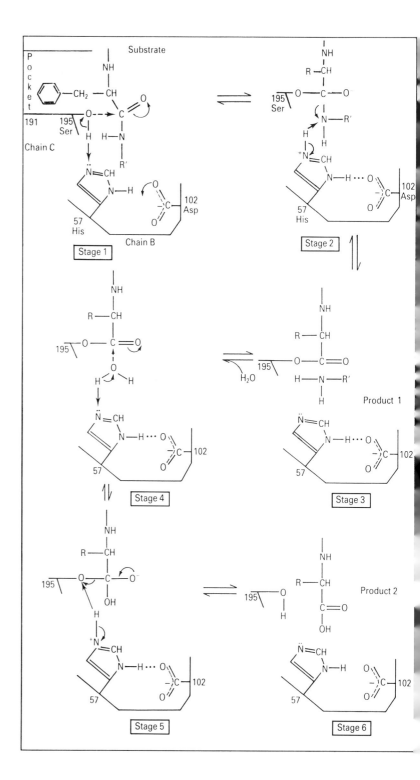

FIGURE 5.5   Possible mode of action of chymotrypsin

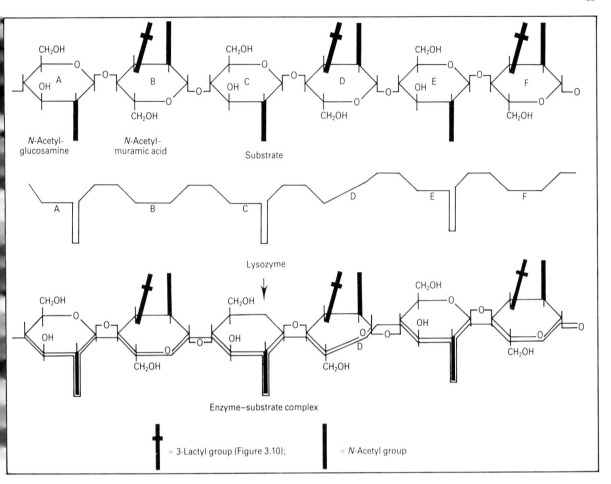

FIGURE 5.6 Binding of the peptidoglycan backbone to lysozyme results in distortion in the substrate

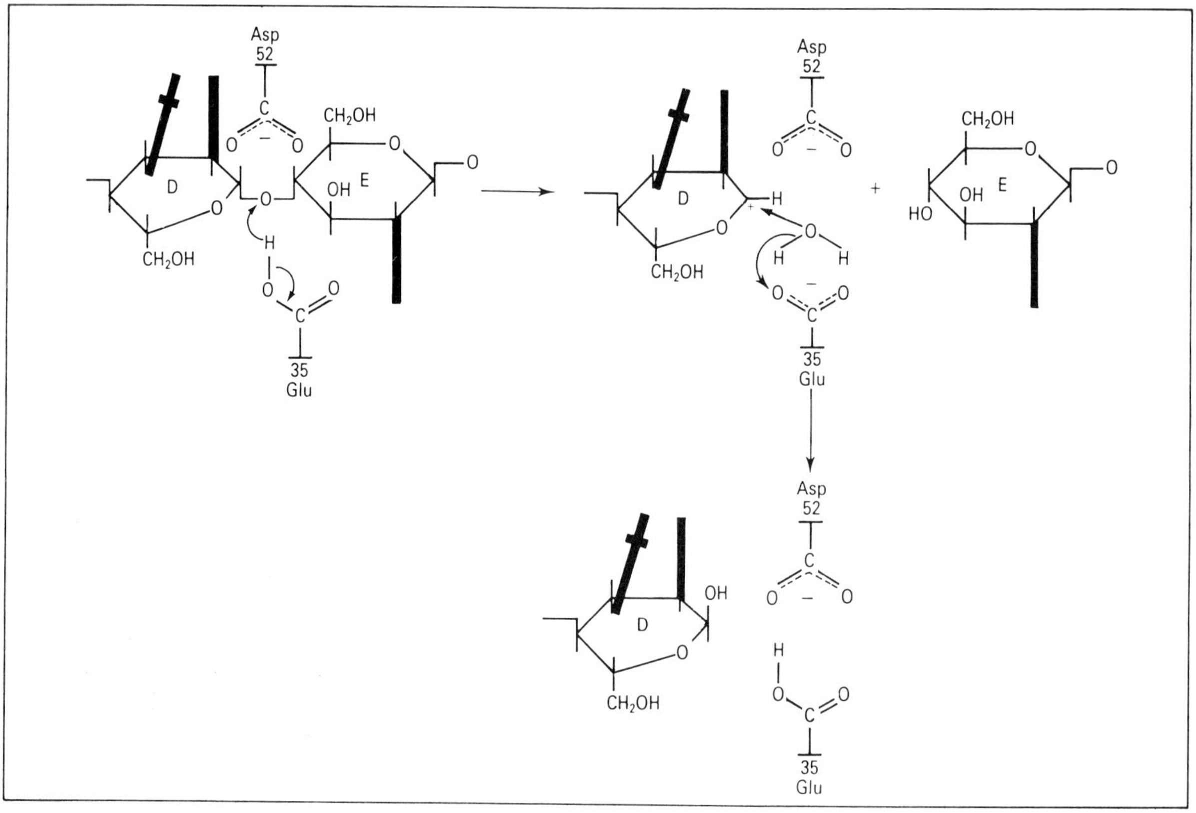

FIGURE 5.7   Mechanism of action of lysozyme

D. Complex formation is promoted by hydrogen bonding and non-polar interactions. The distortion in residue D is believed to reduce the activation energy which contributes to the effectiveness of the hydrolysis of the glycosidic linkage between residues D and E.

The identification of the cleaved bond directed the search for the catalytic groups. Two amino acid residues emerged as candidates: an aspartic acid at position 52 and a glutamic acid at position 35 which lie within different environments close to but on different sides of the glycosidic bond. At optimum pH 5, aspartate-52 in its polar surroundings is deprotonated whereas glutamate-35 is protonated and may act as an acid. It has been proposed that glutamate-35 donates H^+ to the oxygen of the glycosidic linkage between residue D and E (Figure 5.7). The bond is cleaved with residue D forming a carbonium ion promoted by the ring distortion and stabilized by the electronegative aspartate and the pyranose ring oxygen atom. Residues E and F are released from the active site. The hydroxyl group of a water interacts with the carbonium ion intermediate whilst the H^+ restores glutamate-35 to its acidic form. Upon the departure of residues A, B, C and D, a new catalytic cycle may commence.

Suggested further reading

DIXON, M. and WEBB, E. C. (1979) *Enzymes*, 3rd edn, Longman, London

Enzyme Nomenclature: Recommendations (1984) of the Nomenclature Committee of the International Union of Biochemistry, Academic Press, Orlando

FOSTER, R. L. (1980) *The Nature of Enzymology*, Croom Helm, London

HAMMES, G. G. (1982) *Enzyme Catalysis and Regulation*, Academic Press, New York

CHAPTER 6

Enzyme kinetics

6.1 Factors influencing the rate of an enzyme-catalysed reaction

The general equation of a one-substrate enzymic reaction:

$$E + S \rightleftharpoons ES \rightleftharpoons P + E$$

indicates that the substrate will bind to the enzyme to form an enzyme–substrate complex which will either yield product and free enzyme or the reactants (Section 5.1). The concentrations of enzyme [E] and substrate [S] available to form ES will influence the rate of product formation whose concentration will increase with time until an equilibrium is achieved since the reaction is reversible. Initially, the enzyme will cycle between substrate binding and product release. Because of the nature of substrate binding and catalysis (Section 5.4), factors such as pH and temperature are also important.

The catalytic activity of an enzyme is usually assayed by incubating a mixture containing a known [S] and [E] at a suitable pH for an appropriate length of time. After incubation, the appearance of product (or sometimes the disappearance of substrate) is estimated. A common approach is the measurement of its concentration-dependent capacity to absorb light in a spectrophotometer either directly or after a chemical reaction which produces a coloured solution. The activities of enzymes which utilize NAD or NADP in oxidized or reduced form (Figure 5.3a) are generally assayed directly at a wavelength of 340 nm where NAD(P)H but not NAD(P)$^+$ exhibits an absorbance maximum (Figure 6.1). If a substrate is converted into a product by an oxidoreductase

FIGURE 6.1 Absorption spectra of NAD$^+$ and NADH

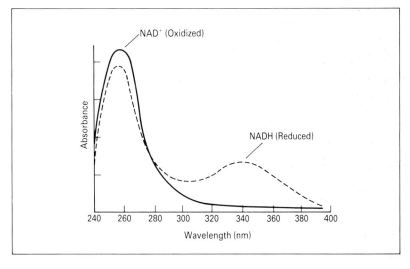

(Section 5.3) which requires $NAD(P)^+$ as coenzyme, the resultant $NAD(P)H$ may be measured at this wavelength. Where $NAD(P)^+ \leftrightarrow NAD(P)H$ conversions do not apply, the product may be linked to a further reaction which involves these coenzymes.

The activity of enzymes can be expressed in a number of ways:

1. The recommended unit of enzyme activity is the katal, which is the amount of activity that converts 1 mol of substrate s^{-1}. Frequently, the activities are expressed in microkatals (μkat), nanokatals (nkat) etc. corresponding to reaction rates of μmol, nmol s^{-1} respectively.

2. An older term, the International Enzyme Unit (IU), is defined as the amount of enzyme which will catalyse the transformation of 1 μmol of substrate min^{-1} under standard conditions.

Other related terms are:

FIGURE 6.2 Progress curve of typical enzyme-catalysed reaction

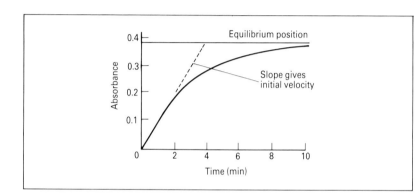

FIGURE 6.3 Effects of (a) enzyme concentration and (b) substrate concentration on reaction rate when enzyme and substrate are incubated for a constant time

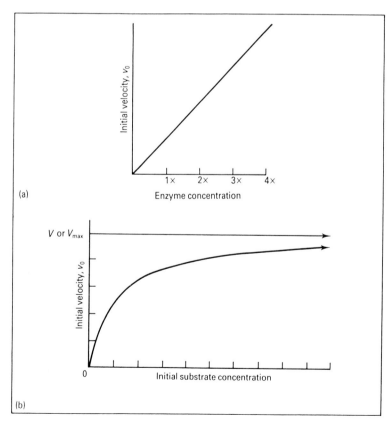

1. The specific activity of an enzyme preparation is kat kg^{-1} of protein or IU mg^{-1} of protein.
2. The molar activity is kat mol^{-1} of enzyme.
3. The turnover number of an enzyme is the number of molecules of substrate transformed per active site of the enzyme min^{-1}.

In an enzyme–substrate reaction mixture at a constant temperature, the reaction velocity decreases as a function of time (Figure 6.2). This decline may occur for numerous reasons:

1. The approach to an equilibrium and the associated influence of the reverse reaction.
2. The depletion of the substrate leads to the reduced occupancy of active sites.
3. The product(s) of the reaction may inhibit the enzyme or change the pH if the medium is inadequately buffered.
4. The enzyme may undergo some progressive inactivation at the temperature or pH of the reaction due to instability.

Enzymes are therefore studied within their initial velocity (v) range, i.e. at the initial stage before these factors exert an influence on the reaction. The initial velocity may be determined from the slope of a tangent to the curve at time zero (v_0).

The rate of an enzyme-catalysed reaction depends directly on the concentration of the enzyme when the substrate is present in excess (Figure 6.3a). This is because of the provision of additional catalytic sites to which the substrate may bind with concomitant rate enhancement.

The concentration of substrate also influences the initial velocity but not in a simple manner (Figure 6.3b). At a constant [E], the hyperbolic plot obtained with different initial substrate concentrations shows that the rate is initially proportional to [S], i.e. first order with respect to substrate. (In the orders of chemical reactions, the reaction is first order when its rate is proportional to the first power of the concentration of just one reactant.) At extremely high substrate concentrations, the reaction rate approaches a constant rate (Section 6.2). This is the maximum velocity (V or V_{max}) attainable for this particular [E]. The available active sites of all the enzyme molecules are occupied by the substrate; the enzyme is saturated. To increase the rate, additional active sites must be made available by the addition of more enzyme. The reaction rate at V is independent of [S] and is zero order with respect to substrate. Between the extremities, the reaction is a mixture

of zero- and first-order kinetics. This behaviour of an enzyme led to the concept of an enzyme–substrate complex intermediate and the underpinning of modern enzyme kinetics by the Michaelis–Menten equation (Section 6.2).

Each enzyme exhibits maximum activity at a characteristic pH called its optimum pH (Figure 6.4a). The bell-shaped plot illustrates that limited departures from this pH leads to a reduced enzymic performance due to changes in the ionization of contact and catalytic amino acid residues (Section 5.2). pH changes also modify ionic substrates. If a COO$^-$ group of an aspartate is required to bind a positively charged substrate, protonation would reduce the force of attraction and decrease the affinity of the enzyme for the substrate although it becomes more positively charged. The stability of the enzyme may be compromised by pH-induced conformational changes with loss of activity. This may occur on either or both sides of the optimum pH or in combination with the above effects.

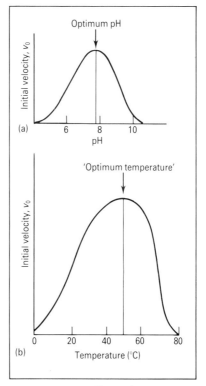

FIGURE 6.4 Effects of (a) pH and (b) temperature on reaction rate when enzyme and substrate are incubated for a constant time

The temperature at which an enzymic reaction is measured profoundly affects v_0 (Figure 6.4b). Enzymic reactions occur slowly at 0°C because of the low level of molecular kinetic energy which limits substrate–enzyme collisions and the attainment of the transition state (Section 5.1). Increasing temperature promotes both these events. The approximately twofold rate enhancement per 10°C rise reflects the activation energy requirement to achieve the transition state. At higher temperatures, product formation declines due to conformational changes in the enzyme by thermal denaturation which reduces the effective [E]. The maximum rate of substrate conversion into product is time dependent. As the duration of incubation is extended, the plot in Figure 6.4(b) is displaced to the left.

6.2 Steady-state enzyme kinetics

A basic theory of enzyme action was proposed in 1913 when Michaelis and Menten developed a mathematical expression to rationalize the hyperbolic plot of v_0 as a function of [S]. The Michaelis–Menten equation aims to describe the interrelationship between the parameters pertaining to an enzymic reaction. This accomplishment was based on two assumptions:

(i) the enzyme–substrate complex (ES) is in equilibrium with free enzyme and substrate in solution; i.e. $E + S \rightleftharpoons ES$ and
(ii) the formation of this complex is essential for product formation; i.e. $ES \rightarrow P + E$.

The current derivation of their equation incorporates a further assumption, introduced by Briggs and Haldane in 1925:

(iii) [ES] is constant; i.e. in a steady-state in which the formation and breakdown of ES are dynamically balanced. The Michaelis–Menten equation is accordingly derived in Figure 6.5.

The Michaelis–Menten equation

$$v_0 = \frac{V[S]}{K_m + [S]}$$

relates the components of an enzymic reaction, [S] and [E], to velocity, initial and maximum, through a rate constant, called K_m, the Michaelis constant, where

$$K_m = \frac{\text{rate of breakdown of the ES complex}}{\text{rate of formation of the ES complex}}$$

V or (V_{max}) is defined as the maximum velocity of an enzymic reaction. K_m is defined as the substrate concentration at which an enzyme demonstrates 50% of its maximum velocity (Figure 6.6). K_m is therefore the [S] at which half of the active sites of the enzyme are occupied. The K_m is a constant characteristic of an enzyme for its conversion of a substrate. V is dependent upon [E] which is thereby represented in the equation. Modern enzyme kinetics is founded upon this equation which allows the rate of the reaction at any [S] to be calculated, if K_m and V are known. This is of importance in understanding the behaviour of metabolic pathways (Section 10.5). The smaller the value of K_m the greater the enzyme's affinity for the substrate and the quicker the reaction: the largest K_m represents the rate-limiting reaction in a metabolic pathway.

To estimate K_m and V, the initial rate is measured at several different substrate concentrations. However, the hyperbolic plot of initial velocity as a function of [S] is inadequate to determine V accurately since at an [S] of $10 \times K_m$ only approximately 90% V is achieved (Figure 6.7a). At greater concentrations, additional problems such as substrate insolubility, formation of non-productive enzyme–substrate complexes through substrate inhibition mechanisms and salt effects may be encountered. To obtain an accurate estimation of V and hence K_m, enzymologists rearranged the Michaelis–Menten equation to produce linear plotting methods, e.g. Lineweaver–Burk, Eadie–Hofstee (Figure 6.7b,c) and other plots. The Lineweaver–Burk plot (derivation in Figure 6.8) is a popular method although the use of reciprocals results in points nearest to the origin representing the highest rates and [S] values and emphasizes less precise measurements at low [S] with less accent on more accurate higher rates. The Eadie–Hofstee plot aims to improve the accuracy of V and K_m data by improvements in the weighting and separation of points and the exactness of the line but suffers from compounding errors by not retaining

FIGURE 6.5 Derivation of the Michaelis–Menten equation using the steady-state assumption

General equation: $E + S \underset{k_{-1}}{\overset{k_1}{\rightleftharpoons}} ES \underset{k_{-2}}{\overset{k_2}{\rightleftharpoons}} P + E$

Objective: To define a general expression for v_0, the initial velocity of the reaction

Derivation: v_0 = initial rate of product formation = k_2 [ES]

Unfortunately, k_2 and [ES] cannot be measured directly. Therefore, find an alternative expression for v_0 in measurable variables, i.e. [E], [S]

(i) Consider the formation of ES:

$$\therefore \frac{d[ES]}{dt} = k_1[E][S]$$

As the steady-state assumption is justifiable only where $[S] > 1000 \times [E]$:

(a) differentiate between free and combined enzyme and
(b) ignore ES formation by the reverse direction, $P + E \overset{k_{-2}}{\rightleftharpoons} ES$ because the reverse reaction is negligible initially:

$$\therefore \frac{d[ES]}{dt} = k_1([E_t] - [ES])[S] \text{ where } E_t = \text{total enzyme (free and combined forms)}$$

(ii) Consider the breakdown of ES, i.e. in forward and reverse directions:

$$\frac{-d[ES]}{dt} = k_{-1}[ES] + k_2[ES]$$

(iii) Consider ES in a steady-state in which [ES] is constant: i.e. rate of ES formation = rate of ES breakdown

$$\therefore k_1([E_t] - [ES])[S] = k_{-1}[ES] + k_2[ES]$$

(iv) Group the constants:

$$\frac{([E_t] - [ES])[S]}{[ES]} = \frac{k_{-1} + k_2}{k_1}$$

(v) The rate constant grouping is denoted by K_m, the Michaelis constant

(vi) From $\frac{([E_t] - [ES])[S]}{[ES]} = K_m$, solve for [ES]

$$\therefore \frac{[E_t][S]}{[ES]} - \frac{[ES][S]}{[ES]} = K_m$$

$$\therefore \frac{[E_t][S]}{[ES]} - [S] = K_m$$

$$\therefore \frac{[E_t][S]}{[ES]} = K_m + [S]$$

$$\therefore [ES] = \frac{[E_t][S]}{K_m + [S]}$$

Since $v_0 = k_2[ES]$, substitute for [ES]

$$\therefore v_0 = \frac{k_2[E_t][S]}{K_m + [S]}$$

Also, [S] is so high that essentially all the enzyme is present as ES, i.e. the enzyme is saturated and the maximum velocity, V, is achievable, but

$$V = k_2[E_t]$$

$$v_0 = \frac{V[S]}{K_m + [S]}$$

This is the Michaelis–Menten equation.

the independence of the variables. Computerized line-fitting techniques have been applied to the plotting of kinetic data. Variations from the characteristic plot may indicate contamination by activators, inhibitors or impurities. The properties of enzymes catalysing two-substrate reactions can be studied by varying the concentration of each substrate in the presence of a saturating concentration of the other substrate and employing standard graphical procedures.

$$v_0 = \frac{V[S]}{K_m + [S]}$$

when

$$v_0 = \tfrac{1}{2}V$$

then

$$\frac{V}{2} = \frac{V[S]}{K_m + [S]}$$

Divide by V:

$$\tfrac{1}{2} = \frac{[S]}{K_m + [S]}$$

Cross multiply:

$$K_m + [S] = 2[S]$$
$$K_m = [S]$$

FIGURE 6.6   The relationship between K_m and substrate concentration when the rate is equal to 50% of maximum velocity

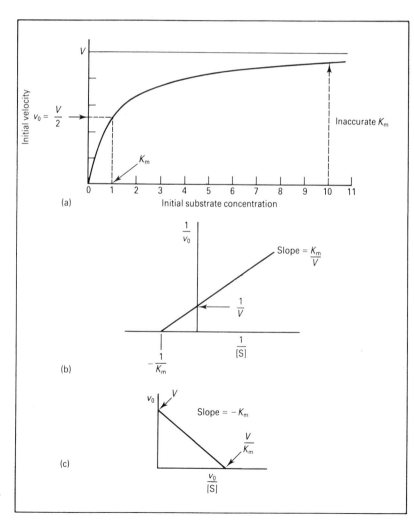

FIGURE 6.7   Graphical procedures for the estimation of V and K_m. (a) Plot of initial velocity versus substrate concentration. (b) Lineweaver–Burk plot. (c) Eadie–Hofstee plot

FIGURE 6.8 Derivation of the Lineweaver–Burk equation and its use in the Lineweaver–Burk plot

The Michaelis–Menten equation: $v_0 = \dfrac{V[S]}{K_m + [S]}$

Take reciprocals of both sides: $\dfrac{1}{v_0} = \dfrac{K_m + [S]}{V[S]}$

Rearrange: $\dfrac{1}{v_0} = \dfrac{K_m}{V[S]} + \dfrac{[S]}{V[S]}$

Reduce to the Lineweaver–Burk equation: $\dfrac{1}{v_0} = \dfrac{K_m}{V} \cdot \dfrac{1}{[S]} + \dfrac{1}{V}$

Use of Lineweaver–Burk equation in the plotting method:

If $\dfrac{1}{v_0} = 0$;

then $0 = \dfrac{K_m}{V} \cdot \dfrac{1}{[S]} + \dfrac{1}{V}$

$\therefore \dfrac{K_m}{V} \cdot \dfrac{1}{[S]} = \dfrac{-1}{V}$

$\therefore \dfrac{1}{[S]} = -\dfrac{\dfrac{1}{V}}{\dfrac{K_m}{V}}$

$\therefore \dfrac{1}{[S]} = \dfrac{-1}{K_m}$

If $\dfrac{1}{[S]} = 0$;

then $\dfrac{1}{v_0} = \dfrac{K_m}{V} \cdot 0 + \dfrac{1}{V}$

$\therefore \dfrac{1}{v_0} = \dfrac{1}{V}$

6.3 Enzyme inhibition

In addition to substrate concentration, two groups of compounds alter the rate of an enzymic reaction by specific mechanisms. Activators are compounds which combine with an enzyme or enzyme–substrate complex to effect an increase in activity without being modified by the enzyme. Inhibitors are compounds which decrease the rate of an enzyme-catalysed reaction. Inhibitors are divided into two categories: irreversible and reversible inhibitors. Irreversible inhibition involves the covalent bonding of the inhibitor to a functional group at the active site or elsewhere on the enzyme. Because the effective concentration of the enzyme is progressively declining, irreversible inhibition cannot be analysed by Michaelis–Menten kinetics. This type of inhibition is frequently used to obtain information regarding the functional amino acids

at the active site of the enzyme (Section 5.2). Irreversible inhibitors have been exploited to provide pesticides, e.g. parathion is an active inhibitor of insect acetylcholinesterase upon which normal propagation of nervous impulses relies. Suicide inhibition is a form of irreversible inhibition in which the substrate in the first catalytic cycle is converted into a chemically reactive product which remains bound to the active site through covalent bonding. The enzyme is rendered permanently inactive. Such inhibitors have potential as drugs.

Reversible inhibitors are not covalently bound to the enzyme. Reversible inhibition is characterized by an equilibrium between free and inhibitor-bound enzymic forms. Therefore, steady-state kinetics may be applied to the analysis of these inhibitions. The inhibitor may be removed from the enzyme–inhibitor (EI) complex by simple methods to furnish active enzymes. Of the various forms of reversible inhibition which have been identified through kinetic studies, competitive, non-competitive and uncompetitive inhibition will be considered here.

Competitive inhibitors are inhibitors which have an effect on the K_m but not on the V of an enzyme-catalysed reaction. The V is unchanged because the number of functional active sites is not altered but a greater substrate concentration is required to achieve the maximum utilization of the sites. Consequently, the K_m for the substrate increases. Competitive inhibition may be overcome by the addition of more substrate to the enzyme reaction mixture. Competitive inhibitors often bear a structural similarity to the substrate and compete with the substrate for the active sites of the enzyme, i.e. they are isosteric. However, competitive inhibitors are not necessarily structurally analogous to the substrate, e.g. salicylate inhibition of 3-phosphoglycerate kinase, and may bind to a site distinct from the active site, e.g. L-isoleucine inhibition of threonine deaminase from *Escherichia coli*. The classical example of competitive inhibition is the action of malonate on succinate dehydrogenase (Figure 6.9) which advanced the elucidation of the tricarboxylate cycle (Section 12.4). Inhibitors of this reaction achieve their effects by ionic bonding to the contact amino acid residues (Section 5.2).

Non-competitive inhibition is characterized by a change in V but not K_m and is not reversed by additions of substrate. This type of inhibition occurs when an inhibitor binds to a site other than the active site on the free enzyme or enzyme–substrate complex. Non-competitive inhibitors interfere with either the formation of ES complex or its breakdown to yield product. Examples include heavy metal (e.g. mercury, lead) ions which bind to strategically positioned sulphydryl groups and modulate the enzyme's conformation.

Uncompetitive inhibitors bind only to a formed ES complex. This type of inhibition, characterized by equal effects on both V and K_m, is rare in one-substrate reactions but may occur as a type of product inhibition in reactions with multiple substrates and products. Figure 6.10 illustrates mechanistic and plot differences between the discussed inhibitions. Table 6.1 summarizes the effect of inhibitors on Lineweaver–Burk plot parameters. Graphical methods are available for the estimation of K_i, the inhibition constant. In competitive inhibition, for example

$$K_i = \frac{[E][I]}{[EI]}$$

FIGURE 6.9 Competitive inhibition of succinate dehydrogenase. (a) The reaction. (b) Some inhibitors

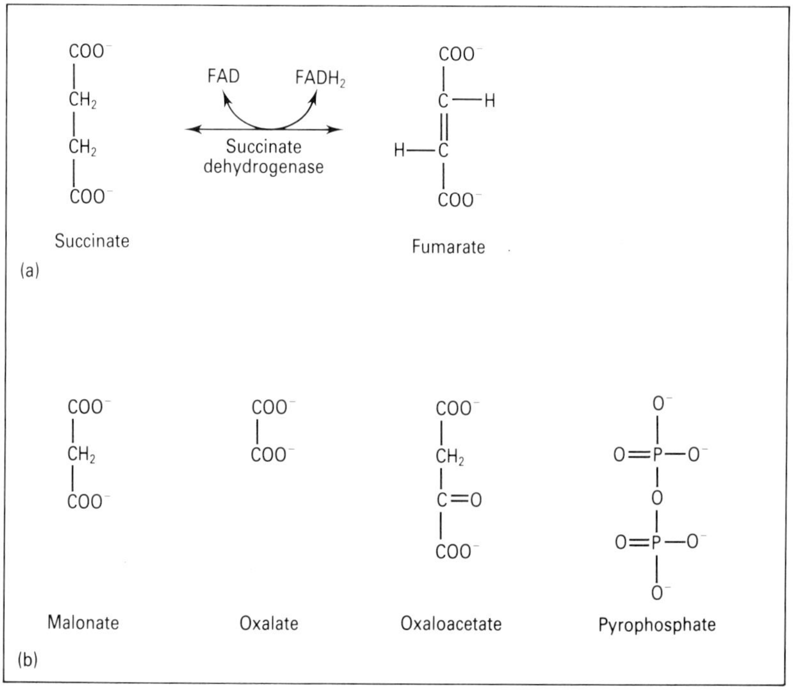

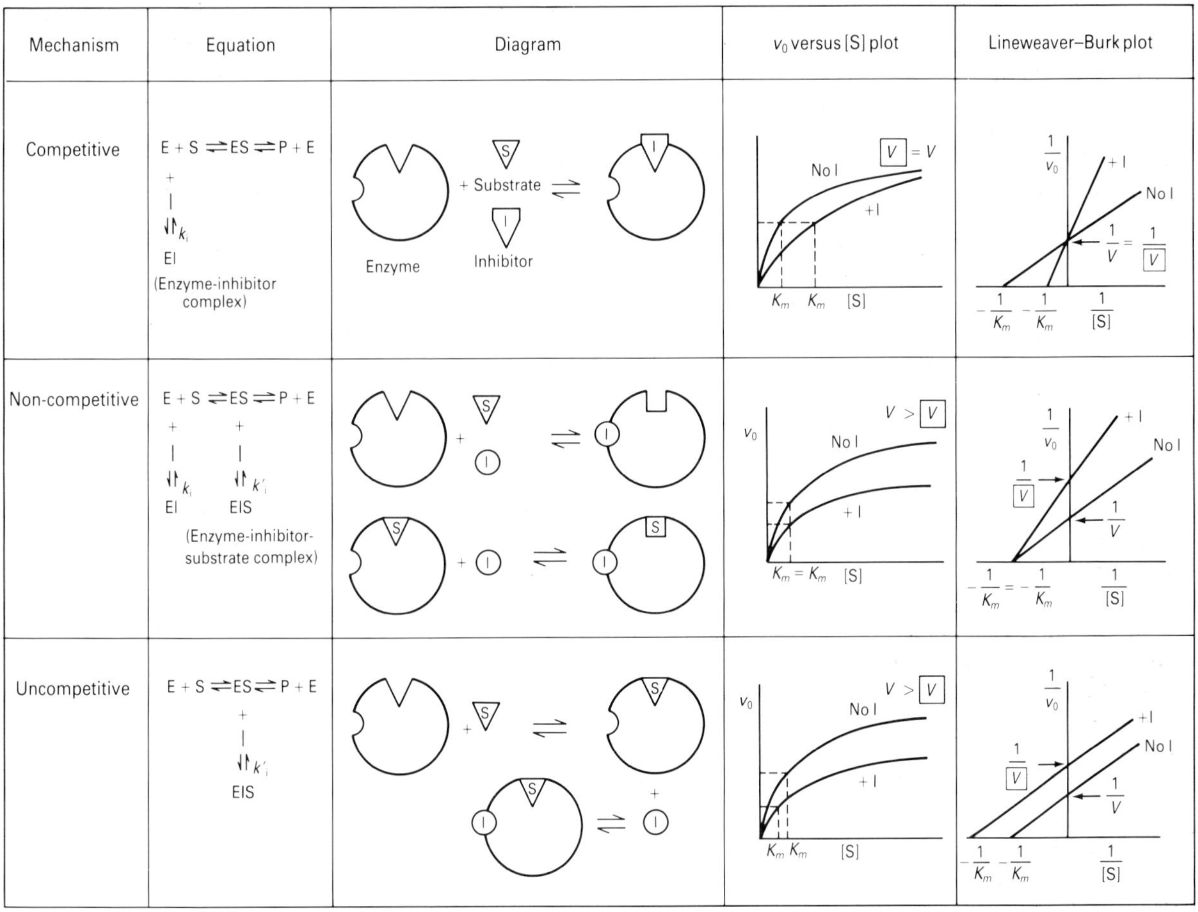

Mechanism	Equation	Diagram	v_0 versus [S] plot	Lineweaver–Burk plot
Competitive	E + S $\rightleftharpoons$ ES $\rightleftharpoons$ P + E + I $\updownarrow k_i$ EI (Enzyme-inhibitor complex)	Enzyme · Inhibitor + Substrate $\rightleftharpoons$	No I, $\boxed{V} = V$, +I; K_m K_m [S]	$\frac{1}{v_0}$, +I, No I, $\frac{1}{V} = \frac{1}{\boxed{V}}$; $-\frac{1}{K_m}$ $-\frac{1}{K_m}$ $\frac{1}{[S]}$
Non-competitive	E + S $\rightleftharpoons$ ES $\rightleftharpoons$ P + E + + I I $\updownarrow k_i$ $\updownarrow k'_i$ EI EIS (Enzyme-inhibitor-substrate complex)		v_0, No I, +I, $V > \boxed{V}$; $K_m = K_m$ [S]	$\frac{1}{v_0}$, +I, No I, $\frac{1}{\boxed{V}}$, $\frac{1}{V}$; $-\frac{1}{K_m} = -\frac{1}{K_m}$ $\frac{1}{[S]}$
Uncompetitive	E + S $\rightleftharpoons$ ES $\rightleftharpoons$ P + E + I $\updownarrow k'_i$ EIS		v_0, No I, +I, $V > \boxed{V}$; K_m K_m [S]	$\frac{1}{v_0}$, +I, No I, $\frac{1}{\boxed{V}}$, $\frac{1}{V}$; $-\frac{1}{K_m}$ $-\frac{1}{K_m}$ $\frac{1}{[S]}$

FIGURE 6.10 Mechanisms of reversible inhibition

TABLE 6.1 Intercepts on axes of a Lineweaver–Burk plot in the absence and presence of inhibitors

	Intercept on $1/v$ axis	Intercept on $1/[S]$ axis	Slope
No inhibitor	$\frac{1}{V}$	$\frac{-1}{K_m}$	$\frac{K_m}{V}$
Competitive inhibitor	$\frac{1}{V}$	$\dfrac{-1}{K_m\left(1 + \dfrac{[I]}{K_i}\right)}$	$\dfrac{K_m}{V}\left(1 + \dfrac{[I]}{K_i}\right)$
Non-competitive* inhibitor	$\dfrac{1}{V}\left(1 + \dfrac{[I]}{K_i}\right)$	$\dfrac{-1}{K_m}$	$\dfrac{K_m}{V}\left(1 + \dfrac{[I]}{K_i}\right)$
Uncompetitive inhibitor	$\dfrac{1}{V}\left(1 + \dfrac{[I]}{K'_i}\right)$	$\dfrac{-1}{K_m\left(1 + \dfrac{[I]}{K'_i}\right)}$	$\dfrac{K_m}{V}$

* K may be K_i or K'_i depending on mechanism.

6.4 Allostery

Some enzymes when their v_0 is plotted as a function of [S] do not show the hyperbolic curve of Figure 6.3(b) but a sigmoidal curve (Figure 6.11). The rate of the reaction at a given [S] is increased or decreased by the addition of specific substances, i.e. activators or inhibitors. Enzymes which exhibit this behaviour are called allosteric enzymes based on a concept developed earlier to explain the oxygenation/deoxygenation of haemoglobin (Section 4.7). In addition to the substrate-binding site (active site), allosteric enzymes possess other sites to which inhibitors and activators, termed allosteric effectors, may bind and influence catalytic events through induced conformational changes in the enzyme (Figure 6.12).

Most allosteric enzymes contain numerous subunits. In most of these enzymes, e.g. pyruvate carboxylase (Section 12.6), both catalytic and regulatory sites are located on the same polypeptide chain whilst some, e.g. aspartate carbamoyltransferase, carry the catalytic and regulatory sites on different subunits. Through the sigmoidal shape of their v_0 against [S] plot (Figure 6.11), X-ray crystallographic and other studies, it is known that many allosteric enzymes display cooperativity of substrate binding even in the absence of allosteric effectors. This cooperativity may be positive or negative. In positive cooperativity, when one binding site is occupied, subsequent binding to other sites occurs more readily. In negative cooperativity, successive binding occurs with decreasing ease. In the presence of an allosteric activator, the curve

tends towards a hyperbola, whilst in the presence of an inhibitor, the curve becomes more sigmoidal. The structure of the allosteric enzyme is particularly suited to a role in the regulation of metabolic pathways. The end products of a metabolic pathway frequently bind to an allosteric site on the first enzyme of the pathway as a negative effector to reduce the rate of synthesis of the end product. This form of control is called feedback inhibition (Figure 6.13). As the end product F increases in concentration, it diffuses to the allosteric enzyme (E_A) causing a reduced synthesis of its product B which, in turn, lowers enzymic reaction rates in the remainder of the pathway. Conversely, allosteric enzymes may be stimulated by positive effectors which are not end products of pathways but other metabolites that induce conformational changes in enzymes to enhance their activities. These allosteric enzymes are termed heterotropic since the effector

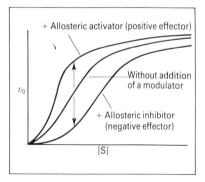

FIGURE 6.11 Effect of substrate concentration on the initial velocity of an allosteric enzyme in the presence and absence of specific modulators

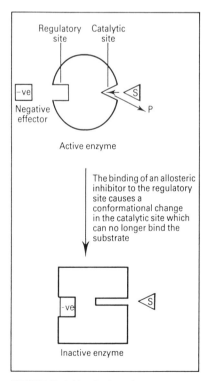

FIGURE 6.12 Induced conformational change in an allosteric enzyme

FIGURE 6.13   Feedback inhibition

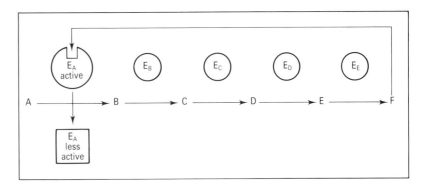

and substrate are different ligands. In some enzymes, the substrate creates a positive cooperative effect by binding to the catalytic sites not allosteric sites. Such enzymes are called homotropic. This homotropic cooperativity is advantageous in the utilization of accumulated substrate and may also be useful because it enables larger rate changes for smaller changes in the substrate concentration.

Two main models, the concerted (or symmetry) model of Monod, Wyman and Changeux (MWC) and the sequential model of Koshland, Némethy and Filmer (KNF), form the basis of approaches to explain the sigmoidal relationship between v_0 and [S] (Figure 6.11) in molecular terms. Although

most allosteric enzymes are composed of at least four subunits, for simplicity the principles of these models will be outlined employing a dimer.

(i) The MWC model proposes that two different conformation states, called R and T, exist in equilibrium (Figure 6.14). The R (relaxed) conformation is composed of subunits which have a high affinity for substrate and activator and is therefore the active form. The T (tense) conformation is composed of subunits which have a high affinity for inhibitor but low affinity for substrate and is the inactive form. The basis of this model is that both subunits of the dimer can only exist in the same conformational state, i.e. RR or TT but not RT conformations. The RR and TT conformations

FIGURE 6.14   The concerted (or symmetry) model of Monod, Wyman and Changeux (MWC). (a) Initial equilibrium. (b) In the presence of activator. (c) In the presence of inhibitor

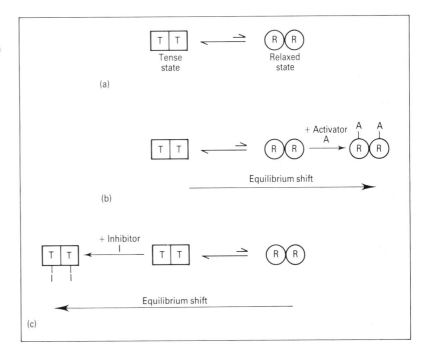

exist in equilibrium. In the absence of activator, the TT form predominates. When the first activator molecules bind to the few RR molecules, the equilibrium responds by a conformational shift from TT to RR to produce more active enzyme molecules which increase the rate of substrate transformation. Progressive increases in activator concentration result in a concomitant increase in TT to RR conversions. The sigmoid curve then approaches the non-allosteric hyperbolic plot. Inhibitors may bind to the TT conformation, the equilibrium responds by means of RR to TT conversions with a concomitant reduction in active sites. The sigmoid curve then becomes more pronounced. Negative cooperativity cannot be accounted for by this model.

(ii) The KNF model is an extension of the principle of induced fit (Section 5.2). The effectors modify subunit conformation directly and not through a shift in an assumed equilibrium between two forms. This model proposed that ligand-bind-ing sites within analogous conformations may have differing affinities for the same ligand. The binding of an effector to its allosteric site in one subunit induces conformational changes within that subunit which then induces conformational changes in the other subunit. A conformation equivalent to RT which is not allowed in the MWC model is therefore a requisite of the KNF model. If the effector is an activator (Figure 6.15a), its binding to the first subunit will effect a conformational change that will enhance substrate binding to the same subunit and also induce a conformational change in the second subunit to increase its affinity firstly for the activator and then for substrate. Inhibitors function in lowering the affinity of the active sites for the substrate through conformational changes in both subunits (Figure 6.15b).

Negative cooperativity may be accounted for by this model. Neither model can satisfactorily explain the action of some allosteric proteins for which more complex models are required.

FIGURE 6.15 The sequential model of Koshland, Némethy and Filmer (KNF). Allosteric effect of (a) an activator and (b) an inhibitor

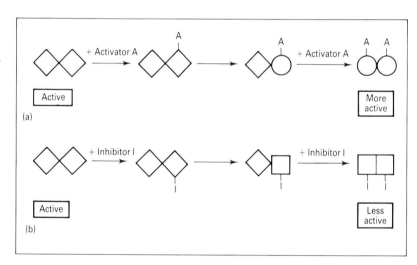

6.5 Isoenzymes

Isoenzymes or isozymes are families of oligomeric enzymes which catalyse the same reaction but differences in their subunit composition modify the rate at which each molecular species transforms substrate. Isoenzymes may be divided into primary or secondary isoenzymes. Primary isoenzymes are the products of multiple gene loci which code for distinct protein molecules or are the products of multiple alleles at a single gene locus (called allo-enzymes). Secondary isoenzymes are derived by post-translational modifications including glycosylation. Because of differences in their amino acid composition, primary isoenzymes may be detected by variations in their electrophoretic mobility.

Lactate dehydrogenase (LDH) is a primary isoenzyme which catalyses reversibly the oxidation of lactate to pyruvate. Six tetrameric isoenzymes of human LDH have been identified and are denoted as LDH_1 (A_4), LDH_2 (A_3B), LDH_3 (A_2B_2), LDH_4 (AB_3), LDH_5 (B_4) and LDH_X (C_4). LDH_1 and LDH_5 predominate in heart muscle and liver respectively. A structurally distinct isoenzyme, LDH_X, which occurs only in spermatozoa and the gametogenic cells of mature testes permits the utilization of a wider range of substrates and may confer the metabolic flexibility necessary to counter the environmental changes experienced by spermatozoa during the fertilization processes. LDH A and B chains form two homogeneous and three heterogeneous types. The A_4 type has a lower K_m for pyruvate than the B_4 type. The other isoenzymes exhibit kinetics relative to the proportions of each type of subunit. The tissue distribution of LDH isoenzymes, however, demonstrates major variation from species to species contributing to the difficulties in the provision of a rational explanation of the physiological roles of A and B homo- and hetero-tetramers. Rather than variations in enzyme kinetics, other biological advantages such as differential binding to subcellular organelles or differential rates of protein degradation may be important.

Within any vertebrate including man most organs demonstrate different LDH isoenzyme patterns. Being a cytoplasmic isoenzyme, LDH_1 increases significantly in the blood circulation after a heart attack because of its release from damaged cells. This is one example of the use of isoenzyme levels in the diagnosis of clinical disorders.

Suggested further reading

CORNISH-BOWDEN, A. (1979) *Fundamentals of Enzyme Kinetics*, Butterworths, London

FERSHT, A. (1985) *Enzyme Structure and Mechanism*, 2nd edn, Freeman, New York

CHAPTER 7

Nucleic acids

7.1 The structure of nucleotides

Nucleic acids are polynucleotide chains in which ribonucleotides and deoxyribonucleotides are the monomeric units (Section 1.4) of ribonucleic acid (RNA) and deoxyribonucleic acid (DNA) respectively. Nucleotides are composed of three component parts: a heterocyclic ring structure, a pentose sugar and a phosphate group, each of which contributes to the chemistry of the unit. Figure 7.1 illustrates that the heterocyclic compound is a nitrogen-containing ring structure which is either a derivative of pyrimidine or purine. Because of their chemically basic nature (Section 2.5), they are referred to as nitrogenous bases. A purine can be considered as a pyrimidine ring to which a five-membered imidazole ring has been fused. Conventional numbering of the atoms in a pyrimidine is clockwise whereas in purines the six-membered ring is numbered anticlockwise. It is these nitrogenous bases which are responsible for the important biological properties of nucleic acids.

The interaction of either D-ribose or 2-deoxy-D-ribose with a nitrogenous base gives rise to a nucleoside, either a ribonucleoside or deoxyribonucleoside. The bond according to carbohydrate nomenclature is a β-glycosidic bond (Section 3.4)

involving the C-1 atom of the sugar and the N-1 atom of a pyrimidine or the N-9 atom of a purine and so is either a C-1′→N-1 or C-1′→N-9 glycosidic linkage. To distinguish between the carbons of the heterocyclic compound and the sugar, those of the sugar are denoted by a prime superscript. The suffix -idine indicates that the nucleoside contains a pyrimidine base whereas -osine denotes the presence of a purine base. Nucleoside nomenclature is clarified in Table 7.1. Because thymine is a major base of DNA but has an infrequent occurrence in RNA (Section 7.2) the ribonucleoside is called ribosylthymine whilst thymidine refers to the deoxyribonucleoside.

The addition of one, two or three phosphate groups to the sugar of a nucleoside by ester linkage (alcoholic-OH + acid→ester) derives a nucleotide. The nomenclature of the nucleotide is based upon the name of the nucleoside plus the position and number of the phosphate groups, e.g. adenosine 3′-monophosphate, guanosine 5′-triphosphate. Although phosphorylation may occur at the 2′, 3′ or 5′ positions of a ribonucleoside and at the 3′ or 5′ positions of a deoxyribonucleoside, the 5′-nucleotides are of major biological importance.

TABLE 7.1 Nomenclature of nucleosides

Base	Abbreviation	Ribonucleoside	Deoxyribonucleoside
Cytosine	C	Cytidine	Deoxycytidine
Uracil	U	Uridine	Deoxyuridine
Thymine	T	Ribosylthymine	Thymidine
Adenine	A	Adenosine	Deoxyadenosine
Guanine	G	Guanosine	Deoxyguanosine

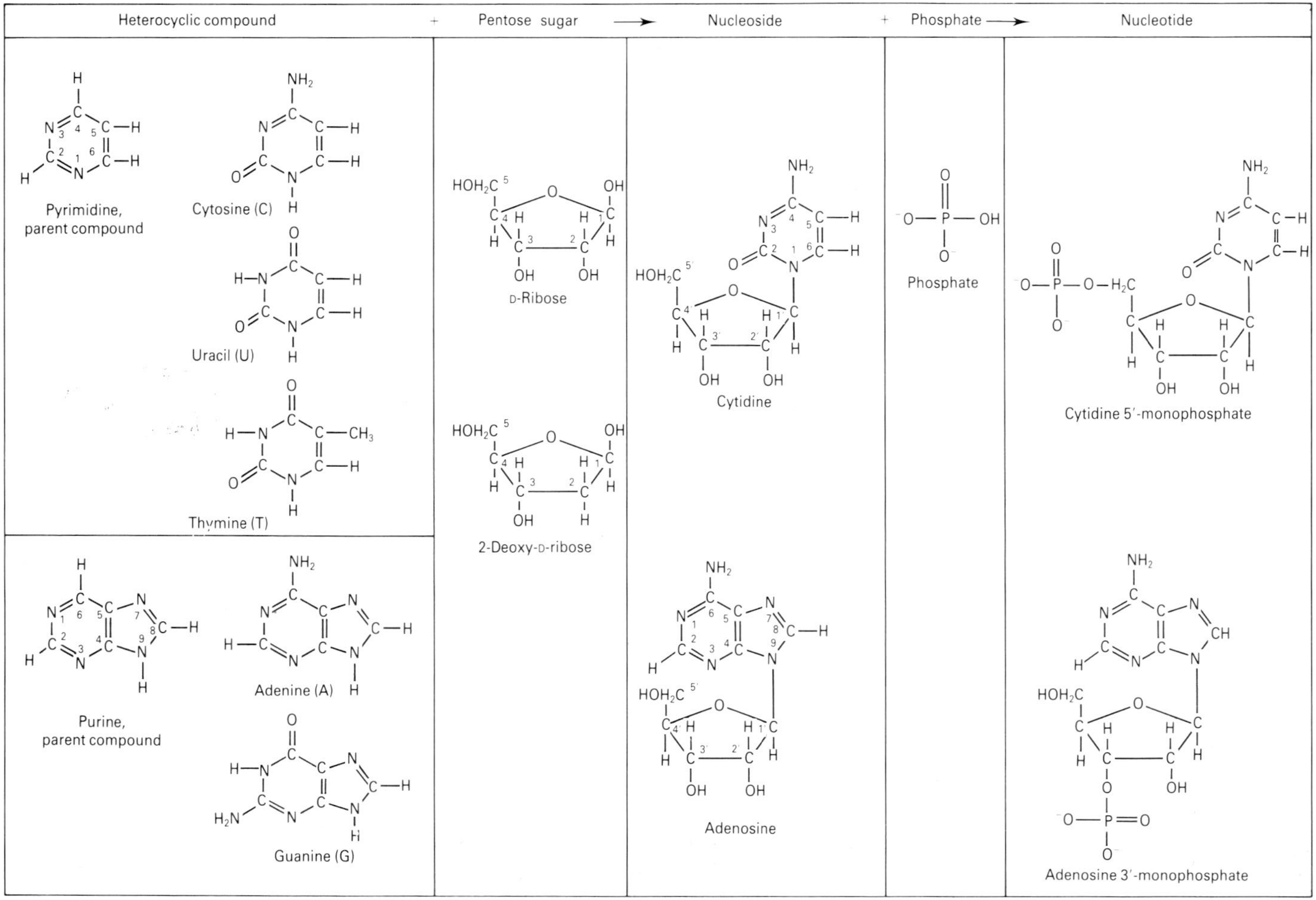

FIGURE 7.1 The nature of nucleotides

5′-Ribonucleotides are denoted as NMP, NDP and NTP whereas 5′-deoxyribonucleotides are denoted as dNMP etc., e.g. adenosine 5′-triphosphate (ATP), deoxyadenosine 5′-triphosphate (dATP).

The nucleoside 5′-monophosphates are sometimes referred to as adenylate, deoxyadenylate, uridylate, guanylate, cytidylate and thymidylate because of the presence of the phosphate group.

7.2 Polynucleotide chains

Identification of the component pentose sugar confirms whether the polynucleotide chain is RNA or DNA. Both RNA and DNA contain the same two purine bases, adenine (A) and guanine (G) whereas they differ in their content of the pyrimidine bases. RNA contains cytosine (C) and uracil (U) but DNA contains cytosine and the 5-methyl derivative of uracil called thymine (T). In addition to these bases, called major bases, DNA and RNA also contain altered or less common bases called minor bases. In DNA, the minor bases are usually methylated derivatives of the major bases which play a special role in the functioning of the polynucleotide. RNAs, especially transfer RNAs, also contain minor bases, e.g. inosine, pseudouridine (in which uracil is linked through C-5, not N-1, to ribose), dihydrouridine, ribosylthymine and methylated derivatives of nucleosides (Figure 7.2). Minor bases are mainly modified versions of major bases.

Individual monomeric nucleotides are polymerized by the formation of phosphodiester linkages (Section 1.4) so that RNA may be described as a linear polyribonucleotide having a ribose–phos-

phate backbone with 3′,5′-phosphodiester internucleotide links (Figure 7.3a). Strands of DNA may be similarly described as a polydeoxyribonucleotide having a deoxyribose–phosphate backbone with 3′,5′-phosphodiester internucleotide links (Figure 7.3b). Single phosphorus–oxygen bonds permit the rotation of nucleoside moieties. Linear nucleic acids have two ends termed the 5′-end and 3′-end. Because the biosynthesis of nucleic acids utilizes nucleoside 5′-triphosphates, the 5′-end exhibits a terminal phosphate whereas a terminal hydroxyl group is located at the 3′-end. At physiological pH, the phosphate groups, but not the heterocyclic bases, are ionized. The size of nucleic acids demands that their structures can be represented in a convenient short form. Of a number of abbreviated representations, the system currently favoured employs the one-letter symbol for the bases written linearly with the 5′-end at the left and the 3′-end at the right. The tetraribonucleotide in Figure 7.3 may be denoted as AGCU and its deoxyribonucleotide counterpart as AGCT.

FIGURE 7.2 Some minor nucleosides found in transfer RNA. (a) Inosine. (b) Pseudouridine. (c) 5,6-Dihydrouridine. (d) Ribosylthymine. (e) 7-Methylguanosine. (f) 6,6-Dimethyladenosine

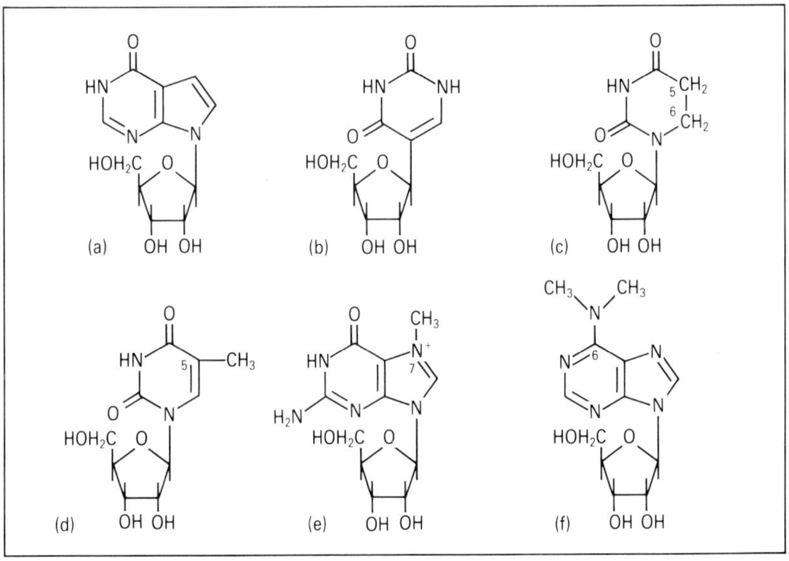

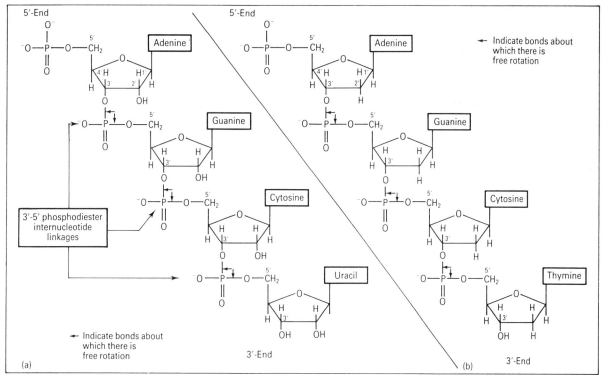

FIGURE 7.3   Tetranucleotide sequences representing nucleic acid structure. (a) RNA. (b) DNA

7.3 The structure of DNA

The size of DNA varies according to its source (Table 7.2). Chemical analysis of the base composition of various DNA molecules revealed that the relative amounts of the heterocyclic bases varied between species (Table 7.3) but were constant within a species irrespective of age and tissue of origin. The ratios A/T, G/C and purine/pyrimidine approximate to 1 so that the number of adenine residues equals thymine residues (i.e. A = T), the number of guanine residues equals cytosine residues (i.e. G = C) and the number of purine residues equals pyrimidine residues (i.e. A + G = T + C). The ratio G + C/A + T indicates the characteristic chemical composition of DNA from a given organism.

With the exception of single-stranded DNA viruses, DNA occurs as a double-helical (duplex) molecule. In 1953, Watson and Crick constructed a model of DNA compatible with available X-ray diffraction data, chemical data on base composition, knowledge of the three-dimensional structure of nucleotides and the stereochemistry of hydrogen bond formation between different bases. The

TABLE 7.2   The size of DNA in different organisms

Organism	Molecular weight	Base-pairs
SV40 virus	3×10^6	5×10^3
Adenovirus	1.4×10^7	2.1×10^4
Escherichia coli	2.2×10^9	4.6×10^6
Mouse cells	1.5×10^{12}	2.3×10^9
Human cells	1.8×10^{12}	2.8×10^9

TABLE 7.3 Base equivalence in DNA from various sources

| Organism | Base composition (mol. %) | | | | Base ratios | | | |
	A	G	C^*	T	$\dfrac{A}{T}$	$\dfrac{G}{C}$	$\dfrac{A+G}{T+C}$	$\dfrac{G+C}{A+T}$
Human	30.4	19.6	20.6	30.1	1.01	0.95	0.99	0.66
Ox	29.0	21.2	22.5	28.7	1.01	0.94	0.98	0.76
Rat	28.6	21.4	21.5	28.4	1.01	0.99	1.00	0.75
Salmon	28.9	22.4	21.6	27.1	1.07	1.04	1.05	0.79
Carrot	26.7	23.1	23.2	26.9	0.99	1.00	0.99	0.86
Wheatgerm	27.3	22.7	22.8	27.1	1.01	1.00	1.00	0.84
Yeast	31.7	18.3	17.4	32.6	0.97	1.05	1.00	0.56
E. coli	24.7	26.0	25.7	23.6	1.05	1.10	1.03	1.07
Staphylococcus aureus	30.8	21.0	19.0	29.2	1.05	1.11	1.07	0.67

*Including 5-methylcytosine if present

Watson–Crick model (Figure 7.4) showed DNA to consist of two not three polynucleotide chains arranged with the sugar–phosphate backbone on the outside and the bases on the inside located perpendicular to the axis of the duplex. The two strands of the DNA duplex are antiparallel, i.e. the 3′,5′-phosphodiester internucleotide linkages in each chain lie in opposing directions. The strands are complementary in that the thymine always pairs with adenine and cytosine always pairs with guanine. This arrangement explains why the DNA duplex contains equimolar amounts of purines and pyrimidines as indicated by chemical analysis. Base-pairing is the result of their ability to interact by the formation of hydrogen bonds (Section 2.2). Thymine may form two hydrogen bonds with adenine while cytosine may form three hydrogen bonds with guanine (Figure 7.5). These bonding arrangements are not exclusive since hydrogen bonds may occur with other nucleotides, e.g. the minor bases found in tRNA.

The Watson–Crick model portrays the double-stranded DNA molecule as a right-handed helix. This means that when the molecule is viewed from one end the top surface of the helix spirals towards the right. Each turn of the helix contains ten base-pairs, measures 3.4 nm in length and corresponds to the major periodicity (Section 4.5) attained by X-ray crystallography. The distance of 0.34 nm occupied by one nucleotide is consistent with the experimental minor periodicity. The two helical strands are held together by the hydrogen bonds between complementary base-pairs. In addition, within a polar environment vertical hydrophobic interactions occur between adjacent non-polar heterocyclic bases to create stacking which contributes to the stability of the duplex structure. The crossing of the antiparallel chains creates external helical grooves of different dimensions called major and minor grooves. These grooves are the sites of contact with DNA-binding proteins which interact according to their sequence-specificity. More specific proteins tend to bind to the major grooves, less specific proteins, e.g. histones (Section 9.4), to the minor grooves.

DNA can assume different forms called A-DNA, B-DNA, C-DNA, D-DNA and Z-DNA (zig-zag), depending upon their chemical microenvironment. These forms exhibit different major and minor periodicities, different angles of base-pairing, different dimensions of major and minor grooves and either more or less than ten base-pairs per helical turn. The Watson–Crick model represents the most stable form, B-DNA, which is the predominant intracellular form. Certain regions of B-DNA containing alternate purine and pyrimidine residues may adopt the only left-handed helical form, Z-DNA. This transformation may be important in the regulation of gene expression, i.e. the switching on and off of genes, a process which governs all cellular activities.

The DNA molecules of prokaryotes and numerous viruses are circular in that each chain is continuous. To enhance packaging in vivo the axis of the duplex may be twisted into a supercoil or superhelix (Figure 7.6) which may be either right-handed or left-handed. The number of crossover points varies with the source of DNA.

FIGURE 7.4 Diagram of Watson–Crick model of DNA

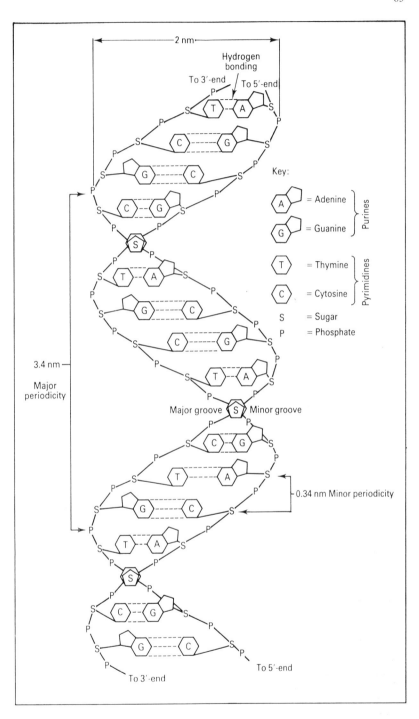

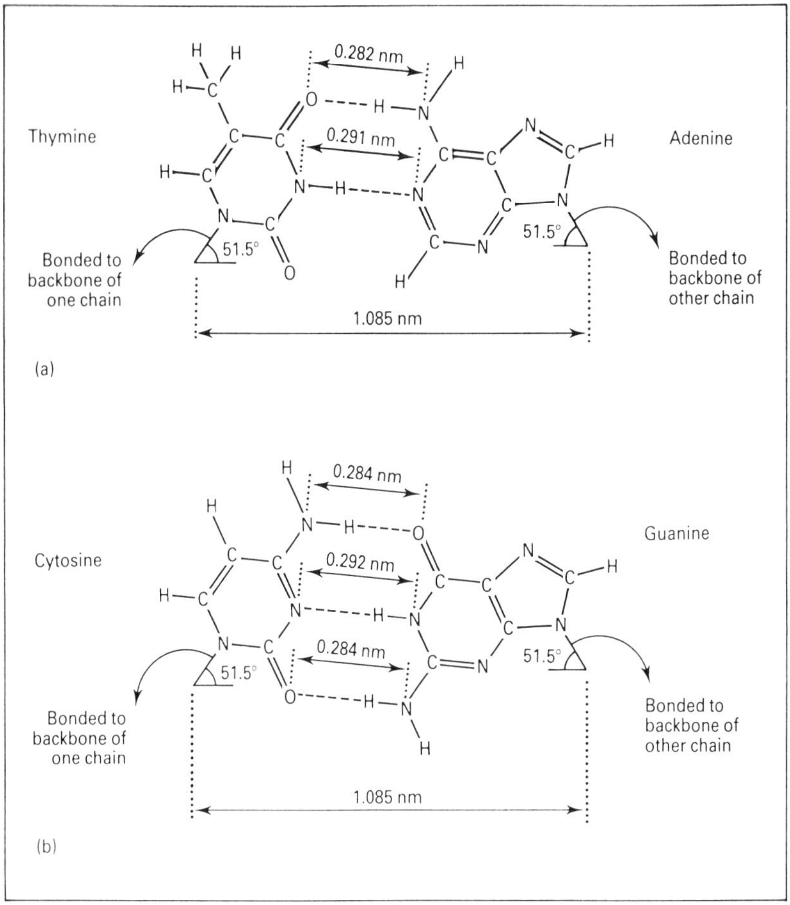

FIGURE 7.5 Dimensions and hydrogen bonding of nucleotide pairs. (a) Thymine to adenine. (b) Cytosine to guanine

(a)

(b)

FIGURE 7.6 An example of supercoiling of DNA

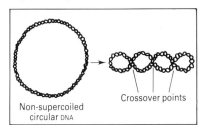

Non-supercoiled circular DNA

Crossover points

7.4 The structure of RNA

In RNA viruses, RNA serves as a genetic material. More commonly, the sole function of RNA resides within the process of protein synthesis (Section 1.6). There are three main forms of RNA called messenger RNA (mRNA), transfer RNA (tRNA) and ribosomal RNA (rRNA). Some physical characteristics of RNA isolated from a prokaryote are listed in Table 7.4. Traditionally RNAs are differentiated by their rate of sedimentation in a centrifugal field (expressed in Svedberg units, denoted as S). Except in certain viruses, RNAs are single-stranded molecules and in contrast to DNA exhibit significant variations in the proportions of bases. However, RNA molecules do contain regions of base-pairing induced by hydrogen bonding. As

much as 70% of the bases may participate in base-pairing. Apposing bases which are not complementary may be looped out to facilitate the pairing of other bases. Although in percentage terms present in small amounts, the largest number of individual RNA molecules are mRNAs.

The transcription of DNA produces RNA molecules called transcripts. The process involves base-pairing in which U pairs with A of the DNA template. The primary structure of an RNA molecule is thereby complementary to a region of one strand of the DNA molecule. When a particular protein is no longer required by the cell, synthesis of the mRNA is inhibited to conserve materials and the mRNA template is degraded by

TABLE 7.4   RNA Molecules in *E. coli*

Type	Approximate relative amount (%)	Sedimentation coefficient (S)	Molecular mass (kDa)	Number of nucleotides
Messenger RNA (mRNA)	2		Heterogeneous	
Transfer RNA (tRNA)	16	4	24–31	73–93
Ribosomal RNA (rRNA)	82	23	1200	2900
		16	560	1540
		5	36	120

nucleases. Therefore, mRNAs have short intra-cellular life spans generally measured in minutes for prokaryotic mRNAs or hours for eukaryotic mRNAs. This accounts for the relatively low amount determinable in the cell at any given time.

A length of DNA which contains the genetic message for a start signal, one polypeptide chain and a stop signal (Section 17.5) is termed a cistron and the complementary transcript is called mono-cistronic mRNA. An mRNA which encodes several different polypeptide chains is called a polycistronic mRNA molecule. An mRNA molecule may be divided into regions. In pro-karyotes, alignment of amino acids seldom com-mences at the 5′-end of the mRNA but at a nuc-leotide sequence located within the molecule. The frontal untranslated RNA bases constitute the leader section (Figure 7.7a). Additional untrans-lated sequences may be found at the 5′-end and 3′-end. Within polycistronic mRNA, such sequences of 1–400 bases may also be located internally and are termed spacers or intercistronic regions.

Eukaryotic mRNAs exhibit three distinctive structural features (Figure 7.7b). They are usually monocistronic. All have a 5′-cap consisting of a single residue of 7-methylguanosine linked uniquely through a 5′–5′ triphosphate bridge to the first nucleotide which is methylated at the 2′-OH position. The cap, which is added at an early stage during transcription, promotes translation by increasing mRNA binding to the 40S ribosomal subunit and by binding initiation factors involved in protein synthesis. Most mRNAs have a poly-A tail of 50–150 consecutive adenosine residues at the 3′-end, the function of which remains obscure although enhancement of stability has been sug-gested. In eukaryotic cells, mRNA is not produced directly from the DNA template. The transcript is one of the additional types of RNA called hetero-geneous nuclear RNA (hnRNA) which may be five times longer than the subsequent mRNA molecule. The precursor molecule is processed into mRNA by splicing (i.e. the elimination of redundant sequences) in which the characteristic end sequences are preserved.

The smallest RNA molecules, tRNAs, deliver

FIGURE 7.7 Comparative structures of messenger RNA. (a) Polycistronic prokaryotic RNA transcript. (b) Monocistronic eukaryotic mRNA

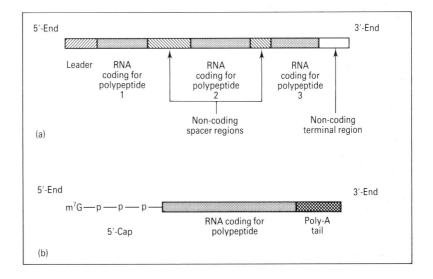

and position amino acids in the correct order in the growing polypeptide chain according to the mRNA template. Each amino acid has at least one specific tRNA molecule; leucine, arginine and serine have the maximum of six different tRNAs. In 1965, the first primary sequence of a tRNA, that of yeast alanine tRNA, was attained. Because certain regions of the sequence would be complementary if the chain was folded in a particular manner, the structure was presented as the two-dimensional cloverleaf diagram (Figure 7.8a). In actuality, the three-dimensional structure determined by X-ray crystallography resembles an inverted letter L (Figure 7.8b). All tRNA molecules demonstrate

similar structural features. As well as the major bases, tRNAs contain a number of minor bases (Section 7.2). At the 5'-end is located a guanosine or cytidine residue. All tRNAs contain the trinucleotide sequence CCA at the 3'-end. Attachment of the amino acid for which the tRNA is specific occurs through esterification involving the 3'-OH group. The tRNAs exhibit regions of base-pairing and non-hydrogen-bonded areas create loops, i.e. loop I (containing 5,6-dihydrouridine), loop II (the anticodon loop), loop III (the variable loop) and loop IV (containing ribosylthymine). Variability in tRNA size (Table 7.4) results from differences in the numbers of nucleotides contained

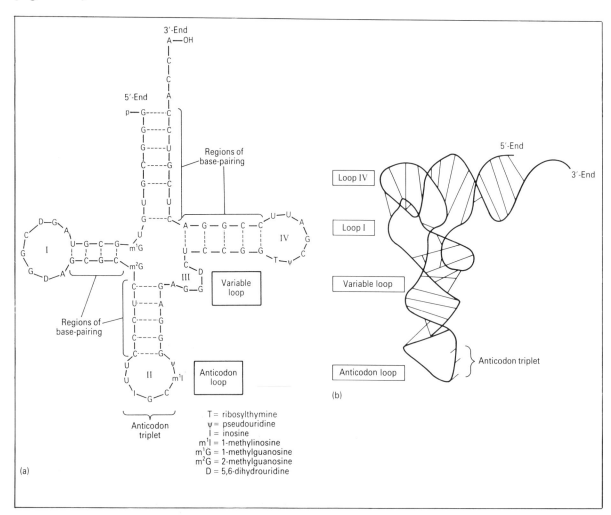

FIGURE 7.8   Structure of transfer RNA. (a) The cloverleaf diagram of yeast alanine tRNA. T, ribosylthymine; Ψ, pseudouridine; I, inosine; m¹I, 1-methylinosine; m¹G, 1-methylguanosine; m²G, 2-methylguanosine; D, 5,6-dihydrouridine. (b) The three-dimensional conformation of yeast phenylalanine tRNA

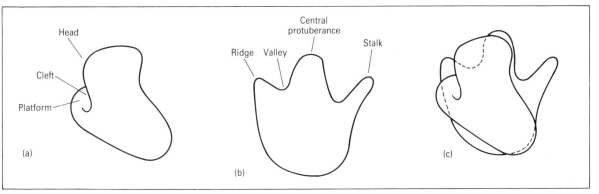

FIGURE 7.9   The 70S ribosome of *Escherichia coli*. (a) The small (30S) subunit. (b) The large (50S) subunit. (c) The intact ribosome. (Reproduced with permission from the *Annual Review of Biochemistry*, Vol. 54 © 1985 by Annual Reviews Inc.)

within the loop I and/or loop III. Amino acids are correctly positioned by base-pairing between nucleotide triplets on the mRNA, called codons, and a defined nucleotide triplet on the tRNA, called the anticodon, contained within loop II.

Ribosomal RNA, the most abundant of the RNAs in the cell, is the major component of ribosomes, the protein-synthesizing structures of the cell (Section 9.6). In prokaryotes, there are three species of rRNA each of which is present within each 25 nm long 70S ribosome. Ribosomes consist of two subunits, designated large and small (Figure 7.9). In *Escherichia coli*, the large subunit (50S, 1.6×10^6 Da) consists of 34 proteins (designated L1–L34) ranging in molecular mass from 5.4 kDa to 29.4 kDA and one molecule each of 23S and 5S rRNA. The proteins occur singly except for the four molecules of L7 and L12. Ten methylated bases and three pseudouridine residues are found in 23S rRNA but 5S rRNA, located on the central protuberance, lacks minor bases. The small subunit (30S, 9×10^5 Da) consists of 21 proteins (designated S1–S21) ranging in molecular mass from 8.3 kDa to 61.2 kDA and a single molecule of 16S rRNA which contains nine methylated bases. The secondary structures of 16S and 23S rRNAs have been elucidated (Figure 7.10). Non-Watson–Crick base-pairings are present, e.g. G–U, G–A, A–C pairs.

Ribosomal architecture in eukaryotes is similar but a fourth 5.8S rRNA and a larger number of proteins have been identified. Eukaryotic ribosomes are larger (80S) with a large subunit (60S, 2.7×10^6 Da), containing 5S, 5.8S and 26–28S rRNAs (3400–4700 nucleotides) and more than 50 polypeptides, and a small subunit (40S, 1.3×10^6 Da) containing 18S rRNA (1800 nucleotides) and about 40 polypeptides. In prokaryotic and eukaryotic ribosomes, two-thirds of their weight is due to the rRNA content.

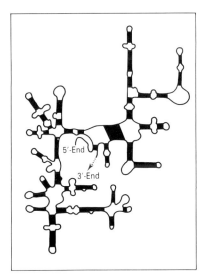

FIGURE 7.10   A section of the secondary structure of 16S rRNA. ■■■ , Regions of hydrogen bonding; □, regions of non-complementary bases

Ribosomal RNAs of the same sedimentation coefficient from various sources demonstrate a high degree of evolutionary conservation of structure. It is believed that rRNA features prominently in the assembly and function of ribosomal subunits. The 3'-terminus of the 16S rRNA is involved in the binding of mRNA to the ribosome and 23S rRNA has been implicated in peptidyl transfer during protein synthesis (Section 17.6).

7.5 Some properties of nucleic acids

All heterocyclic bases found in nucleic acids may exist in two forms, depending upon the environmental pH. The transformation, called tautomerism, involves proton exchange between atoms in the molecule. Keto–enol tautomerism, also called lactam–lactim tautomerism (Figure 7.11), results from the electron-withdrawing effect of the oxygen atom creating slight electropositivity in the imino-hydrogen atom which migrates to the electronegative oxygen to produce an enol group. At physiological pH, the bases of nucleic acids are in the keto form which promotes hydrogen-bonded base-pairing. Local intracellular pH variations therefore may effect deviations from normal base-pairing arrangements.

All nucleic acids demonstrate an absorption maxima at approximately 260 nm. The precise value for a given nucleic acid depends upon its base composition since the absorption of ultraviolet light is a property conferred by the conjugated bond systems of the heterocyclic bases, each of which absorbs at different wavelengths (Table 7.5).

When a solution of double-stranded DNA is subjected to extremes of pH or is heated, a decrease in viscosity and an increase in UV absorption is recorded. Because the heterocyclic bases are highly ordered due to hydrogen bonding and hydrophobic interactions, the UV absorption at 260 nm of the duplex structure is lower than for the random conformation of single-stranded DNA. Through this relationship, duplex and single-stranded DNA are described as hypochromic and hyperchromic respectively. The unfolding of the duplex strands into single chains is referred to as denaturation. The heat denaturation of DNA may

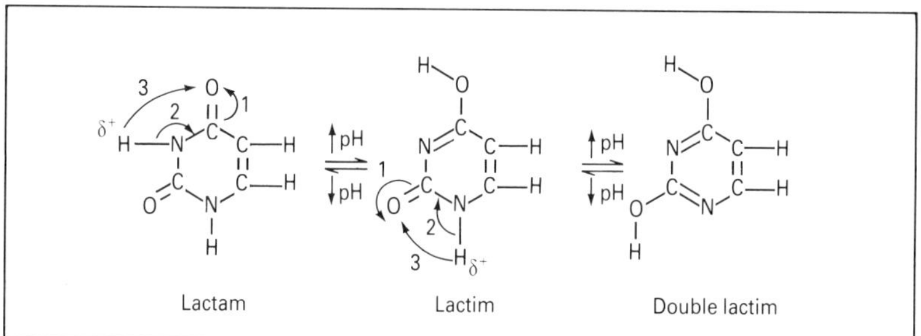

FIGURE 7.11   Tautomerism of uracil

TABLE 7.5   The absorption maxima of heterocyclic bases of nucleic acids at pH 7.0

Heterocyclic base	Absorption maximum/maxima (nm)
Adenine	260
Guanine	246, 276
Cytosine	268
Uracil	258
Thymine	266

be referred to as melting because, since hydrogen bonds mutually reinforce, the denaturation occurs over a small temperature range. The temperature at which 50% of the DNA is denatured is termed the transition or melting temperature, T_m (Figure 7.12a). The T_m value of DNA depends upon its $G+C/A+T$ ratio (Table 7.3), the higher this ratio the higher the T_m value (Figure 7.12b). The importance of the $G+C$ content reflects the triple hydrogen bonding in this base-pair (Figure 7.5) which requires a higher temperature for its disruption.

If the denaturation of the DNA is incomplete with about 12 intact consecutive base-pairs, a return to favourable conditions permits the partially separated strands to re-form the duplex structure spontaneously, a process called renaturation. If the denaturation of the DNA is complete, renaturation may occur but at a markedly lower

rate since complementary sequences must align through collisions before the re-formation of the duplex. Renaturation tends to occur at temperatures 20–25°C below the T_m value. Similar effects may be achieved with RNA molecules due to hydrogen-bonded regions.

Denatured DNA molecules from different species may interact with each other to create hybrid duplexes in which regions of a DNA strand from one species have base-paired with a disparate DNA strand. Such hybridizations permit the identification of like genes within different species and the determination of evolutionary relationships between species. Hybridization may also occur between a single DNA strand and an RNA molecule; the process is called DNA–RNA hybridization. Such techniques have proved valuable in the isolation and purification of genes and their corresponding RNAs.

Renaturation of DNA is governed by reassociation kinetics. The reassociation rate obeys the Law of Mass Action (Section 2.3) and is concentration dependent, i.e. the higher the concentration of DNA, the faster the renaturation. The relationship between the initial DNA concentration (C_0) and the concentration of unrenatured DNA (C) at time (t) is given by the equation:

$$\frac{C}{C_0} = \frac{1}{(1+kC_0t)}$$

where k is an association rate constant dependent upon temperature and the length of the DNA fragments. Several values of C_0 are used to measure C as a function of time and a graph of C/C_0 versus $\log_{10} C_0t$ is plotted. Such plots can be employed in the determination of the complexity of (number of bases in) a repeating sequence and the number of copies of that sequence per DNA preparation.

Reassociation curves (called C_0t curves) for bacterial and bacteriophage DNA are simple smooth one-step curves (Figure 7.13a) which suggests that these molecules contain very few repeated sequences. With DNA extracted from eukaryotic cells and processed to produce strands of uniform length, the curve is more complex (Figure 7.13b). The DNA renatures at different times. Almost immediately, DNA containing several hundred to several million copies per cell of one or more short sequences renatures. This class is called highly repetitive DNA. Because highly repetitive DNA is found as a minor band (a satellite) next to the main band of chromosomal DNA after caesium

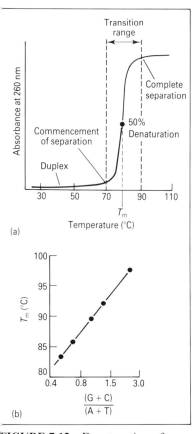

FIGURE 7.12   Denaturation of DNA. (a) A melting curve profile of DNA. (b) The relationship between T_m and $(G+C)$ content

chloride equilibrium centrifugation (Section 18.1), it is also termed satellite DNA. Middle repetitive DNA containing sequences repeated ten to several hundred times per cell is next to reassociate. Last to reassociate are sequences which are present as a single copy per cell and classified as unique DNA.

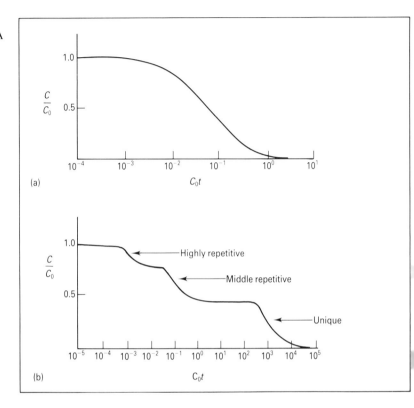

FIGURE 7.13 Reassociation kinetics of (a) λ bacteriophage DNA and (b) mouse DNA

Suggested further reading

Adams, R. L. P., Knowler, J. T. and Leader, D. P. (1986) *The Biochemistry of Nucleic Acids*, 10th edn, Chapman and Hall, London

Mainwaring, W. P., Parrish, J. H., Pickering, J. D. and Mann, N. H. (1982) *Nucleic Acid Biochemistry and Molecular Biology*, Blackwell, Oxford

Szekely, M. (1980) *From DNA to Protein – The Transfer of Genetic Information*, Macmillan, London

CHAPTER 8

Lipids

8.1 The classes of lipids

Lipids are a structurally and functionally diverse group of compounds which have the common feature of being largely non-polar molecules. They are insoluble in water but soluble in the lipid solvents which are a variety of non-polar solvents including chloroform, methanol, hexane and ether either used singly or as cocktails. Numerous classes of lipids contain fatty acid residues. Lipids can be classified into the following major groups: fatty acids, waxes, acylglycerols, phosphoacylglycerols, plasmalogens, sphingolipids, eicosanoids, terpenes and steroids.

8.2 Fatty acids

Fatty acids are carboxylic acids originally isolated from fats. They consist of a long hydrocarbon chain terminating in a carboxyl group. They may be either saturated, i.e. contain no double bonds, or unsaturated, i.e. contain double bonds. The saturated fatty acids conform to the general formula: $CH_3–(CH_2)_n–COOH$ (Table 8.1). At physiological pH, they exist in an ionized form: $CH_3–(CH_2)_n–COO^-$ (Section 2.1). Because of the variable position of the double bonds in unsaturated fatty acids, it is not possible to write a general formula. The fatty acids which frequently occur in nature have an even number of carbon atoms, generally in the range of $C_{12}–C_{20}$, although shorter and longer, branched and cyclic chain acids and odd-numbered fatty acids do occur. The double bond(s) in unsaturated fatty acids is rarely conjugated. Each double bond introduces rigidity into the structure (Section 1.2). In most naturally occurring fatty acids, the double bond is of the *cis* configuration (Figure 8.1) which creates a rigid bend in the long aliphatic chains and renders them sensitive to oxidation.

The carboxylate (COO^-) is normally water soluble but the long hydrocarbon chain repels water (hydrophobic) rendering the entire molecule water insoluble. Because fatty acids have both hydrophobic and hydrophilic regions they are referred to as amphipathic molecules (amphi = both). Resultant from the amphipathic property, fatty acids in a polar environment organize themselves into micelles in which the hydrocarbon chains are directed towards the interior of the structure with the carboxylate groups on the outside in contact with the polar solvent. The structure is held together by weak non-covalent attractive forces called van der Waals forces between the hydrocarbon chains.

TABLE 8.1 Some important naturally occurring fatty acids

Saturated fatty acids (acylates)	Abbreviation	Name		Structure
		Common	Systematic	
	12:0	Laurate	n-Dodecanoate	$CH_3(CH_2)_{10}COO^-$
	14:0	Myristate	n-Tetradecanoate	$CH_3(CH_2)_{12}COO^-$
	16:0	Palmitate	n-Hexadecanoate	$CH_3(CH_2)_{14}COO^-$
	18:0	Stearate	n-Octadecanoate	$CH_3(CH_2)_{16}COO^-$
	20:0	Arachidate	n-Eicosanoate	$CH_3(CH_2)_{18}COO^-$
Unsaturated fatty acids (acylates)	$16:1^{\Delta9}$	Palmitoleate	cis-9-Hexadecenoate	$CH_3(CH_2)_5CH=CH(CH_2)_7COO^-$
	$18:1^{\Delta9}$	Oleate	cis-9-Octadecenoate	$CH_3(CH_2)_7CH=CH(CH_2)_7COO^-$
	$18:2^{\Delta9,12}$	Linoleate	cis cis-9,12-Octadecenoate	$CH_3(CH_2)_4(CH=CHCH_2)_2(CH_2)_6COO^-$
	$18:3^{\Delta9,12,15}$	Linolenate	all cis-9,12,15-Octadecenoate	$CH_3CH_2(CH=CHCH_2)_3(CH_2)_6COO^-$
	$20:4^{\Delta5,8,11,14}$	Arachidonate	all cis-5,8,11,14-Eicosatetraenoate	$CH_3(CH_2)_4(CH=CHCH_2)_4(CH_2)_2COO^-$

Saturated fatty acids under systematic nomenclature contain the syllable, -an-, while unsaturated fatty acids contain the syllable, -en-
Δ denotes double bond
Δ^9 denotes double bond position, i.e. between C-9 and C-10 on numbering from the carboxyl carbon atom
Δ^5 denotes double bond position, i.e. between C-5 and C-6

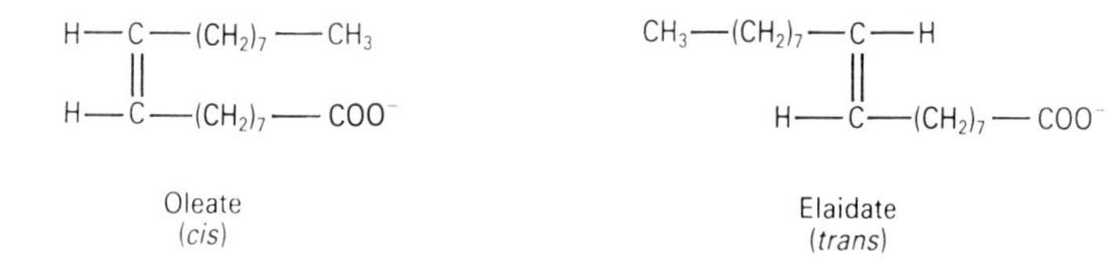

FIGURE 8.1 An example of cis–trans isomerism in unsaturated fatty acids

Oleate (cis)

Elaidate (trans)

8.3 Waxes

A wax is the water-insoluble ester product of the interaction of a single long chain fatty acid and a long chain alcohol (Figure 8.2a). These compounds have a variety of functions including protective and metabolic functions (Section 1.6).

FIGURE 8.2 General structure of
(a) waxes, (b) triacylglycerols,
(c) phosphoacylglycerols and
(d) plasmalogens

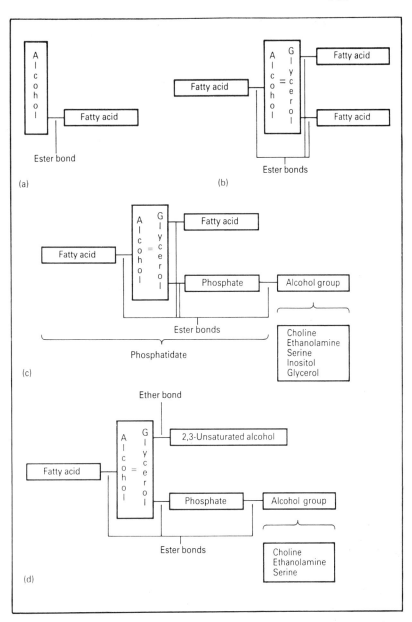

8.4 Acylglycerols

Acylglycerols (formerly called glycerides) are esters in which one, two or three fatty acids have reacted with the alcohol, glycerol. The two CH_2OH groups of glycerol cause difficulties for D, L nomenclature (Section 1.3). The remedy was the introduction of stereospecific numbering, indicated by the prefix *sn*, and based on the designation of L-glycerol 3-phosphate as *sn*-glycerol 3-phosphate (Figure 8.3). The *sn* system allows accurate description of the structures of mixed triacylglycerols in which the *sn*-1

Glycerol

L-Glycerol 3-phosphate
or D-glycerol 1-phosphate
sn-glycerol 3-phosphate

L-Glycerol 1-phosphate
or D-glycerol 3-phosphate
sn-glycerol 1-phosphate

position is frequently occupied by a saturated fatty acid and the *sn*-2 position by an unsaturated fatty acid.

Esterification by one fatty acid (called acylation) of the glycerol results in a monoacylglycerol, by two fatty acids yields a diacylglycerol and by three fatty acids yields a triacylglycerol (Figure 8.2b). Only a small amount of free fatty acids is found in tissue, the bulk of the fatty acids being stored as triacylglycerols. Triacylglycerols may be composed of only one fatty acid, either saturated (e.g. tri-palmitin) or unsaturated (e.g. triolein), or a mixture of saturated or unsaturated fatty acids. Since acyl groups have lost the negative charge of the fatty acid during esterification, they are electrically neutral and so the triacylglycerols they compose are termed neutral fats. Most neutral fats, e.g. olive oil or butter, are complex mixtures of simple and mixed triacylglycerols containing a variety of fatty acids differing in chain length and degree of saturation. In general, animal triacylglycerols are composed of long chain saturated fatty acids and tend to be solid at room temperature (fats) whereas plant triacylglycerols tend to contain unsaturated fatty acids and are liquid at room temperature (oils).

8.5 Phosphoacylglycerols

Phosphoacylglycerols (formerly called phospho-glycerides) are composed of glycerol in which *sn*-1 and *sn*-2 hydroxyl groups are esterified with fatty acids and the *sn*-3 hydroxyl group is esterified with phosphoric acid. This derives the parent compound, phosphatidate (Figure 8.2c), which is the simplest phosphoacylglycerol. Only a small amount of phosphatidate is present in cellular membranes but it serves as an intermediate in the synthesis of the major membranous phosphoacyl-glycerols. The phosphate group is further esterified by an alcoholic hydroxyl group. The major groups of phosphoacylglycerols include phosphatidyl-cholines (formerly lecithins), phosphatidylethanol-amines (formerly cephalins), phosphatidylserines, phosphatidylglycerols and phosphatidylinositols, in which the second alcoholic group is supplied by choline, ethanolamine, serine, glycerol and inositol respectively.

In water or aqueous media, the phosphoacyl-glycerols (and also plasmalogens and sphingo-myelins) assume a characteristic shape (Figure 8.4a). One end of the molecule is polar due to the electronegative phosphate and sometimes an elec-tropositive group. The long hydrocarbon chains of the fatty acids are non-polar and remain hydro-phobic. Like fatty acids, these amphipathic mol-ecules can in a polar environment form micelles but preferentially assume a bilayer formation (Figure 8.4b) which serves as the fundamental structure of cellular membranes. Bilayer formation is a spontaneous event due to the hydrophobicity of the hydrocarbon chains reinforced by van der Waals' forces which favour close packing of these

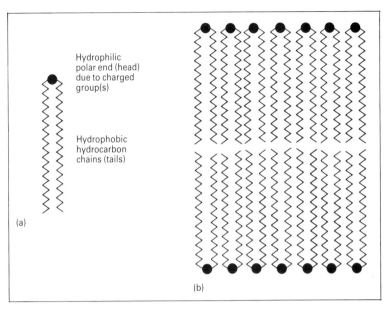

FIGURE 8.4 Amphipathic phosphoacylglycerols. (a) Structural representation. (b) The formation of a lipid bilayer

Hydrophilic polar end (head) due to charged group(s)

Hydrophobic hydrocarbon chains (tails)

(a)

(b)

chains to such an extent that, on disruption, the bilayer may re-form. Additional stability of the bilayer is afforded by interactions between the polar groups and the polar solvent.

8.6 Plasmalogens

Plasmalogens are a class of lipids abundant in nerve and skeletal muscle cell membranes. Structurally, they are similar to phosphoacylglycerols except that a 2,3-unsaturated alcohol is substituted by an ether linkage at *sn*-1 (or *sn*-2) carbon rather than a fatty acid in ester linkage (Figure 8.2d). The term phosphatidal in the names of individual compounds, e.g. phosphatidalcholine, distinguishes them from phosphoacylglycerols. The functional role of plasmalogens in biological tissues has not been elucidated.

8.7 Sphingolipids

Sphingolipids are common constituents of membranes which are similar in structure to phosphoacylglycerols except that the alcohol is the amino alcohol, sphingosine (Figure 8.5b). Linkage of the fatty acid does not involve an ester linkage but an amide linkage to give a parent compound, ceramide (Figure 8.5a). Phosphorylation of a ceramide followed by esterification yields a sphingomyelin (Figure 8.5c). Brain and nervous tissue are rich in sphingomyelins. Another class of derivatives of ceramides called cerebrosides are abundant in brain membranes (but are also found in other tissues). Cerebrosides are glycosylated ceramides, frequently containing D-glucose or D-galactose (Figure 8.5d). Cerebrosides are therefore glycolipids. If the glycosylation of the ceramides involves an oligosaccharide chain, the products are called gangliosides. Gangliosides are important components of specific receptor sites which bind neurotransmitter molecules during the chemical transmission of a nervous impulse from nerve cell to nerve cell.

8.8 Eicosanoids

The eicosanoids are four families (Figure 8.6) of highly active biological molecules which are oxygenated derivatives of unsaturated C_{20} fatty acids (eicosaenoates) and are biosynthesized by the action of different enzyme systems. The cyclo-oxygenase system yields prostaglandins, one of which a pivotal prostaglandin H_2 is acted upon by the enzyme, thromboxane synthase to yield thromboxane A_2 (TXA_2) which may be converted to TXB_2 (Figure 15.10). Arachidonate metabolism by two lipoxygenase systems yields leukotrienes and lipoxins.

Prostaglandins (Figure 8.6a), so named because it was thought that they originated from the pro-state gland in man and animals, can be synthesized by a variety of animal tissues. Structurally, they are a group of C_{20} monocarboxylic acids which contain an internal cyclopentane ring. The number of C=C double bonds in the prostaglandin hydrocarbon chain is indicated by a subscript number, i.e. PG_1, PG_2 or PG_3. Although all prostaglandins have an α-hydroxyl group at C-15 (except PGG), they differ in the position of ring substituent carbonyl and hydroxyl groups. Each variation is identified by a letter of the English alphabet, e.g. D, E, F, G, H or I (Figure 15.10) although originally Swedish E and F for *e*ther soluble and *f*osfat (phosphate) soluble respectively.

Biological activity of these compounds is achieved by small quantities, e.g. in the nanogram (10^{-9}g) range. Prostaglandins have a variety of physiological roles in different tissues including modulation of the following: hormone action; the inflammatory response; blood flow; ion transport across membranes; transmission of nervous impulses. PGE_2 is employed in obstetrics to induce labour. Frequently the action of one prostaglandin is antagonistic to that of another. They have very short half-lives since they are rapidly degraded upon their delivery to lung tissue.

Thromboxanes (Figure 8.6b) are so named because they were originally isolated from thrombocytes (blood platelets). Thromboxane synthesis also takes place in lung and kidney. Thromboxanes differ from prostaglandins in the ring structure which is, in the case of thromboxanes, a cyclic ether. Their biological function involves the promotion of blood clotting by platelet aggregation and vasoconstriction.

Leukotrienes (Figure 8.6c) are so named because they are synthesized by leukocytes (white blood cells) and contain three conjugated double bonds. Their nomenclature is similar to that of prostaglandins. The leukotrienes of biological interest have four double bonds; LTA_4, LTB_4, LTC_4, LTD_4 and LTE_4 (Figure 15.10). Although their biological effects especially the constriction of the bronchioles in asthmatics had been observed in the late 1930s, the elucidation of leukotrienes as the causative agents was not reported until 1979. LTC_4 and LTD_4 are potent contractors of smooth muscle, being especially effective as bronchoconstrictors and vasoconstrictors. LTB_4 is extremely active in the modulation of the migration of polymorphonuclear leukocytes.

The discovery of lipoxins (Figure 8.6d) was announced in 1984. These substances contain a conjugated tetraene and are synthesized by leukocytes. LXA provokes slow-onset but long-lasting contractions of lung tissue strips and inhibits the activity of certain leukocytes.

FIGURE 8.5 General structures of sphingolipids. (a) Ceramides. (b) Sphingosine. (c) Sphingomyelins. (d) Cerebrosides

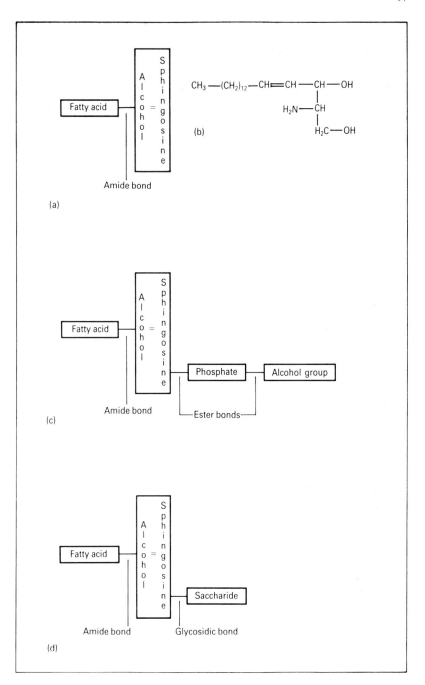

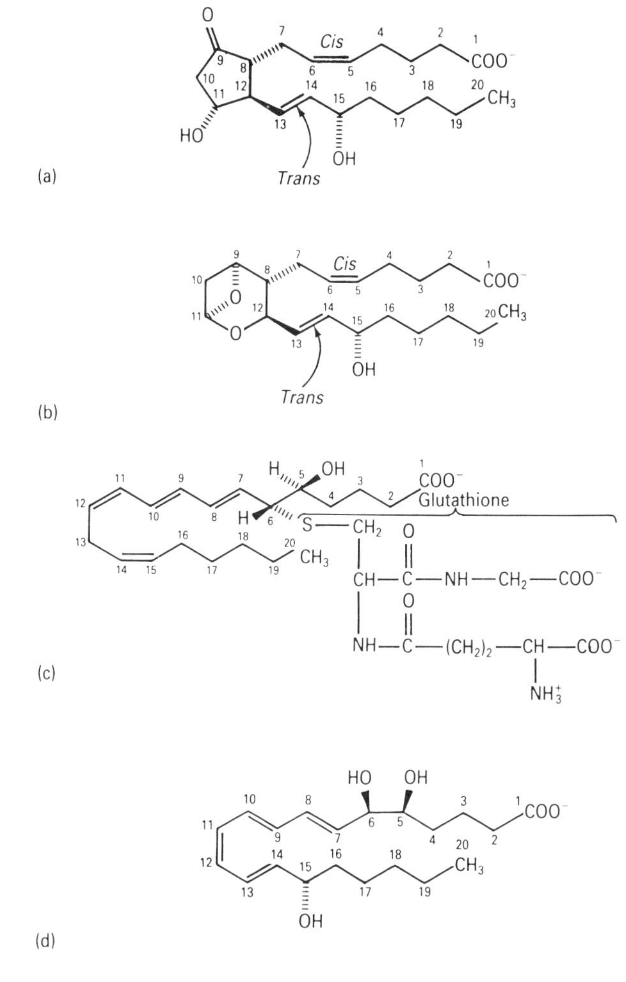

FIGURE 8.6 Example structures
from eicosanoid families. (a)
Prostaglandin E$_2$ (PGE$_2$). (b)
Thromboxane A$_2$ (TXA$_2$). (c)
Leukotriene C$_4$ (LTC$_4$). (d) Lipoxin
A (LXA)

8.9 Terpenes

Terpenes and steroids (Section 8.10) are structurally unrelated to previous classes of lipid in that their structures do not contain or are not derived from fatty acids. They are considered as lipids because of their solubility characteristics.

Terpenes are polymers of isoprene (Figure 8.7a) and are found as constituents of a variety of biological substances, e.g. vitamins A, E and K, rubber, chlorophyll (Figure 14.1) and the important electron carriers, ubiquinone (Figure 8.7b, Section 13.2) and plastoquinone (Figure 8.7c, Section 14.4).

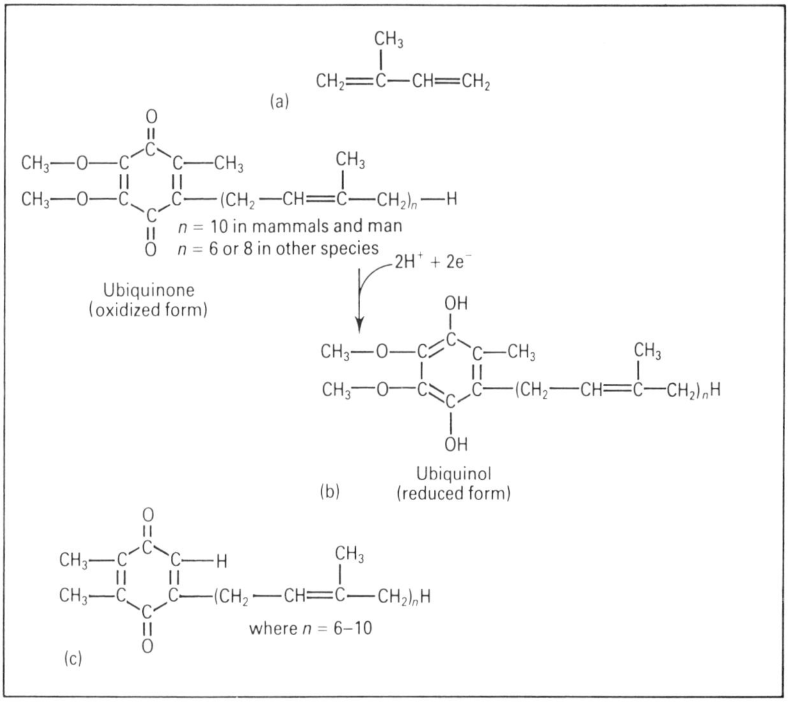

FIGURE 8.7 Structures of some isoprenoid compounds. (a) An isoprene (2-methylbutadiene) unit. (b) Ubiquinone and ubiquinol (oxidized and reduced Q). (c) Plastoquinone

8.10 Steroids

The steroids are an important class of lipid because of their wide range of biological activities often at very minute concentrations. Structurally, they consist of four fused hydrocarbon rings, labelled A, B, C and D (Figure 8.8a). Rings A, B and C are six-membered cyclohexane rings while ring D is cyclopentane. Chemically, the non-linear arrangement is called a perhydrocyclopentano-phenanthrene ring system, which has a characteristic numbering convention for its carbon atoms. The properties of the individual steroids are determined by the substituent groups attached to the ring system. The nature and position of these groups determine with which cells and cellular molecules the steroid can interact.

Many steroids have an alcohol group and strictly should be referred to as sterols. The most abundant sterol is cholesterol which is an important membrane constituent either in free (Figure 8.8b) or esterified form. Cholesterol possesses a planar steroid ring system, a polar 3β-hydroxyl group and a hydrophobic tail which makes the molecule amphipathic in character enabling orientation of the hydroxyl group towards aqueous media whilst the rings and tail penetrate the hydrophobic regions of membranes. Cholesterol is also a precursor for the synthesis of steroid hormones (Section 15.8), vitamin D and bile salts (Figure 8.8c).

Testosterone (Figure 15.12), synthesized by the testes, and oestradiol (Figure 15.12) synthesized by the ovaries, are the hormones responsible for the sexual development and the promotion and maintenance of sex characteristics in the male and female respectively. Progesterone (Figure 15.12) gives rise to other steroids and, in the female, prepares the uterus for the implantation of the ovum as well as preventing ovulation during pregnancy. Oestradiol and progesterone together are largely responsible for the regulation of the menstrual cycle. Combinations of synthetic progestogens and oestrogens are employed in contraceptive pills to prevent pregnancy or regulate menstruation. Cortisol (Figure 15.12), synthesized by the adrenal

FIGURE 8.8   Structures of steroids. (a) The steroid ring system. (b) Cholesterol. (c) A bile salt, glycocholate (choloylglycine)

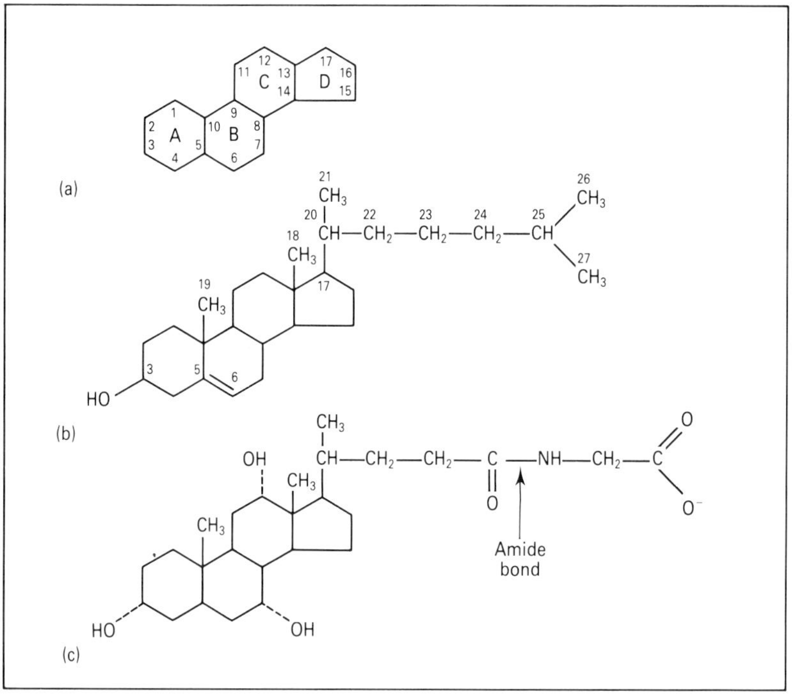

8.11 Circulatory lipid complexes

cortex, has an important role in the regulation of cellular metabolism, especially of carbohydrates but also influences that of fatty acids and proteins. It also exhibits anti-inflammatory properties by stabilizing certain membranes of tissue mast cells.

Because of their amphipathic properties, bile salts act in the emulsification of fats in the small intestine to aid absorption of dietary fat. The

principal bile salts are derivatives of cholic acid which is synthesized from cholesterol and contain an amide linkage to an amino acid (Figure 8.8c). Minor bile acids differ from cholic acid by virtue of their loss of at least one substituent hydroxyl group at positions 3, 7 or 12. Note that the prefix in glycocholate does not refer to a carbohydrate moiety but to the amino acid, glycine.

Cholesterol, triacylglycerols and phospholipids are transported in the circulatory system in association with proteins. Five distinct classes of lipoproteins called chylomicrons, very-low-density (VLD) lipoprotein, low-density (LD) lipoprotein, high-density (HD) lipoprotein and very-high-density (VHD) lipoprotein have been described. The largest lipoproteins are the chylomicrons which have the lowest density because of their high triacylglycerol and low protein content.

The main roles of these lipoproteins are as follows. Chylomicrons, which are synthesized by

the intestine, appear in the blood following a fat-containing meal to deliver dietary triacylglycerols to adipose tissue and the liver. VLD lipoprotein, synthesized by the liver and intestinal cells, transports endogenous triacylglycerols, esterified cholesterol and phospholipids to adipose tissue. The triacylglycerols delivered by chylomicrons and VLD lipoprotein are hydrolysed within the capillaries by lipoprotein lipase and the released fatty acids enter the adipocytes. LD lipoprotein, produced following the hydrolysis of triacylglycerols from VLD lipoprotein, transports cholesterol as cholesterol linoleate to peripheral tissues. HD lipoprotein, synthesized by the liver, carries cholesterol and phospholipids from peripheral tissues to the liver. VHD lipoprotein, also synthesized by the liver, transports mainly phospholipids.

Cholesterol biosynthesis occurs mainly in the liver and intestine and LD lipoprotein delivers the cholesterol to other cell types. LD lipoprotein binds to specific plasma membrane receptors located within regions called coated pits. The receptor–LD lipoprotein complex undergoes endocytosis (Section 9.3) during which it is encompassed by the plasma membrane and internalized as a vesicle. The vesicle makes contact and fuses with lysosomes containing a variety of hydrolytic enzymes including proteases and esterases which release amino acids and cholesterol from the complex. This free cholesterol can be employed in membrane biosynthesis or re-esterified for intracellular storage mainly as cholesterol oleate or palmitoleate. Free cholesterol also inhibits the activation and synthesis of the enzyme hydroxymethylglutaryl-CoA reductase which controls the rate of cholesterol biosynthesis (Section 15.8). In this way, dietary cholesterol may suppress endogenous cholesterol synthesis. The accumulation of intracellular cholesterol also prevents the replenishment of the LD lipoprotein receptors thereby inhibiting LD lipoprotein uptake by the cell.

Suggested further reading

MEAD, J. F., ALFIN-SLATER, R. B., HOWTON, D. R. and POPJAK, G.(1986) *Lipids: Chemistry, Biochemistry and Nutrition*, Plenum, New York

GURR, M. I. and JAMES, A. T.(1980) *Lipid Biochemistry – an Introduction*, 3rd edn, Chapman and Hall, London

CHAPTER 9

Eukaryotic cellular organization

9.1 Prokaryotic and eukaryotic cells

The comparison of the physical characteristics of prokaryotic and eukaryotic cells in Section 1.1 requires some expansion. Figure 9.1 illustrates the internal structure of a bacterium. The organism is encompassed by a rigid cell wall, rich in carbohydrates and amino acids (Section 3.7), which is irregularly anchored to the plasma (or cell) membrane. The plasma membrane exhibits numerous invaginations called mesosomes to which large circular molecules of bacterial DNA are frequently attached. Mesosomes function in bacterial respiration and cell division. The prokaryotic plasma membrane demonstrates a high level of organization since it performs certain functions for which eukaryotic cells have evolved distinct organelles, e.g. cellular respiration. Molecules of protein-free DNA are located within the cytoplasm in an amorphous region called the nuclear region. Some small circular molecules of DNA called plasmids are found outside this region. Plasmids con-

tain certain genes advantageous to the welfare of the organism, e.g. genes governing resistance to certain antibiotics. Because of their independent replication, plasmids are employed as vectors to permit the insertion of foreign genes into bacteria during genetic engineering (Section 19.3).

The contents of the cell excluding the nuclear region are collectively called the cytoplasm. The aqueous phase of the cytoplasm is termed the cytosol. The cytosol contains many proteins in solution including metabolic enzymes and intracellular transport proteins, many small organic molecules which are involved in metabolic processes, coenzymes, cations, e.g. Mg^{2+} and Ca^{2+}, anions, e.g. HCO_3^-, HPO_4^{2-}, and, in aerobic cells, oxygen. Within the cytoplasm, the ribosomes may exceed 10 000 in number. Although freely distributed, during protein synthesis numerous ribosomes may become bound to mRNA to form polyribosomes (Section 17.6). Numerous intracellular granules are present within the cytoplasm. These may contain reserve fuel molecules such as starch, glycogen (Section 3.6) and lipid (Section 8.4) and enzymes concerned with synthetic or degradative processes. The bacterium may possess one or many flagella which extend from the cytoplasm through the cell wall and are responsible for the motility of the organism. The surface of several bacteria including *Escherichia coli* exhibit fine fibrillar structures called fimbriae, the proteins of which interact with glycosphingolipids of host cells. This interaction may be the initial stage in the infection of host tissue.

Eukaryotic cells may be unicellular organisms, e.g. protozoa, or aggregate to constitute the tissues

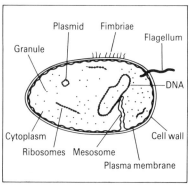

FIGURE 9.1   Schematic diagram of a bacterium

of multicellular organisms. Figure 9.2 depicts a schematic transverse section through a eukaryotic (animal) cell whose major feature is the variety of intracellular membrane-bound organelles. The principal structures identifiable within an animal cell are the nucleus, nucleolus, mitochondria, endoplasmic reticulum, Golgi apparatus, ribosomes, lysosomes, peroxisomes and plasma membrane. Plant cells may contain additional features such as a cell wall, plasmodesmata, large vacuoles and chloroplasts (Section 9.5).

The plant cell wall is a thick protective and supportive polysaccharide-containing layer. The cell wall is unlikely to have an appreciable involve-ment in the regulation of the exchange of materials between plant cells and their environment. This role as in animal cells is a function of the plasma membrane. Plasmodesmata are cytoplasmic bridges which intrude through adjacent cell walls to provide cytoplasmic continuity and the circulation of materials between cells. Although vacuoles are present in animal cells, they are significantly larger and more abundant in plant cells. In some cases, the single membrane-bound vacuole of a plant cell occupies much of the cytoplasm and displaces the other organelles into peripheral locations. Vacuoles function as reservoirs for water, metabolic products and intermediates.

FIGURE 9.2 Schematic diagram of a eukaryotic (animal) cell

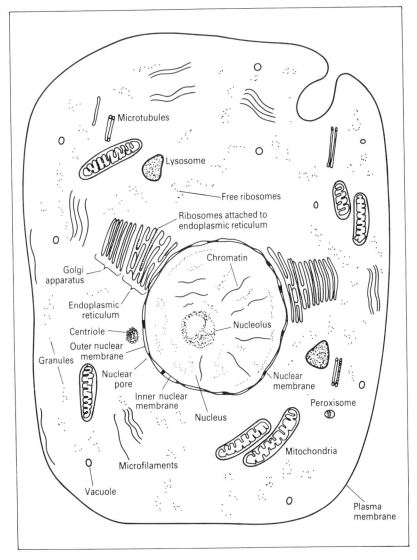

9.2 The plasma membrane: structure

The plasma membrane (Figure 9.2) encapsulates the cell and physically separates the cytoplasm from the external environment. All substances which enter or leave the cell must pass through the plasma membrane which plays an important role in the selective uptake of nutrients from the extracellular medium and the discharge of waste products of metabolism from the cell. The plasma membrane is the most extensively researched and best understood of all cell membranes and its properties have led to the development of models of membrane structure from the fundamental lipid bilayer composed of amphipathic phospholipids (Section 8.5) to the currently most widely accepted model called the fluid mosaic model.

The plasma membrane (Figure 9.3) is a phospholipid bilayer which incorporates various proteins and cholesterol. In eukaryotic cells, all membrane proteins expose at least one oligosaccharide chain to the outside of the cell, never to the inside. Some glycoproteins bind externally to the polar groups of the phospholipid and are termed peripheral (or extrinsic) proteins. Other proteins from the extracellular milieu may in turn adhere to these proteins. Proteins termed integral (or intrinsic) proteins appear positioned within the membrane from which, unlike the loosely bound peripheral proteins, they are not readily displaced. All integral proteins contain within their structure at least one hydrophobic segment which embeds within the membrane. Additionally, there may be a substantial hydrophilic polypeptide mass exposed mainly (or entirely) on one side of the membrane or more evenly distributed on both sides of the membrane. The hydrophobic regions consist largely of hydrophobic amino acids which interact with the non-polar hydrocarbon chains of the membranous lipids. These hydrophobic intramembranous regions appear to be α-helical in nature and perpendicular to the membrane surface. The integral proteins which extend across the entire membrane consist of a central hydrophobic segment and terminal hydrophilic segments, one of which anchors the protein in the cytoplasm while the other projects outwards from the lipid bilayer. Protein molecules may span the membrane in such a manner as to create a narrow channel which may connect the cell cytoplasm to the outside milieu. These channels play an important role in the determination of the ionic status and thereby the activity of the cell (Section 9.3).

Many of the glycoproteins function as cell-surface receptors, i.e. as binding sites of unique conformational shapes, each of which specifically binds a certain molecule of a complementary configuration called a ligand. When occupied by its ligand, the folding pattern of the polypeptide chains of the receptor changes to cause conformational change in an associated membranous protein so that a signal is transmitted across the membrane from its external environment to the inside of the cell where an enzyme-mediated biological response is manifested.

The plasma membrane exhibits asymmetry with

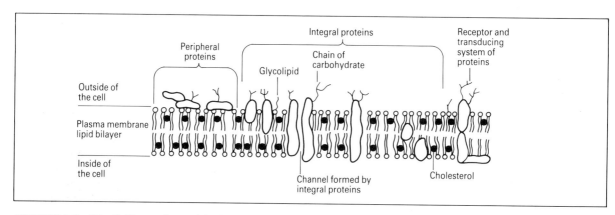

FIGURE 9.3   The fluid mosaic model of membrane structure

respect to some lipids. The outer monolayer of an erythrocyte's membrane, for example, contains only phosphatidylcholine and sphingomyelin (Section 8.7) whereas the inner monolayer contains phosphatidylethanolamine, phosphatidylserine and phosphatidylinositol (Section 8.5). Glycolipids are located only in the outer monolayer. The monolayers exhibit selective location of a wide variety of enzymic activities.

Phosphoacylglycerols, sphingomyelins and cholesterol are incorporated into the lipid bilayer because of their amphipathic character (Chapter 8). The plasma membrane of human erythrocytes has a high cholesterol content, about 45% of the total lipid content. The bilayer formed from natural phospholipids is essentially a liquid in that it exhibits random motions consistent with the liquid state. Their hydrocarbon tails may move more freely about in the plane of the monolayer without losing their hydrophobicity which is responsible for their mutual attraction. Membranous proteins embedded within the membrane can also move laterally but are limited in the magnitude of such migrations by their interactions with other components located internal to the membrane.

This property of molecular movement within the membrane is referred to as membrane fluidity.

Membrane fluidity is determined by the packing of the hydrocarbon tails of the lipids within the membrane. Lipids with long saturated tails decrease membrane fluidity because their parallel tails can form extensive hydrophobic interactions. Shorter chain lengths increase membrane fluidity because of the limitations imposed upon interactions between adjacent chains. Unsaturation of the hydrocarbon tail introduces a *cis* double bond which causes a bend in the tail (Section 8.2). This lowers the numbers of hydrophobic interactions between adjacent tails and enhances membrane fluidity. Therefore, both the length and the degree of unsaturation of the hydrocarbon chains influence the fluidity of biological membranes. Cholesterol molecules, because of their rigid planar non-polar ring structure, can intercalate between the phospholipids near to their hydrophilic heads with which the polar hydroxyl groups may interact. Cholesterol molecules can fit compactly with the kinked unsaturated hydrocarbon chains and promote hydrophobic interactions which reduce the fluidity of natural membranes.

9.3 The plasma membrane: transport mechanisms

Access to the cytoplasm may be gained by extracellular substances by a number of mechanisms depending on the chemistry and size of the molecule and the type of cell. The mechanisms are passive transport, facilitated diffusion, active transport and endocytosis. In general, the more non-polar a substance the more lipid soluble it is and the more readily it passes through the plasma membrane by dissolving in the lipid regions. Small molecules, e.g. butyramide, may enter the cell from a medium of high concentration to increase the internal low concentration. This concentration-dependent migration of molecules is called diffusion or passive transport and does not involve the interaction with membranous proteins.

A variety of non-lipid soluble small molecules, e.g. sugars and amino acids, can nevertheless pass through the plasma membrane. The mechanism involved is facilitated (or mediated) diffusion in which transport is enhanced by specific integral membranous proteins called carriers. Carrier

proteins demonstrate certain properties similar to enzymes. They are permeant specific, e.g. glucose but not fructose or dissaccharides may enter the erythrocyte by facilitated diffusion. Carriers are pH dependent and can be competitively inhibited (Section 6.3) by compounds structurally similar to that of the permeant. The carrier proteins also exhibit saturation kinetics. Thus, the rate of transport progressively increases with increasing concentration of permeant until it becomes independent of concentration and remains constant (cf V_{max}, Figure 6.3b).

A carrier which transports a single molecule in one direction is called a uniport system. Alternatively, a carrier may carry two molecules simultaneously in the same direction, i.e. a symport system. Thirdly, a carrier may exchange one molecule for another and therefore transport them in opposite directions, i.e an antiport system (Figure 9.4).

Facilitated diffusion speeds up the rate at which

FIGURE 9.4 Mechanisms for facilitated transport. (a) Uniport mechanism. (b) Symport mechanism. (c) Antiport mechanism

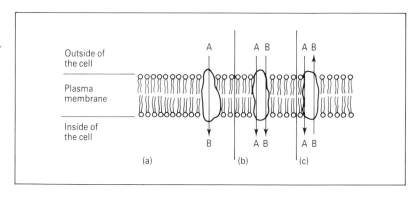

the normal concentration equilibrium is established across the membrane but does not transport substances against a concentration gradient. To transport substances against a concentration gradient, energy is required and the process is called active transport. Active transport is also carrier mediated; the carriers demonstrate the properties listed above for passive carriers. The carriers of active transport, however, require coupling with a source of energy, usually ATP (Section 10.4), although the energy may not be used directly in the movement of the permeant in all active transport systems. Active transport is the mechanism by which cations, e.g. Na^+, K^+ and Ca^{2+}, are transported through the narrow channels of the plasma membrane (Figure 9.3).

Macromolecules and large particles penetrate the impermeable barrier by the process called endocytosis in which material to be absorbed is engulfed by an area of the plasma membrane which forms an enclosed vesicle. There are three mechanisms of endocytosis; phagocytosis, pinocytosis and receptor-mediated endocytosis (Figure 9.5).

In phagocytosis, large particles bind to the surface of the cell by hydrophobic interactions, surface tension or through attachment to specific cell-surface receptors. Particle–cell contact initiates a series of biochemical events which result in the envelopment of the particle by the membrane. The particle is drawn into the cell and is degraded by the lysosomal enzymes.

Pinocytosis is a non-specific process in which minute droplets of extracellular fluid are engulfed by the plasma membrane. On detachment from the plasma membrane, pinocytic vesicles of less than 1 nm in diameter containing ions and small molecules migrate inward and may fragment into

smaller vesicles or fuse to become larger. Receptor-mediated endocytosis is absolutely specific. The receptors, e.g. low-density (LD) lipoprotein receptors, may reside in specific areas of the plasma membrane called coated pits or may be scattered over the membrane and migrate on occupancy by the ligand to a specific area, e.g. insulin receptors. At these sites, the inner side of the plasma membrane has a thick coating of a fibrous protein called clathrin. Polymerization of clathrin causes the coated pit to form a coated vesicle with an external lattice of clathrin. During internalization, the clathrin meshwork dissociates and the vesicles fuse with one another to form large vesicles called endosomes. As the endosome migrates inward, the membranous receptors, e.g. LD lipoprotein receptor, lose their affinity for the ligand through the acidification of their environment and become clustered at one end of the vesicle which has now assumed a tubular form. The structure is known as a CURL (compartment for the uncoupling of receptor and ligand). Detachment of the tubular portion affords a mechanism by which empty receptors may be recycled back to the plasma membrane. The ligands may be subsequently degraded following fusion of the vesicular portion with lysosomes. It should be noted that the above description of endocytosis does not apply to all ligands and receptors. Indeed, the intracellular transport and processing of receptor–ligand systems have been categorized into four general modes:

1. Recycling receptors which transport their ligand to lysosomes, e.g. LD lipoprotein receptor.
2. Recycling receptors which do not transport their ligand to lysosomes, e.g. transferrin receptor.

3. Non-recycling receptors which transport their ligand to lysosomes, e.g. EGF (epidermal growth factor) receptor.

4. Non-recycling receptors which do not transport their ligand to lysosomes, e.g. immunoglobulin A receptor.

FIGURE 9.5 Mechanisms of endocytosis. (a) Phagocytosis. (b) Pinocytosis. (c) Receptor-mediated endocytosis

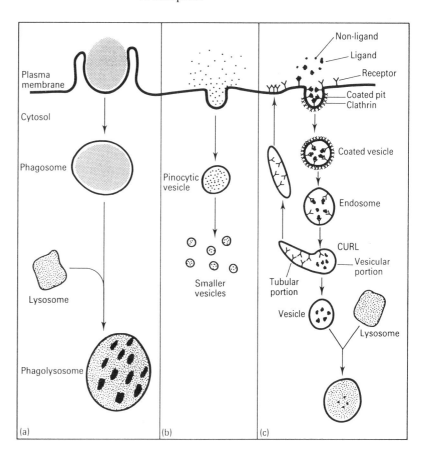

9.4 Nuclear structures

The nucleus of a cell (Figure 9.2) is the largest subcellular organelle, measuring approximately 4–6 μm in diameter. It is surrounded by the nuclear membrane which segregates nuclear material from the cytoplasm. The nuclear membrane differs from other cellular membranes. At various regions, its double membrane is fused together to form nuclear pores through which large molecular complexes such as ribosome precursors and mRNA may pass.

The nucleus contains a particulate semifluid mass called the nucleoplasm which is in part organized into one or more spherical bodies called nucleoli. A nucleolus, like the nucleus, is mainly composed of chromatin but is not enveloped by a membrane. The role of a nucleolus is the synthesis of ribosomal RNA molecules. Cells active in protein synthesis require an active synthesis of ribosome subunits. These cells exhibit enlarged nucleoli whereas cells exhibiting little protein synthesis have reduced frequently crescent-shaped nucleoli.

Chromatin is the nuclear material which stains with basic dyes. The chromatin is not evenly dispersed throughout the nucleus but may be clumped into dark staining regions near the inner nuclear membrane referred to as peripheral chromatin. Between the peripheral chromatin and the nucleolar chromatin lie lightly staining regions called dispersed chromatin. During an early stage in cell division, the chromatin material becomes packaged into chromosomes which are readily stained structures. In resting cells, the chromatin is not as amorphous as staining patterns may suggest.

Chromatin contains deoxyribonucleic acid (DNA) and a greater quantity of various proteins. The proteins of greatest structural relevance are the lysine- and arginine-containing histones and non-histone proteins. Five types of histones have been classified: H1, H2A, H2B, H3 and H4. Ionic interactions between these proteins and the phosphate groups of DNA are responsible for the ultrastructure of chromatin in which DNA is coiled around octamers of histones to form nucleosomes (Figure 9.6). H1 is an accessory protein also bound to DNA but not part of the nucleosome. Chromatin material can be thought of as repetitive nucleosomes interlinked by the continuous strand of DNA and positioned within the nucleus by non-histone proteins.

FIGURE 9.6   Structure of chromatin

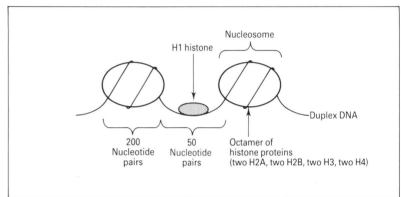

9.5 Electron-transporting organelles

Two organelles, the mitochondrion and the chloroplast, have extensive internal membranes which support electron-transport systems necessary for the production of energy. Mitochondria are found in most eukaryotic cells whereas chloroplasts are restricted to plant cells.

Various shapes of mitochondria have been recorded, i.e. oval, round, cylindrical etc., but they (Figure 9.7) are commonly observed as oval organelles about 1–2 μm long and 0.5–1 μm wide. Their numbers and distribution are closely related to the capacity of the cell for aerobic energy production, e.g. the human hepatocyte may contain 500 to 2000 mitochondria whereas the erythrocyte does not generate energy through the involvement of oxygen as a terminal acceptor and has no mitochondria. All mitochondria have two separate membranes, an outer and an inner membrane, which exhibit permeability differences. The inner membrane is impermeable to many metabolic intermediates. Embedded within the inner membrane is a wide range of carrier molecules to facilitate the transport of essential materials into and out of the organelle. The outer membrane, however, is less restrictive being freely permeable to most small molecules and ions. The membranes are separated by a fluid-filled intermembrane space (or 'O' compartment) in which very few activities have been detected, e.g. the maintenance of the relative concentrations of adenine nucleotides (Section 10.4).

The inner membrane surrounds the aqueous matrix (or 'M' compartment) which contains most of the enzymes associated with aerobic oxidative processes, e.g. tricarboxylate cycle (Chapter 12).

The other enzymes necessary for these processes are peripheral or integral inner membrane proteins. The matrix contains discrete double-helical strands of circular DNA and ribosomes. Unlike nuclear DNA, mitochondrial DNA is not complexed with protein. The majority of mitochondrial proteins are however directed by nuclear DNA. In yeast, the mitochondrial DNA contains the code for its unique tRNA molecules, rRNA molecules of its own ribosomes and mRNA from which only six subunits of three inner-membrane respiratory-chain enzymes are translated. The primary structure of these proteins is determined by a genetic code (Section 17.5) which, although triplet in character, reads differently from that pertaining to prokaryotes and the eukaryotic nucleus and chloroplast.

The inner membrane exhibits numerous folds called cristae which invaginate into the matrix. Irrespective of shape, by increasing the length of membrane, cristae enable the membrane to house large numbers of electron-transport assemblies and associated ATP-synthesizing enzymes. The inner membrane of a single mitochondrion may contain 5000 to 20 000 electron-transport assemblies. The description of the mitochondria as the power-houses of the cell is entirely due to these structures within the inner membrane. Passage of electrons over the carriers comprising these assemblies

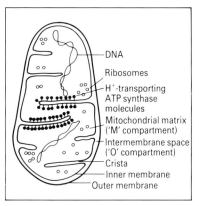

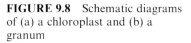

FIGURE 9.7   Schematic diagram of a mitochondrion

FIGURE 9.8   Schematic diagrams of (a) a chloroplast and (b) a granum

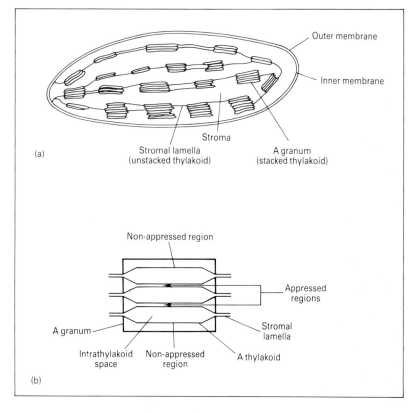

provide the energy from which a form of chemical energy suitable for use by the cell is generated (Chapter 13).

Chloroplasts are exclusive to the cells of green plant tissue. Their role is the capture of electromagnetic energy and its conversion into chemical energy during photosynthesis (Chapter 14). The cells of simple plants, e.g. algae, may contain a single chloroplast while higher plants have numerous chloroplasts per cell. The chloroplast is also surrounded by two distinct membranes (Figure 9.8a). Like its mitochondrial counterpart, the chloroplast inner membrane contains electron-transport assemblies and ATP-synthesizing enzymes. Additionally within this membrane reside light-harvesting complexes (LHC) which interact with the photons of light. The inner membrane is extensively folded but the folds do not invaginate the central compartment called the stroma. Rather they give rise to disc-shaped saccules called thylakoids. Thylakoids stack to form aggregate structures called grana which superficially may be considered to resemble stacks of coins (Figure 9.8b). During the stacking process, however, internal membrane components undergo rearrangement so that appressed granal regions become rich in a LHC containing photosystem II (PS II) while non-appressed regions become rich in photosystem I (PS I) and an ATP synthase. Membranous interconnections between adjacent grana are termed stromal lamella. The outer surface of the inner membrane is in contact with the aqueous stroma which contains most of the enzymes for carbohydrate synthesis (Section 14.6). Enclosed within the membrane is the intrathylakoid space which extends through stacked and unstacked regions.

9.6 Organelles associated with protein synthesis

Three organelles may be considered within this section: the ribosome, endoplasmic reticulum and Golgi apparatus (Figure 9.2). The ribosomes may be found free in the cytoplasm or attached to membranes especially the endoplasmic reticulum (ER). Free ribosomes participate in the synthesis of intracellular proteins whilst ribosomes bound to the ER synthesize proteins destined for the cell surface as membrane components or secretions and lysosomes. The structure (Section 7.4) and function of ribosomes (Section 17.6) in either case is the same.

The endoplasmic reticulum is an extensive network (or reticulum) of continuous folded membranes with a complex shape. The folds create inner cavities called cisternae. The endoplasmic reticulum may be described as rough or smooth (RER or SER) depending on the attachment of ribosomes which give a rough appearance to the structure. Polypeptides assembled on RER are synthesized with an additional section of variable length called a signal or leader sequence at their N-terminus. This extension facilitates the insertion of the polypeptide chain into the membrane and, upon fulfilling its function, it is cleaved from the chain by a protease associated with the membrane. The role of the ER includes the post-translational processing of proteins which may be defined as the enzymic modification of a polypeptide chain after its synthesis, e.g. by glycosylation, hydroxylation and the formation of disulphide bonds. These modified proteins are then encapsulated in a vesicle derived from the ER membrane which transports them to the cis face of the Golgi apparatus.

Named after its discoverer, the Golgi apparatus is a stack of flattened membranes each of which encloses a cisterna. The Golgi apparatus functions in the sorting of glycoproteins and is highly ordered being composed of three distinct compartments, cis, medial and trans compartments, through which the glycoproteins progress and are segregated into those destined for lysosomes, plasma membrane or secretions. They emerge from the trans face of the trans compartment in the appropriate vesicle. The Golgi apparatus is also the major site of the synthesis of glycosphingolipids (Section 8.7) of the outer monolayer of the plasma membrane.

9.7 Lysosomes and microbodies

Lysosomes and microbodies are single-membrane organelles each of which possess a discrete series of enzymes. Lysosomes (Figure 9.2) contain a wide variety of hydrolases which, at acidic pH, collectively are capable of degrading most classes of biological molecules. To protect the cell from autolysis, enzymic activation involves the metabolic acidification of the lysosomal milieu. Lysosomes feature significantly in endocytosis (Section 9.3).

The microbodies include the peroxisomes (present in both animal and plant cells) and glyoxysomes (located in only plant cells). Peroxisomes (Figure 9.2) contain non-digestive enzymes which produce or degrade hydrogen peroxide. For example, alcohol oxidase catalyses the oxidation of primary alcohols yielding hydrogen peroxide which is reduced by catalase to water. Catalase, however, is not confined to peroxisomes since it may be detected in significant quantities in the cytosol. Glyoxysomes contain the enzymes for the glyoxylate cycle (Section 12.8).

9.8 The cytoskeleton

The cytoskeleton is the remaining fibrous framework following the treatment of eukaryotic cells with non-ionic detergents under conditions in which most of the cellular proteins are extracted. The cytoskeleton consists of at least three distinct cytoplasmic systems of aggregated protein: microfilaments, microtubules and intermediate filaments (Figure 9.2). These structures may be identified by the diameter of their fibres: microfilaments 5–7 nm, microtubules about 25 nm and intermediate filaments 8–10 nm.

Both microfilaments and microtubules undergo carefully regulated disassembly to and reassembly from their component molecules chiefly actin and tubulin respectively. They influence cell shape. Microfilament roles include cell locomotion, cell adhesion, cell division and endocytosis. The structural status of microfilaments may be modulated by over 30 different proteins some of which, e.g. ankyrin, spectrin and vinculin may connect microfilaments to the integral proteins of the plasma membrane, the lateral movement of which may be thus limited (Section 9.2).

Microtubules are hollow cylinders which may serve as cables along which organelles and vesicles move and are positioned in the cytoplasm. They are important structural elements of centrioles and the mitotic spindle to which chromosomes attach during cell division. At least four tubulin-associated proteins including clathrin (Section 9.3) have been identified.

Tissue-specific intermediate filaments have been classified into vimentin filaments, glial filaments, neurofilaments, desmin filaments and cytokeratin filaments. Although each type of filament is composed of a different protein, the various proteins demonstrate remarkable sequence homology. Their functions are unknown. There are at least nine different proteins associated with intermediate filaments.

Suggested further reading

BERNS, M. W. (1983) *Cells*, 2nd ed, Saunders, Philadelphia
DE DUVE, C.(1984) *A Guided Tour of the Living Cell*, Scientific American Books, New York
FINEAN, J. B., COLEMAN, R. and MICHELL, R. H. (1984) *Membranes and their Cellular Functions*, 3rd ed, Blackwell, Oxford

FULTON, A. B. (1984) *The Cytoskeleton*, Chapman and Hall, London
POSTE, G. and CROOKE, S. T. (eds) (1986) *New Insights into Cell and Membrane Transport Processes*, Plenum, New York
SILVER, B. L. (1985) *The Physical Chemistry of Membranes*, Allen and Unwin, London

CHAPTER 10

Principles of cellular metabolism

10.1 Biological energetics

Living cells require energy. The ultimate source of energy is the thermonuclear fusion of hydrogen atoms to form helium which occurs at the surface of the sun according to the equation:

$$4H \rightarrow 1He + 2 \text{ positrons} + \text{energy}$$

(a positron is a particle which has the same mass as an electron but has a positive charge). The energy is transported to Earth as sunlight (light energy) which is converted into chemical energy by green plants and certain microorganisms by the process of photosynthesis (Chapter 14). The chemical energy is stored primarily in carbohydrates synthesized by the reduction of atmospheric carbon dioxide. Also, oxygen is produced from water as a by-product and released into the atmosphere. These products of photosynthesis are vital for aerobic organisms which do not contain the necessary molecular apparatus for the above transformations of energy. Such organisms obtain their energy by utilizing molecular oxygen to oxidize energy-rich plant products. This process called respiration produces amongst other products, carbon dioxide which is returned to the atmosphere to be subsequently utilized in photosynthesis. This cycle of events is called the carbon cycle (Figure 10.1).

FIGURE 10.1 The carbon cycle

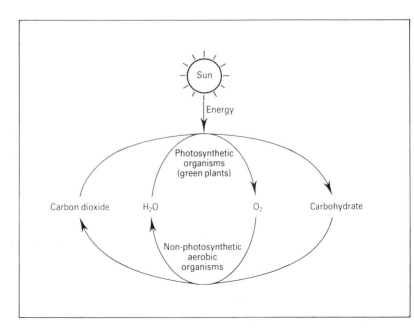

Cycles feature prominently in biological systems, e.g. nitrogen cycle (Section 16.1). These cycles involve a series of chemical reactions in which the initial reactant is regenerated but a valuable material is simultaneously produced and becomes available to cells. Within a single cell, the utilization of nutrients or the removal of toxic waste products may involve cycles, e.g. tricarboxylate cycle (Chapter 12) or the urea cycle (Section 16.5) respectively. However, during most of the reactions of any cycle, energy is lost and cannot be used profitably by the cell. Therefore, although nutrients may recycle, energy flow is linear and irreversible.

10.2 Equilibrium thermodynamics

The study of the energetics of any system is described as thermodynamics, the principles of which were elucidated from the quantitative analysis of energy transformations in simpler physical and chemical systems. These principles have been applied in an attempt to rationalize energy flow in living organisms.

The first law of thermodynamics is related to the principle of conservation of energy. The law in essence states that although energy can be converted from one form to another, it cannot be created or destroyed so that whenever one form of energy is produced, there is a reduction of the same magnitude in another form of energy. The second law of thermodynamics conveys the principle that all spontaneous reactions endeavour to achieve an equilibrium state. During the approach to equilibrium, energy is released so that the system under consideration becomes less ordered, i.e. more random.

The total heat energy of the system is called enthalpy (H). This energy consists of entropy (S) and free energy (G). Entropy is associated with the randomness of molecular motions within the system and tends to increase as free energy is released during reactions. Free energy is available to perform useful work in the system until equilibrium is achieved. At any given temperature and pressure:

$$H = TS + G$$

where T is the absolute temperature. Since biochemists primarily use thermodynamics to consider the progress of a reaction, it is more pertinent to describe the effect of any change in free energy. Changes in free energy are accompanied by concomitant changes in enthalpy and entropy:

$$\Delta G = \Delta H - T\Delta S$$

where Δ denotes change. A biochemical system at equilibrium exhibits no change in its free-energy content, i.e. ΔG is 0, and maximum entropy. However, a system not at equilibrium may proceed spontaneously only by the liberation of free energy, i.e. ΔG is negative, and with a progressive increase in entropy. A system at equilibrium may be altered only by the supply of free energy to it. In this case, ΔG is positive and the entropy decreases. Reactions which liberate free energy are termed exergonic and are considered to be thermodynamically favourable while reactions which consume free energy are endergonic and are thermodynamically unfavourable. If the free energy contained within the reactant(s) is greater than that of the product(s), the reaction may proceed spontaneously since

$$\Delta G = G_{(products)} - G_{(reactants)} = \text{negative value}$$

To permit comparisons of free-energy changes during different reactions, evaluations must be made under agreed conditions, called the standard thermodynamic conditions, of a temperature of 298 K (25°C), a pressure of 1.0 atmosphere, with reactants and products at a concentration of 1.0 mol dm^{-3}. For the general reaction,

$$aA + bB \ldots \rightarrow mM + nN \ldots$$

(where small letters refer to the number of molecules of the substance denoted by the large letter), the actual change in free energy, ΔG, is related to the standard free-energy change, ΔG^0, by the approximation:

$$\Delta G = \Delta G^0 + RT \ln \frac{[M]^m[N]^n \ldots}{[A]^a[B]^b \ldots}$$

where R = the gas constant = 8.3 J K^{-1} mol^{-1}, T = absolute temperature = 298 K and ln = natural logarithm. ΔG^0 may be determined when the system is at equilibrium since, under such conditions,

$\Delta G = 0$ and the above equation rearranges to:

$$\Delta G^0 = -\boldsymbol{R}T\ln\frac{[M]^m[N]^n\ldots}{[A]^a[B]^b\ldots}$$

However, since the system is at equilibrium, the concentration ratio component is the equilibrium constant, K_{eq} (Section 2.3), so that:

$$\Delta G^0 = -\boldsymbol{R}T\ln K_{eq}$$

Therefore, at any temperature, ΔG^0 can be calculated from the equilibrium constant for that reaction. Also, since the $\ln K_{eq}$ component is dimensionless, the units of $\boldsymbol{R}$ ($J\,K^{-1}\,mol^{-1}$) and T (K) result in ΔG having the units of $J\,mol^{-1}$. J denotes the unit of energy called the joule which has been adopted by the International System of Units (Le Système International, abbreviated as SI units).

Standard free-energy change (ΔG^0) measurements demand that the initial concentrations of reactants and products are $1.0\,mol\,dm^{-3}$. Many biochemical reactions liberate or consume protons. To comply with standard thermodynamic conditions, these reactions should proceed at pH 0 (Section 2.4). Since most biochemical reactions occur *in vivo* near pH 7.0, standard free-energy changes for biochemical reactions are measured at pH 7.0 and accordingly denoted as $\Delta G^{0\prime}$. Table 10.1 relates $\Delta G^{0\prime}$ to the equilibrium constant and the direction of the reaction.

TABLE 10.1   The numerical relationship between the equilibrium constant of biochemical reactions, standard free-energy change and the direction of a reaction at pH 7.0 and 25°C

$K_{eq}{}'$ value	$\Delta G^{0\prime}$ ($kJ\,mol^{-1}$)*	Direction
10 000	− 22.8	
1000	− 17.1	
100	− 11.4	Forward reactions
10	− 5.7	
1	0	At equilibrium
0.1	+ 5.7	
0.01	+ 11.4	Reverse reactions
0.001	+ 17.1	
0.0001	+ 22.8	

* Calculated from $\Delta G^{0\prime} = -\boldsymbol{R}T\ln K_{eq}{}' = -2.3\,\boldsymbol{R}T\log K_{eq}{}'$

10.3 Coupled reactions

A thermodynamically favourable reaction may be linked to an unfavourable reaction so that the free energy liberated may be employed to drive the energy-consuming reaction. Interconnected endergonic and exergonic reactions are termed coupled reactions.

Two forms of coupling may occur. (a) The two reactions may be coupled through a common intermediate, i.e.

$$A \rightarrow B;\ \Delta G^{0\prime} = -24\,kJ\,mol^{-1};\ K_{eq}' = 16\,645$$

and

$$B \rightarrow C;\ \Delta G^{0\prime} = +15\,kJ\,mol^{-1};\ K_{eq}' = 0.0023$$

Under standard conditions, A can be spontaneously converted into B because $\Delta G^{0\prime}$ has a negative value and K_{eq}' is greater than 1. Since in the second reaction $\Delta G^{0\prime}$ has a positive value and K_{eq}' is less than 1, B cannot form C. However, C can be produced by the coupling of the reactions since $A \rightarrow B \rightarrow C$ has an overall negative $\Delta G^{0\prime}$ and a K_{eq}' greater than 1, i.e.

$$A \rightarrow C;\ \Delta G^{0\prime} = -9\,kJ\,mol^{-1};\ K_{eq}' = 38.3$$

Coupled reactions illustrate the principle that $\Delta G^{0\prime}$ values are additive. Because of the logarithmic relationship between $\Delta G^{0\prime}$ and K_{eq}' (Section 10.2), $\Delta G^{0\prime}$ is a more convenient representation of the equilibrium constant.

(b) The two reactions may be coupled through the transfer of a chemical group, e.g. phosphate, acyl groups or hydrogen atoms. This mechanism may be summarized as:

$$A \rightarrow B; \Delta G^{0\prime} = -\text{ve}$$
$$X \rightarrow Y; \Delta G^{0\prime} = +\text{ve}$$

but

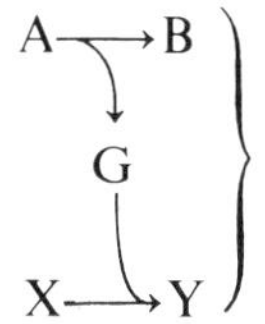

$$\left. \begin{array}{c} A \longrightarrow B \\ \downarrow \\ G \\ \downarrow \\ X \longrightarrow Y \end{array} \right\} \quad \Delta G^{0\prime} = -\text{ve}$$

The transferable group (G) requires a carrier. The most important intracellular carriers are ADP (Figure 10.2), which is phosphorylated to ATP to transport a phosphoryl group, coenzyme A (Figure 5.3c), which is acylated to carry an acyl group, and NAD(P)$^+$ (Figure 5.3a), which is reduced by hydride ions. Therefore an intermediate step occurs in which the transferable group is chemically bonded to its carrier.

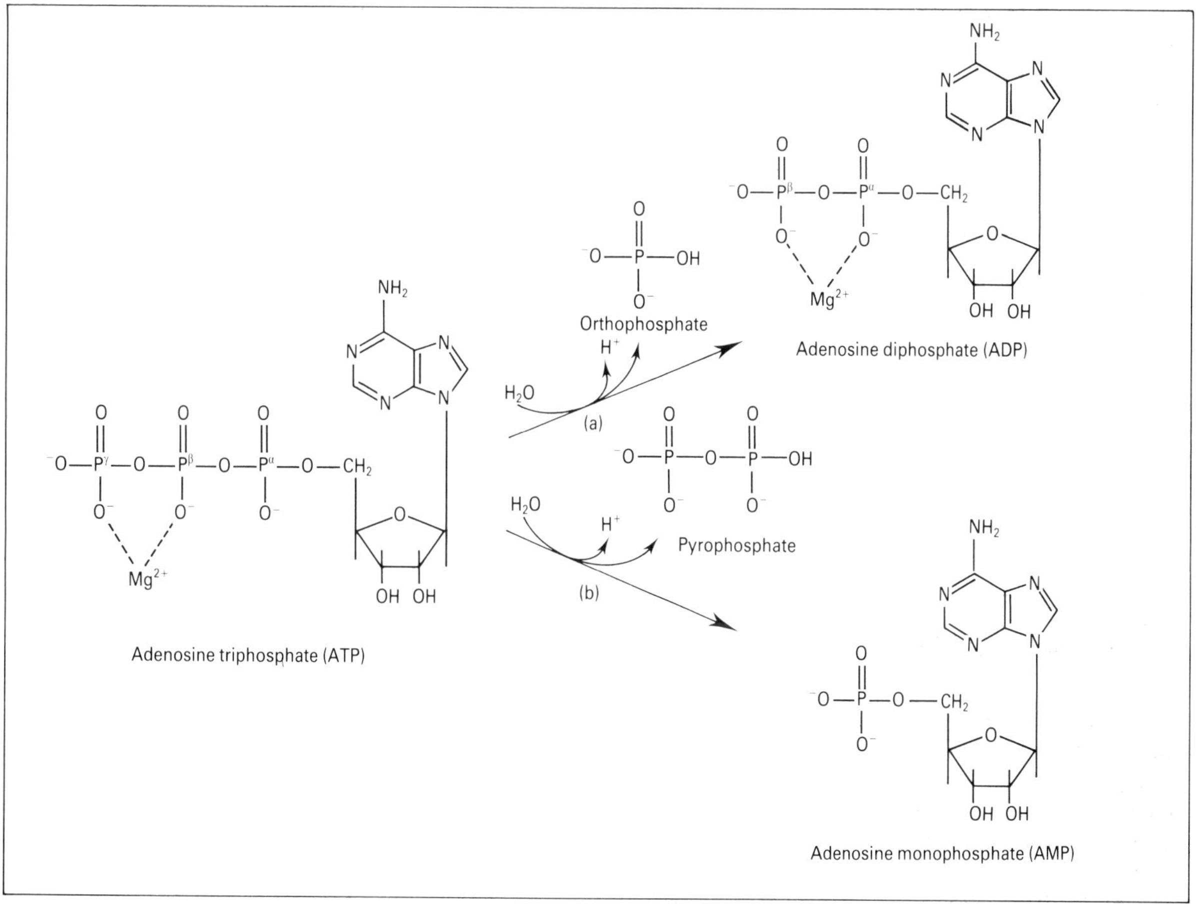

FIGURE 10.2   Hydrolysis of ATP. (a) Orthophosphate cleavage. (b) Pyrophosphate cleavage

10.4 The role of ATP

The major chemical link in cells between exergonic and endergonic reactions is ATP. Magnesium ions are contained within intracellular fluids at relatively high concentrations so that ATP and ADP, because of their electronegativity, exist mainly as magnesium complexes. MgATP occupies an intermediate position on a list of standard free energy of hydrolysis, $\Delta G^{0\prime}$, of phosphate compounds (Table 10.2). This position enables the formation of ATP on the hydrolysis of a phosphoryl group from a phosphate compound with a higher $\Delta G^{0\prime}$ and permits the release of sufficient energy from ATP on its hydrolysis to drive the synthesis of a compound with a lower $\Delta G^{0\prime}$. This principle is illustrated during glycolysis where ATP provides the energy and the phosphoryl group for the production of glucose 6-phosphate and fructose 1,6-bisphosphate but ATP is generated from 1,3-bisphosphoglycerate and phosphoenolpyruvate (Section 11.2). By removing the negative signs, the data can be referred to as the phosphate group transfer potential, e.g. MgATP has a phosphate group transfer potential of 30.5 compared with 13.8 for glucose 6-phosphate. This means that the tendency for ATP to transfer a phosphoryl group is greater than that of glucose 6-phosphate.

The enhancement of phosphate group transfer potential has been accounted for in terms of intramolecular mutual repulsion and resonance stabilization. At pH 7.0, the triphosphate moiety of ATP is almost fully deprotonated. The four electronegative charges repel each other vigorously. When the γ-phosphate group is hydrolysed from ATP, the electrostatic repulsion is reduced. The electrostatic repulsion is partially relieved by the binding of magnesium ions which results in the $\Delta G^{0\prime}$ value for MgATP being approximately 50% lower than that of free ATP. The second factor is the greater stability conferred upon the hydrolysis products by their ability to oscillate rapidly between different structures (Figure 10.3). This resonance enables the electrons in the products to orbit the atomic nucleus at a lower energy level than in ATP.

In addition to orthophosphate cleavage (Figure 10.2a), ATP may be hydrolysed by pyrophosphate cleavage (Figure 10.2b) so called because it produces pyrophosphate and AMP. This mechanism is important since a freely reversible coupled reaction may be converted into an essentially irreversible one by the subsequent removal of pyrophosphate by hydrolytic inorganic pyrophosphatase (Sections 11.5, 14.6, 15.2).

Other nucleoside 5'-triphosphates demonstrate a standard free energy of hydrolysis equivalent to that of ATP. Their intracellular concentrations are low which restricts their function to selected biosynthetic pathways, e.g. uridine triphosphate (UTP) in glycogen biosynthesis (Section 11.5). Nucleoside-diphosphate kinase permits the phosphorylation of (d)NDPs to (d)NTPs at the expense of ATP and vice versa.

ATP may be synthesized by three mechanisms each of which involves coupling: substrate-level phosphorylation, oxidative phosphorylation and photophosphorylation. Substrate-level phosphorylation may be defined as the enzymic phosphorylation of ADP (or other nucleoside 5'-diphosphate) employing energy derived from a coupled reaction

TABLE 10.2 Standard free energy of hydrolysis of some phosphates

Phosphate compound	$\Delta G^{0\prime}$ (kJ mol^{-1})
Phosphoenolpyruvate	−61.9
1,3-Bisphosphoglycerate	−49.4
Creatine phosphate	−43.1
Acetyl phosphate	−43.1
MgATP (to MgADP)	−30.5
MgADP (to AMP)	−30.5
Glucose 1-phosphate	−20.9
Fructose 6-phosphate	−15.9
Glucose 6-phosphate	−13.8

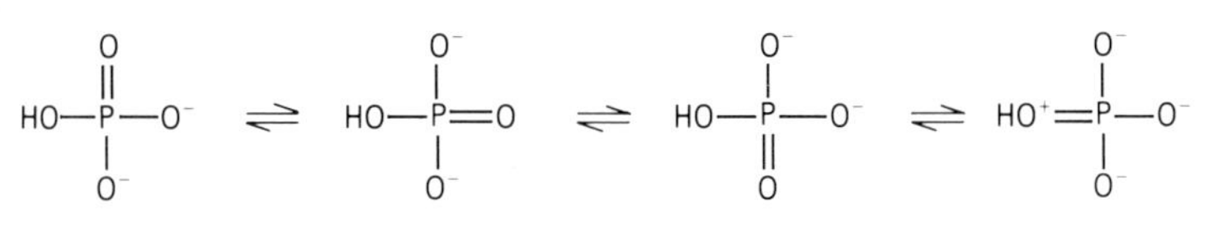

FIGURE 10.3 The major resonance forms of orthophosphate

involving a substrate with a large negative standard free energy of hydrolysis, e.g. 1,3-bisphosphoglycerate (Table 10.2). Such compounds are less stable than their free hydrolysis products.

Oxidative phosphorylation is the process in which the energy for the enzymic phosphorylation of ADP is generated by the transport of electrons from reduced coenzymes to molecular oxygen (Chapter 13). Photophosphorylation is the process in which the energy for the enzymic phosphorylation of ADP is generated by the transport of electrons initiated by the interaction of light with light-harvesting complexes in photosynthetic organisms (Chapter 14).

The function of intracellular ATP can be summarized as the carrier of energy used in: (i) endergonic reactions, e.g. the biosynthesis of macromolecules; (ii) the uptake of nutrients and particles into cells, e.g. active transport, phagocytosis (Section 9.3); (iii) the movement of whole cells, e.g. muscular activity, the migration of leukocytes or their component parts, e.g. chromosomal translocation during cell division and the progression of ribosomes along mRNA during protein synthesis. Although ATP has been viewed traditionally as functioning entirely within the cell, it is now considered that ATP may have an extracellular role at micromolar concentrations, e.g. in cardiac function and smooth muscle contraction.

10.5 Metabolic pathways

The term, cellular metabolism, refers to the chemical processes which occur within the cell. Cellular metabolism is organized into a network of metabolic pathways. A metabolic pathway may be defined as a sequence of coupled enzyme-catalysed reactions (Figure 10.4a). Many metabolic pathways are linear sequences although some important pathways are cyclic. The enzymes of metabolic pathways are not generally organized intracellularly into defined rows but are available as random molecules in the aqueous milieu of a cellular compartment, e.g. cytosol, or as loosely or tightly bound membrane proteins. Certain substrates/products within a metabolic pathway, called intermediates, may serve as substrates for more than one enzyme available within the same cellular compartment. This gives rise to branch points in metabolism (Figure 10.4b). To permit pertinent production of compounds, the activity of metabolic pathways must be regulated (Section 10.6).

Metabolic pathways can be classified as anabolic (from Greek, ana means up) or catabolic (from Greek, cata means down). Anabolic pathways are concerned with synthetic processes and are overall endergonic. Catabolic pathways are concerned with degradation and are exergonic sequences. Catabolism and anabolism are interconnected (Figure 10.4c) through the major chemical link of ATP. Catabolism also provides energy in the form of reducing power (NADPH) necessary for certain biosyntheses (Section 11.8). In general, catabolism is an oxidative process whilst anabolism is a reductive process.

An important principle of cellular metabolism is that catabolic pathways are convergent whilst anabolic pathways are divergent. As many different macromolecules are degraded, the degradation is conducted by the progressive entry of the generated intermediates into other pathways which terminate in a few end products. Conversely, anabolism utilizes a limited number of simple molecules which are processed through a number of major pathways from which, at many branch points, intermediates enter specific pathways leading to individual complex molecules. The intermediates of certain pathways are therefore present within the cell at high concentrations. These pathways constitute the primary metabolism of the cell. Pathways with relatively low concentrations of intermediates are referred to as secondary metabolism, e.g. pentose phosphate pathway (Chapter 11).

Anabolic and catabolic pathways may be segregated into different cellular compartments. In liver cells, the biosynthesis of fatty acids from acetyl-CoA occurs in the cytosol where the enzymes for both biosynthesis and the generation of NADPH are located. The degradation of fatty acids occurs within the mitochondria where the appropriate enzymes and the apparatus for oxidative phosphorylation are located (Section 9.5). Compartmentalization of metabolic pathways necessitates the provision of mechanisms by which

FIGURE 10.4 Some principles of cellular metabolism. (a) A metabolic pathway. (b) Branch points. (c) Coupling of anabolism to catabolism

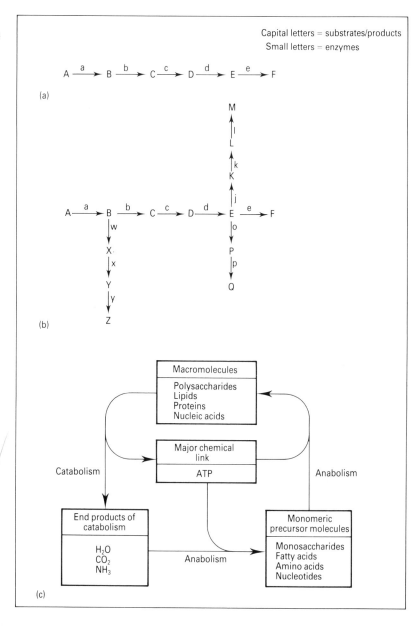

intermediates not soluble in lipids may move between compartments. These mechanisms are the transport and shuttle systems.

A transport system (Section 9.3) utilizes an integral membrane protein called a carrier which specifically binds the molecule or ion to be transported across the membrane. A shuttle system is one which does not convey the actual molecule across the membrane but transfers the functional group or atoms to another substance which may

then permeate the membrane, e.g. glycerol phosphate shuttle (Section 11.3).

Catabolic and anabolic pathways are not always entirely exclusive (Figure 10.5). Frequently they contain a number of common intermediates and sometimes only differ in the chemical mechanism by which reactions are reversed. At least a single modification between the degradative and synthetic pathways is required to facilitate selective regulation of the pathways.

FIGURE 10.5 Regulation of anabolism and catabolism. (a) Exclusive pathways. (b) Partially independent pathways. (c) A substrate cycle

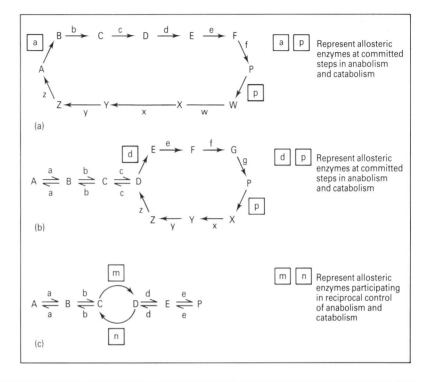

10.6 Intracellular control of metabolism

The simultaneous operation of an anabolic and its opposed catabolic pathway would be unproductive and consume energy. In general, pathways are regulated at the reaction which commits the flow of intermediates to the production of some necessary substance called the end product (Figure 10.5a,b). This committed step proceeds usually with a large negative free-energy change which renders the reaction essentially irreversible. The enzyme at the committed step is usually an allosteric enzyme which can respond to cellular concentrations of a variety of modulators. In many cases, the concentration of end product determines the rate of metabolic flow (flux) through that pathway and thereby controls its own production (Section 6.4). This serves to conserve cellular resources.

By controlling the rate of entry of a metabolite into a particular compartment (Section 10.5), the metabolic flux through that pathway may be controlled by limiting the concentration of an early substrate, e.g. the rate of entry of acyl-CoA into the mitochondrial matrix modulates the rate of the β-oxidation of fatty acids (Section 15.2). Various enzymes may bind in different amounts to membranes of a compartment so that the enzyme is effectively compartmentalized within the same compartment.

Anabolic pathways may be regulated by the availability of energy to drive endergonic reactions. Similarly, catabolic pathways operate in response to demands for energy by anabolic processes. Therefore, intracellular concentrations of nucleotides, e.g. ATP, NAD$^+$ and NADPH, play an important role in the determination of the metabolic flux through certain pathways. Low cytosolic ratios of [ATP]/[ADP] indicate the requirement for energy whilst low [NAD$^+$]/[NADH] ratios imply that energy demands may be satisfied through oxidative phosphorylation. Low [NADP$^+$]/ [NADPH] ratios suggest that reducing power is readily available. In the mitochondrial matrix, [NAD$^+$]/[NADH] ratios are more important because mitochondrial [ATP]/[ADP] exhibit little variation because of the export of ATP to the cytosol (Section 13.5).

The regulation of metabolic pathways may also be considered in terms of the characteristics of each constituent reaction. From the knowledge of actual intracellular concentrations of the reaction products and substrates, the [product]/[substrate] ratio may be calculated and compared with the established value of the equilibrium constant (K_{eq}) of the reaction (Section 10.2). If this ratio is approximately equal to K_{eq} and the resultant ΔG is close to zero, the reaction is deemed to be a near-equilibrium reaction. If this ratio varies appreciably from the K_{eq} and ΔG is large, the reaction is deemed to be a non-equilibrium reaction. A non-equilibrium reaction results when the activity of its enzyme is low compared to the activities of other enzymes in the pathway. This causes the concentration of its substrate to remain high whilst that of the product is greatly reduced due to removal by the successive enzyme. A near-equilibrium reaction occurs if the catalytic activity of its enzyme is high relative to the activities of other enzymes in the pathway. Changes in the substrate concentration in a near-equilibrium reaction produce rapid concomitant alterations in product concentration. Near-equilibrium reactions may also be readily reversed by small additions of product. Their regulation tends to involve unsophisticated mechanisms such as alterations in substrate levels or variations in the concentrations of the appropriate form of a coenzyme. However, increasing the activity of an enzyme catalysing a non-equilibrium reaction will convert larger quantities of its substrate to product and since the successive enzymes function at a higher rate, additional substrates are provided throughout the remainder of the pathway. Therefore an increase in the activity of an enzyme which catalyses a non-equilibrium reaction may generate a significant change in flux whereas alterations in the activity of an enzyme catalysing a near-equilibrium reaction has less influence on the pathway flux. For this reason, non-equilibrium reactions tend to be subject to the complexities of allosteric regulation (Section 6.4) which integrates the regulation of one pathway with that of other pathways.

Metabolic pathways often feature more than one non-equilibrium reaction. The first of these reactions controls the entry of a substrate into that pathway and thereby the generation of flux through the pathway. Subsequent non-equilibrium reactions cannot control the flux through the entire pathway but may regulate the operation of a section of the pathway and maintain levels of intermediates for diversion into branch pathways. Indeed, it is unlikely that any single enzyme is ever truly rate-limiting in a pathway. Quantitative analysis indicates that control of glycolysis is mainly distributed between hexokinase and 6-phosphofructokinase.

When the committed step in both anabolic and catabolic pathways involve the same intermediates, two intermediates may constitute a substrate cycle in which the two participants may be constantly re-formed (Figure 10.5c). Substrate cycles are the location of reciprocal regulation by different allosteric enzymes which catalyse the forward and reverse reactions. Substrate cycling serves to determine the direction of and to amplify the variations in metabolic flux with respect to changes in the concentrations of allosteric effectors (Section 6.4). As a simple example, if the rate of flux from C→D (Figure 10.5c) is three units while the rate from D→C is one unit, the net flux of the pathway will be two units in the direction of C→D. The pathway would then proceed to form P. If a single allosteric effector influences both enzymes $\boxed{m}$ and $\boxed{n}$ so that $\boxed{m}$ is activated tenfold and the activity of $\boxed{n}$ is reduced tenfold, the net flux of the pathway would be 29.9 units in the direction of C→D. The change in the rate of flux is therefore amplified by reciprocal regulation of the substrate cycle. However, a variety of considerations, e.g. the activation (or inhibition) of only one of the enzymes by an effector or the collective consequence of numerous effectors, influence the relationship between substrate cycling and changes in metabolic flux.

Another mechanism employed to 'fine-tune' metabolic flux is that of enzyme interconversion cycles which may be considered as an extension of the principle of substrate cycles. The enzymes involved may exist in two forms, the predominating form being determined by the simultaneous activities of additional enzymes which catalyse the interconversions. The conversion of one form to the other involves covalent modification of the enzyme, frequently by the addition or removal of phosphate groups. Since at physiological pH the phosphate group carries two negative charges, phosphorylation results in the introduction of a highly charged group which induces new bonding arrangements within the protein. The conformational change can be reversed by dephosphorylation. The phosphorylation and dephosphorylation reactions are non-equilibrium reactions which are regulated by allosteric effectors. Other known covalent modifications include adenylylation and ADP–ribosylation reactions.

An important extended example of enzyme interconversion cycles is the reciprocal control of glycogen metabolism involving glycogen synthase and glycogen phosphorylase (Section 11.5). The activities of both enzymes are regulated in concert by phosphorylation and dephosphorylation reactions so that when the synthetic pathway is in operation, the degradative pathway is reciprocally reduced.

In mammals, glycogen synthesis (glycogenesis) is promoted (Figure 10.6) by a glycogen synthase (called synthase *a*) and a less active glycogen phosphorylase *b*. Both are dephosphorylated forms. Glycogen synthase *a* is converted progressively into a less active synthase *b* by the phosphorylation of specific seryl residues catalysed by protein kinase A. Glycogen phosphorylase *b* is phosphorylated at a specific seryl residue (position 14) on each of two identical subunits. Upon phosphorylation by phosphorylase kinase, two dimers may form a more active tetrameric structure. The phosphorylation of the synthase and phosphorylase is not long lasting since the enzymes are rapidly dephosphorylated by specific phosphatases and return to conformations favouring the synthetic pathway. Additionally, both protein kinase A and phosphorylase kinase are also interconverted between different catalytic forms (Section 10.7).

The catalytic powers of the less active forms of the synthase and phosphorylase may be enhanced without the attainment of the catalytic capability of the fully active (*a*) forms. Glycogen synthase *b*, but not synthase *a*, is allosterically modulated by glucose 6-phosphate which serves as its positive effector. Similarly, phosphorylase *b* may be activated by its positive effector, AMP.

Cellular metabolism may also be regulated by the repression or induction of the synthesis of an enzyme (Section 17.8). In the presence of a repressor molecule, synthesis of a pertinent enzyme may be inhibited causing a progressive decrease in the intracellular concentration of the enzyme through normal degradative processes. Conversely, enzyme synthesis may be potentiated by the high concentration of a substrate. Repression and induction mechanisms may be considered as important coarse controls over metabolism.

FIGURE 10.6 Reciprocal regulation of glycogen metabolism by phosphorylation/dephosphorylation reactions

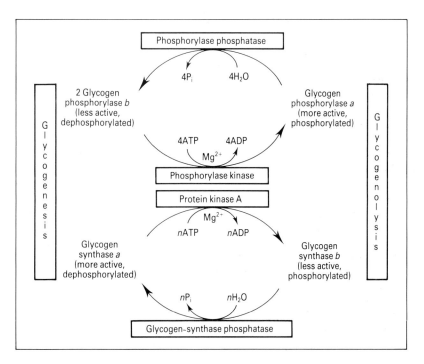

10.7 Extracellular control of metabolism

Intracellular metabolic activity may be modulated in response to extracellular conditions by hormones. Hormones are substances which act as chemical messengers between cells in different locations to alter the activity of the recipient cell. Three classes of hormones have been identified: protein (polypeptide) hormones, steroid hormones and tyrosine-derivative hormones of which there are two distinct groups, the catecholamines and the thyroid hormones. The catecholamine hormones (adrenaline and noradrenaline) are produced by and secreted from the adrenal medulla. The thyroid hormones (thyroxine and triiodothyronine) are elaborated by and secreted from the thyroid gland.

Protein and catecholamine hormones do not enter their target cells (Figure 10.7) but interact with cell-surface receptors and promote the synthesis of intracellular mediators. The hormone therefore transmits its message to the cell and is the first messenger; the mediator produced in response to the first messenger is the second messenger which is responsible for a series of intracellular events culminating in a biological effect. Two important mechanisms of signal transduction from catecholamine and protein hormones have been identified as the adenosine 3',5'-cyclic monophosphate [cyclic AMP (cAMP), Figure 10.7a] and the phosphoinositide (Figure 10.7b) systems.

In the cAMP system, occupancy of an appropriate receptor in the plasma membrane by its complementary hormone triggers the activation of adenylate cyclase via guanine nucleotide-binding regulatory proteins (G proteins). Positive stimuli

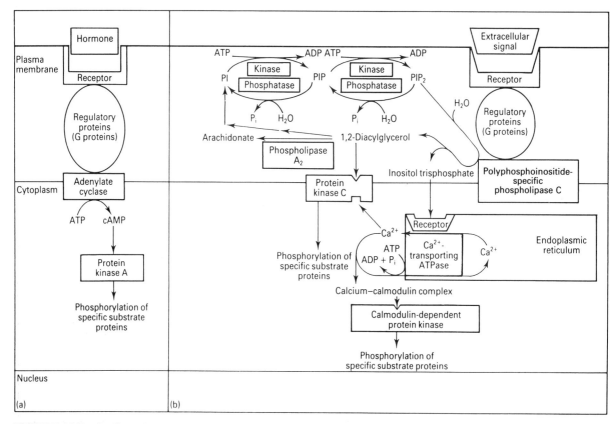

FIGURE 10.7   Outline of two mechanisms of extracellular signal transduction. (a) Cyclic AMP system. (b) Phosphoinositide system

promote the synthesis of cAMP which, as secondary messenger, activates cAMP-dependent protein kinase (protein kinase A) to phosphorylate substrate proteins, the activities of which are regulated by their phosphorylation status (Section 10.6).

The role of the cAMP system can be exemplified by the consideration of the hormonal regulation of glycogen metabolism. The activity of glycogen synthase and phosphorylase are controlled by two hormones, adrenaline and the pancreatic polypeptide hormone, glucagon. Adrenaline stimulates glycogenolysis in both muscle and liver by increasing the amount of the more active phosphorylase a relative to that of phosphorylase b whilst reciprocally reducing the ratio of glycogen synthase a/glycogen synthase b. The main site of glucagon activity is the liver where it plays a major role in the release of glucose for the maintenance of blood glucose levels.

Adrenaline, for example, is released from the

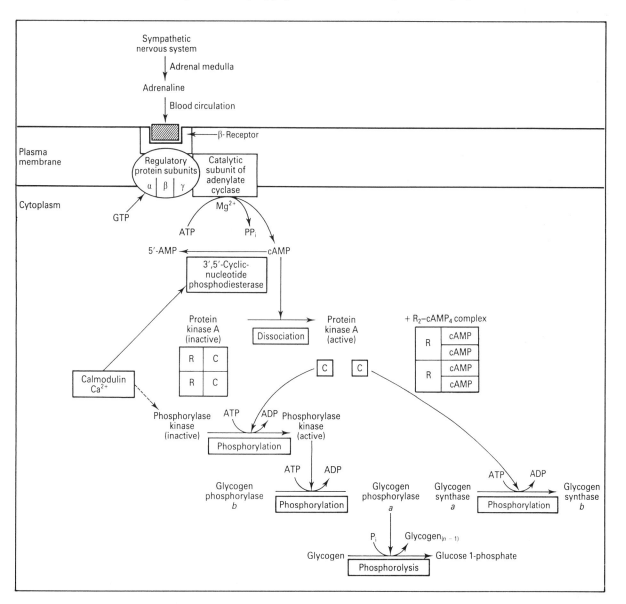

FIGURE 10.8   Amplification cascade in the regulation of glycogen metabolism in skeletal muscle cells by adrenaline

adrenal medulla in response to the activity of the sympathetic nervous system (Figure 10.8). Plasma-membrane receptors are classified into α- and β-adrenergic receptors with respect to their response to adrenaline. Adrenaline exerts its influence by interaction with β-adrenergic receptors which results in the activation of adenylate cyclase. cAMP (Figure 10.9a) interacts with protein kinase A which is a tetrameric structure, composed of two regulatory (R) and two catalytic (C) subunits. The binding of four molecules of cAMP to sites on the regulatory subunits results in the dissociation of the enzyme. This activation releases the active monomeric form of the protein kinase and an inactive R_2–$cAMP_4$ complex. There are two substrates for the protein kinase in this system, one is phosphorylase kinase which is activated by the phosphorylation of a specific serine residue and the other is glycogen synthase *a*. Activated phosphorylase kinase phosphorylates its substrate, glycogen phosphorylase *b*. Phosphorylation of glycogen

synthase renders it less active and so glycogenesis is inhibited whilst glycogen phosphorylase becomes more active stimulating the degradative pathway.

When the production, and thereby the blood concentration, of adrenaline declines, adrenaline diffuses from the β-receptors. Adenylate cyclase is no longer activated, cAMP production ceases and cytosolic concentrations of cAMP are returned to basal levels by the action of 3′,5′-cyclic nucleotide phosphodiesterase which catalyses the hydrolytic cleavage of cAMP and some other cyclic nucleotides. Protein kinase A reassociates into its inactive form and the inhibition of phosphorylase phosphatase (Figure 10.6) is terminated, signalling the stimulation of the synthetic pathway.

The system is called an amplification cascade since the binding of one molecule of adrenaline can cause the formation of numerous molecules of cAMP which may dissociate protein kinase A molecules thereby sequentially promoting the activation of more molecules of phosphorylase kinase

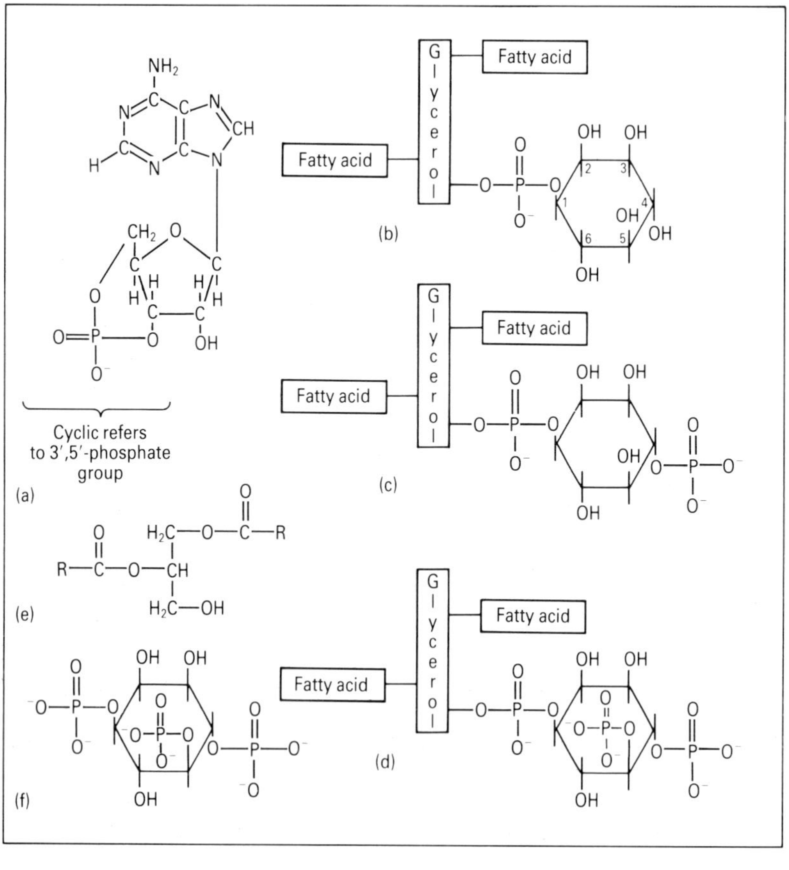

FIGURE 10.9 Structures of some compounds involved in signal transduction. (a) Adenosine 3′,5′-cyclic monophosphate (cyclic AMP, cAMP). (b) Phosphatidylinositol (PI). (c) Phosphatidylinositol 4-phosphate (PIP). (d) Phosphatidylinositol 4,5-bisphosphate (PIP₂). (e) 1,2-Diacylglycerol. (f) Inositol trisphosphate (IP₃)

and inhibition of glycogen synthase to effect the reduction of synthesis and the stimulation of the degradation of glycogen.

The cascade is also subjected to regulation by calcium ions (Ca^{2+}) through calmodulin. Calmodulin, a single polypeptide chain of 148 amino acid residues, may bind up to four calcium ions per molecule to negatively charged amino acid R groups contained within four domains. On binding one or more calcium ions, calmodulin undergoes conformational change to form different Ca^{2+}–calmodulin complexes with different compactness and activities. Through influence on the activity of $3',5'$-cyclic nucleotide phosphodiesterase, activated calmodulin regulates intracellular cAMP levels. Calmodulin is also involved in the regulation of phosphorylase kinase which has the subunit structure $(\alpha, \beta, \gamma, \delta)_4$. The δ-subunit is calmodulin which remains bound to the enzyme even if Ca^{2+} ions are absent. Through binding to this subunit, Ca^{2+} ions may control the activity of this important enzyme. Phosphorylase kinase may therefore be regulated by both protein kinase A and Ca^{2+} ions whose cytosolic concentrations may increase in response to another secondary messenger, inositol trisphosphate.

The phosphoinositide system transduces the extracellular signal delivered by numerous agents including acetylcholine, histamine, vasopressin and adrenaline (Figure 10.7b). Their binding to specific cell surface receptors activates a phosphodiesterase attached to the membrane to hydrolyse membranous phosphatidylinositol 4,5-bisphosphate (PIP_2) into 1,2-diacylglycerol and inositol trisphosphate (Figure 10.9). PIP_2 is present in very small quantities but may be synthesized from and degraded to phosphatidylinositol 4-phosphate (PIP) which is in turn produced from phosphatidylinositol (PI). These three substances are maintained at appropriate intramembranous concentrations by the action of two specific kinases and two specific phosphatases which constitute two substrate cycles. Substrate for the production of the second messengers is provided by delicate adjustments in the activities of the kinases and phosphatases which preserve the equilibrium between the phosphoinositides.

Diacylglycerol production promotes the binding to the cell membrane of cytosolic protein kinase C which is rendered more sensitive to Ca^{2+} ions in its microenvironment and is thereby activated. Protein kinase C catalyses the phosphorylation of seryl and threonyl residues of a broad spectrum of cellular proteins. Alternatively, diacylglycerol may serve as a substrate for enzymes including the Ca^{2+}-dependent phospholipase A_2 which removes from its *sn*-2 position, arachidonate, the precursor of some eicosanoids (Section 8.8). The inositol tris-phosphate diffuses across the cytosol to bind to specific receptors on the endoplasmic reticulum to mobilize Ca^{2+} ions from their intracellular stores by the action of Ca^{2+}-translocation systems and elevate cytosolic Ca^{2+}-ion concentrations. The principal receptor protein for Ca^{2+} ions is calmodulin. Ca^{2+}–calmodulin complexes are capable of activating another protein kinase, calmodulin-dependent protein kinase, and thereby control the phosphorylation of certain proteins.

The action of inositol trisphosphate is curtailed by inositol trisphosphatase which produces inositol 1,4-bisphosphate. Calcium ions may be returned to their membrane stores by the action of a Ca^{2+}-ATPase at the expense of ATP.

Another mechanism whereby extracellular signals may be transmitted across the membrane involves a specific transmembrane glycoprotein comprising an external moiety which recognizes the first messenger and a cytoplasmic domain that possesses a protein–tyrosine kinase activity (Figure 10.10a). Extracellular signals utilizing this mechanism include some growth factors, e.g. epidermal growth factor (EGF), platelet-derived growth factor (PDGF) and some polypeptide hormones, e.g. insulin. Growth factors are polypeptides or glycoproteins which are required for the long-term growth and metabolism of most mammalian cells cultured *in vitro* and may be provided by the supplementation of the culture medium with blood serum. These factors are involved in the regulation of cell proliferation.

The molecular mechanisms by which growth factors exert their influence remain largely unknown. However, on growth factor–receptor interaction, the intrinsic kinase activity catalyses the phosphorylation of target cytoplasmic proteins only on tyrosyl residues. These tyrosine-specific protein phosphorylations may initiate a cascade of biochemical events which ultimately promote DNA synthesis and cell division. Other consequences of the binding of growth factors to their receptors include the hydrolysis of phosphoinositides, a sustained rise in cytoplasmic pH through the activation of an Na^+/H^+ antiport mechanism in the plasma membrane and a transient rise in cytoplasmic free Ca^{2+} concentration. However, EGF-

FIGURE 10.10 Outline of two further mechanisms of extracellular signal transduction. (a) Receptor protein–tyrosine kinase activity. (b) Steroid hormones

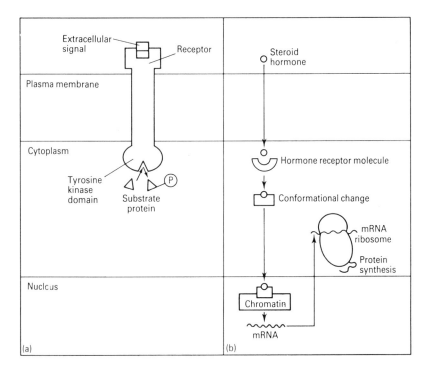

receptor-mediated tyrosyl phosphorylations *per se* probably do not generate the Ca^{2+} concentration changes which are essential for cell proliferation.

Steroid and thyroid hormones must enter their target cells to exert their effect which is manifested as a change in the pattern of protein synthesis. Steroid hormone activity (Figure 10.10b) is limited to responsive eukaryotic cells in which cytosolic protein receptor molecules are located. Thyroid hormones bind to nuclear protein receptor molecules. Steroids may enter a non-target cell by diffusion but, in the absence of appropriate receptors, depart from the cell. In target tissues, the hormone is bound to specific receptor molecules to form a steroid–receptor complex which is activated by its conformational change. The activated complex is the second messenger which migrates into the nucleus where it interacts with specific regions of the chromatin (Section 9.4). Unoccupied receptors and free steroids are capable only of non-specific binding to the chromatin. The specific interaction results in the transcription of particular genes into mRNAs which serve as templates for the ribosomal synthesis of protein. The identification of steroid-unfilled oestrogen receptors within the nucleus has led to the consideration that free steroid hormones may enter the nucleus and bind to specific nuclear receptor molecules in a manner similar to that of thyroid hormones.

Suggested further reading

ATKINSON, D. E. (1977) *Cellular Energy Metabolism and its Regulation*, Academic Press, New York

JONES, M. N. (ed.) (1979) *Biochemical Thermodynamics*, Elsevier, Amsterdam

MARTIN, B. R. (1987) *Metabolic Regulation, A Molecular Approach*, Blackwell, Oxford

OCHS, R. S., HANSON, R. W. and HALL, J. (eds) (1985) *Metabolic Regulation*, Elsevier, Amsterdam

CHAPTER 11

Carbohydrate metabolism

11.1 The pathways of carbohydrate metabolism

Carbohydrates produced during photosynthesis (Section 10.1 and Chapter 14) are utilized as a source of energy and as precursors for the synthesis of many structural and metabolic components. These requirements are satisfied in mammalian and human cells primarily by D-glucose, obtained from the diet or subsequent storage as glycogen (Section 3.6). The glucose is catabolized by a metabolic pathway called glycolysis (Greek, glykos meaning 'sweet' and lysis meaning 'a loosening'). Glycolysis is the major pathway by which glucose is degraded to pyruvate in animals, plants and many microorganisms under both aerobic and anaerobic conditions. Carbohydrate is the only fuel which can be used to generate ATP under anaerobic conditions because glycolysis does not require oxygen. For this reason, glycolysis has a vital role in the energy production of many anaerobic organisms. In cells functioning aerobically, the pyruvate is transported from the cytoplasm into the mitochondria where further metabolism yields additional energy.

A key glycolytic intermediate is glucose 6-phosphate which may serve as a substrate for more than one cytosolic enzyme (Section 10.5). Glucose 6-phosphate is the branch point for glycogen synthesis (glycogenesis) and the pentose phosphate pathway. It may be formed by two routes on the degradation of glycogen (glycogenolysis).

Gluconeogenesis is the sequence of reactions by which glucose or glycogen is synthesized from a wide variety of non-carbohydrate precursors. The predominant starting materials are lactate, glycerol, most amino acids (Section 16.3) and tricarboxylate cycle intermediates. The interrelationships of these pathways are shown in Figure 11.1.

11.2 The reactions of glycolysis

The glycolytic pathway (Figure 11.2) is located in the cell cytosol. The pathway can be divided into three phases: the priming stage, the splitting stage and the energy-conservation stage. The priming stage involves an energy input to the system in the form of two molecules of ATP. This stage consists of three enzymic reactions from glucose to fructose 1,6-bisphosphate.

The hexokinase reaction ensures that the glucose molecules are retained within the cytosol since charged molecules do not cross cellular membranes in the absence of specialized transport mechanisms (Section 9.3). The main group of enzymes which catalyse phosphorylations are called kinases. Kinases bind the $MgATP^{2-}$ complex more readily than free ATP^{4-} (Section 10.4).

Hexokinase occurs in a wide variety of animals, plants and microorganisms. It is an example of the induced-fit model of substrate binding (Section 5.2) in which glucose induces significant alterations in the tertiary structure of the enzyme. The positional changes of the amino acid residues within the

127

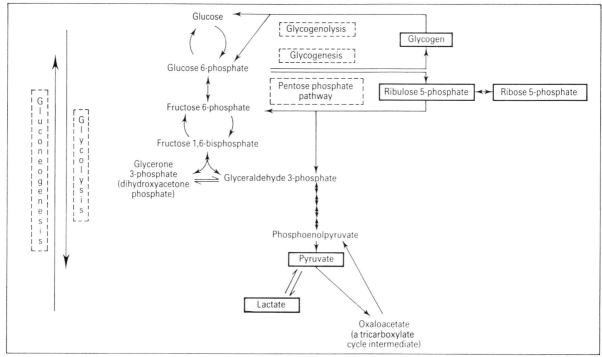

FIGURE 11.1 Summary of carbohydrate metabolism

protein molecule create a more non-polar environment which is conducive to the transfer of the terminal phosphoryl group of ATP to the substrate. Hexokinase isoenzymes are capable of the phosphorylation of at least one other monosaccharide. In some microorganisms and invertebrates, glucokinase, an enzyme highly specific for glucose, catalyses this initial glycolytic reaction.

The readily reversible isomerization of glucose 6-phosphate into its corresponding ketose involves a change of anomeric carbon atom (Section 3.3). The magnesium ion-requiring glucose-6-phosphate isomerase exhibits absolute specificity and establishes the equilibrium at the ratio of 7:3 in favour of glucose 6-phosphate. The second phosphorylation reaction is catalysed by allosteric isoenzymes of 6-phosphofructokinase which is regulated by a variety of effectors (Section 11.11).

In the splitting stage, fructose 1,6-bisphosphate, a six-carbon molecule, is cleaved into two three-carbon molecules, glycerone phosphate (also called dihydroxyacetone phosphate) and glyceraldehyde 3-phosphate, by the enzyme fructose-bisphosphate aldolase. The name of the enzyme is derived from

the chemical nature of the reverse reaction, an aldol condensation. The equilibrium remains vastly in favour of the substrate ($K_{eq} = 10^{-4}$ M) but the reaction proceeds by the mechanism of the removal of products further along the reaction sequence. Another isomerization enables the utilization of the glycerone phosphate in the pathway by its conversion into glyceraldehyde 3-phosphate. The net effect of the first two stages is therefore the conversion of each glucose molecule into two molecules of glyceraldehyde 3-phosphate.

The first reaction of the energy-conservation stage, the conversion of glyceraldehyde 3-phosphate into 1,3-bisphosphoglycerate without the involvement of ATP, reveals the secret of glycolysis as an energy-producing pathway. Glyceraldehyde-3-phosphate dehydrogenase performs the reaction in three stages (Figure 11.3): thiohemiacetal formation and thioester formation to effect the oxidation of the aldehyde group of the substrate followed by phosphorolysis (the cleavage of a bond by the introduction of an orthophosphate group) to yield a mixed acid anhydride which has a large negative standard free energy of hydrolysis

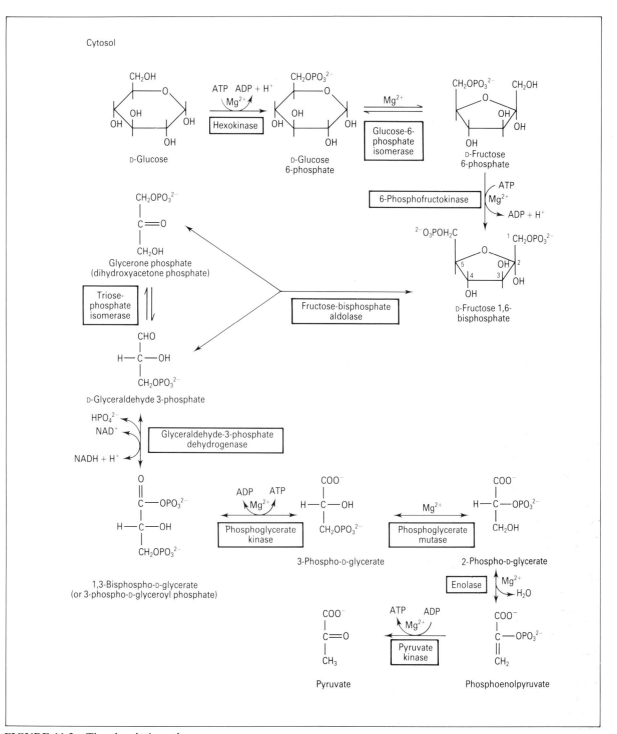

FIGURE 11.2 The glycolytic pathway

FIGURE 11.3 Mechanism of action of glyceraldehyde-3-phosphate dehydrogenase. (Only one of four identical subunits is shown. The reaction mechanism proceeds simultaneously in each subunit)

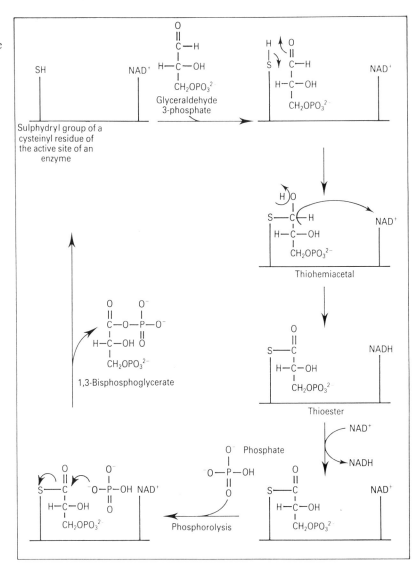

(Section 10.4). A sulphydryl group at the active site of the enzyme is necessary for the formation of the thiohemiacetal intermediate. In thioester formation, enzyme-bound NAD^+ accepts a hydride ion (Figure 5.3a) which in turn reduces coenzymic NAD^+. The destruction of the phosphoanhydride bond during the following reaction releases sufficient free energy to enable ATP synthesis although the reaction is freely reversible. The phosphoglycerate kinase reaction is termed a substrate-level phosphorylation (Section 10.4).

Phosphoglycerate mutase catalyses the transfer of a phosphoryl group from the C-3 position to C-2 position. In general, intramolecular rearrangements of chemical groups are performed by enzymes called mutases. The reaction is freely reversible and proceeds in animal tissues through the utilization of an obligatory intermediate, 2,3-bisphosphoglycerate. In erythrocytes, however, 2,3-bisphosphoglycerate has the additional important role as an allosteric effector in the binding of oxygen by haemoglobin.

2-Phosphoglycerate is converted by the enolase-catalysed elimination of the elements of water from C-2 and C-3 into phosphoenolpyruvate, another intermediate which demonstrates a large negative standard free energy of hydrolysis. In the final reaction of glycolysis, allosteric isoenzymes of pyruvate kinase catalyse the second substrate-level phosphorylation of ADP; the metabolic product is pyruvate. Unlike phosphoglycerate kinase, the pyruvate kinase reaction is not reversible under intracellular conditions.

The glycolytic pathway is not exclusively for the degradation of glucose although glucose is a major substrate in many tissues. Ingested foodstuffs contain other monosaccharides. In general, these monosaccharides are channelled into the glycolytic pathway after conversion to a glycolytic intermediate by a specific short series of reactions.

11.3 NAD$^+$ and glycolysis

The operation of the glycolytic pathway is dependent upon the availability of NAD in the oxidized state which participates as the electron acceptor in the oxidation catalysed by glyceraldehyde-3-phosphate dehydrogenase. As is the case with coenzymes, NAD$^+$ is in limited supply. The reduced

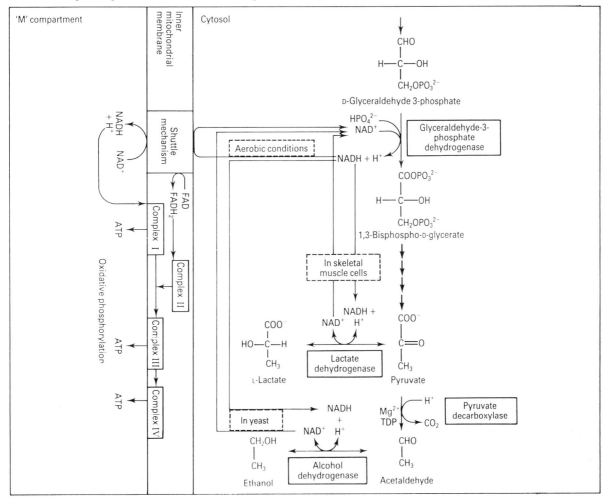

FIGURE 11.4   Some fates of NADH produced in the glyceraldehyde-3-phosphate dehydrogenase reaction under anaerobic and aerobic conditions

NADH must be converted back into NAD^+. Different types of cells achieve the regeneration of NAD^+ by the employment of different metabolic reactions in which a convenient molecule is utilized as an acceptor of NADH-derived electrons. The fate of NADH (Figure 11.4) depends on the existent intracellular conditions.

Under anaerobic conditions, highly active skeletal muscle cells and homolactic bacteria employ pyruvate, convenient as the end product of glycolysis, as a hydride ion (two electrons) acceptor to yield lactate. This reaction is catalysed by lactate dehydrogenase (Section 6.5). Yeast cells also employ pyruvate which is initially decarboxylated into acetaldehyde. This reaction involves the coenzyme, thiamin diphosphate (Figure 12.3), a derivative of the vitamin, thiamin (vitamin B_1). The acetaldehyde is then reduced to ethanol by alcohol dehydrogenase. These anaerobic processes, called fermentations, are of major importance, e.g. in the baking industry as a source of CO_2 to raise dough and in the brewing industry to produce alcohol.

Other adaptations are found in microorganisms and invertebrates.

Under aerobic conditions, a greater energy yield may be derived from the electrons contained within the NADH molecule by their participation in the process of oxidative phosphorylation (Section 10.4). The location of the electron-transport assemblies within the inner mitochondrial membrane necessitates the penetration of the membrane by NADH (Section 9.5). The inner mitochondrial membrane is, however, impermeable to NADH molecules. This obstacle is circumvented by the use of shuttle systems (Section 10.5) which do not transport the NADH molecules across the membrane but transfer the electrons as components of another substance which can transverse the membrane. Two shuttle systems exist for this purpose: the glycerol phosphate shuttle and the malate–aspartate shuttle. Their relative activities are tissue dependent, e.g. the glycerol phosphate shuttle predominates in the cells of mammalian skeletal muscle and brain whilst the malate–aspartate shuttle is

FIGURE 11.5 The glycerol phosphate shuttle

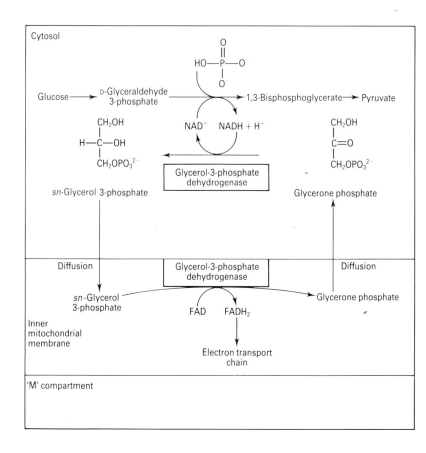

more important in mammalian liver, kidney and cardiac muscle cells.

The glycerol phosphate shuttle (Figure 11.5) utilizes the glycolytic pathway intermediate glycerone phosphate as an acceptor of electrons from NADH. This reversible reaction is catalysed by the cytosolic form of glycerol-3-phosphate dehydrogenase. The product, *sn*-glycerol 3-phosphate, can diffuse into the membrane and the reducing equivalents thus carried are transferred not to mitochondrial NAD$^+$ but to FAD (Figure 5.3e) bound as prosthetic group to another glycerol-3-phosphate dehydrogenase. The oxidation of glycerol 3-phosphate produces glycerone phosphate which

diffuses back into the cytosol. The FAD-linked enzyme is an integral membrane protein suitably positioned on the outside of the inner membrane to effect the transfer of the electrons to Complex II of the respiratory chain (Section 13.2). Glycerol 3-phosphate molecules therefore do not enter the mitochondrial matrix. The employment of FAD creates a free-energy differential which supports the transport of the electrons into the membrane and renders the shuttle mechanism irreversible.

In the malate–aspartate shuttle (Figure 11.6), the acceptor of reducing equivalents is oxaloacetate which is reduced to malate by an isoenzyme of malate dehydrogenase specific to the cytoplasm.

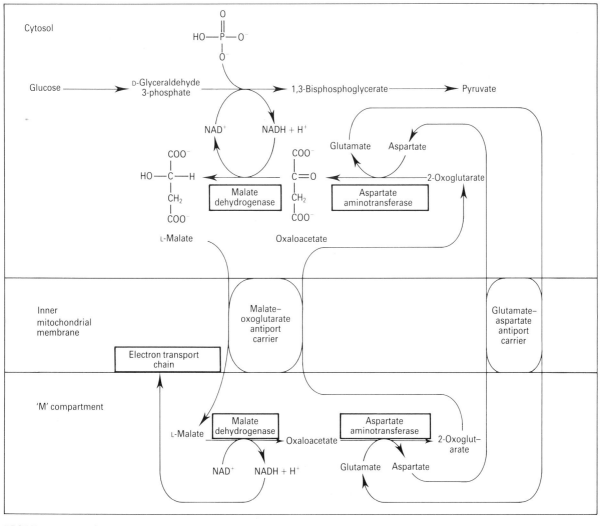

FIGURE 11.6   The malate–aspartate shuttle

The inner mitochondrial membrane has an anti-port transport system (Section 9.3) for malate which is carried by conformational change in the carrier protein in exchange for the tricarboxylate cycle intermediate, 2-oxoglutarate, which is delivered to the outside of the membrane. The malate penetrates the membrane and enters the pool of tricarboxylate cycle intermediates (Section 12.4) in which it is oxidized to oxaloacetate with concomitant NADH production. Oxaloacetate cannot permeate the inner membrane and so cannot be directly utilized as the substrate for the cytosolic malate dehydrogenase. However, aspartate and glutamate can be exchanged across the membrane by the glutamate–aspartate antiport carrier. Mitochondrial oxaloacetate is converted into 2-oxoglu-tarate by the action of the mitochondrial isoen-zyme of aspartate aminotransferase at the expense of glutamate (Section 16.1). In the cytosol, the action of aspartate aminotransferase provides the oxaloacetate for the regeneration of NAD^+.

Both isoenzymes of malate dehydrogenase are NAD linked so that the shuttle in essence transfers electrons from the cytosolic pool of NADH to the mitochondrial pool of NAD^+. Utilization of the same coenzyme results in the direction of the shuttle being determined by the relative concentrations of NADH in each compartment. The shuttle is therefore reversible and can be used to transfer reducing power between the compartments as required.

11.4 The role of glycogen

Glycogen is the major storage polysaccharide found in animal and human tissues (Section 3.6). It is a polymer of glucose in which glucose residues are linked by α-(1→4) glycosidic linkages with branching by α-(1→6) glycosidic linkages (Figure 3.9a,c). Although glycogen synthesis may occur in nearly all animal tissues, the major tissues of storage are skeletal muscles and liver. Glycogen is stored as granules which also incorporate the enzymes for its synthesis and intracellular degradation. In man, glycogen may account for up to 10% and 2% of the wet weight of the liver and skeletal muscle respectively. Since the total quantity of skeletal muscle exceeds that of liver about tenfold, approximately twice as much glycogen is stored in muscle.

The roles of liver and skeletal muscle glycogen, however, differ. Liver glycogen functions as a reservoir of glucose which is released to maintain the concentration of glucose in the blood circulation from which other tissues, e.g. brain, draw their supply of glucose. Liver glycogen levels increase following a meal and progressively decrease to maintain an almost constant blood glucose level. Muscle glycogen serves as a reservoir of glucose mainly for use within the same tissue. Glucose metabolism provides ATP which is necessary during mechanical work. Muscle glycogen levels vary less markedly with food intake than those of liver and its mobilization is triggered by increased muscular activity.

A further importance of glucose storage in polymeric form is that large quantities of small molecules lead to high osmotic pressures within the cells whereas polymerization retains the useful glucose molecules in a form which does not risk membrane lysis. Osmotic pressure may be defined as 'the excess pressure which must be applied to a solution to prevent the passage into it of solvent when the two liquids are separated by a semipermeable membrane'. Since osmotic pressure is concentration dependent, polymerization reduces the concentration of free glucose molecules and thereby alleviates potential osmotic problems.

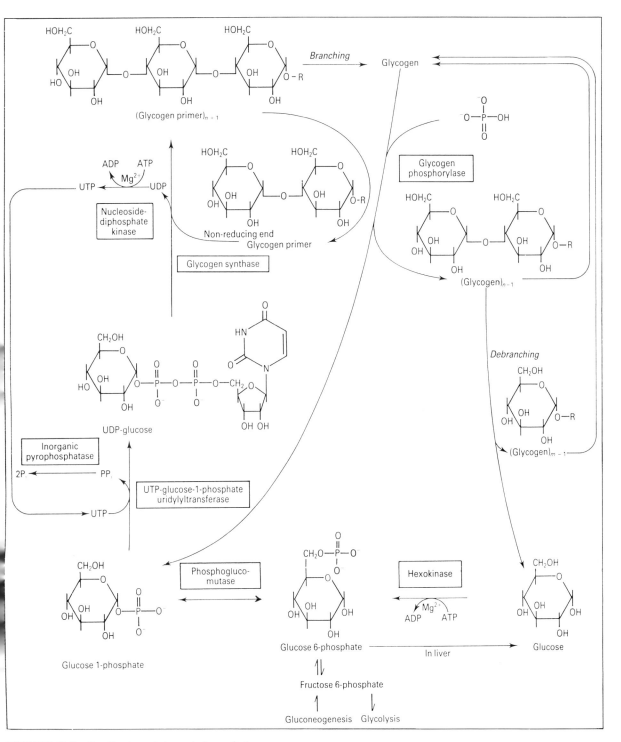

FIGURE 11.7 Synthesis and degradation of glycogen

11.5 Glycogenesis and glycogenolysis

Glycogen synthesis (called glycogenesis) commences from glucose 6-phosphate (Figure 11.7) which may be produced from glucose absorbed from the bloodstream as in skeletal muscle or by gluconeogenesis (Section 11.6) from C_3 compounds, e.g. lactate, as in liver. An intramolecular transfer of the phosphate from the C-6 position to C-1 position is performed by phosphoglucomutase.

The next reaction is unique to the synthetic pathway and involves the formation of uridine diphosphate glucose (UDP-glucose) which serves as the carrier of the glucosyl residue which participates in the elongation of a primer molecule of glycogen. The enzyme, UTP-glucose-1-phosphate uridylyltransferase utilizes both UTP and glucose 1-phosphate in a readily reversible reaction. Synthesis is promoted by the irreversible hydrolysis of pyrophosphate by inorganic pyrophosphatase. The removal of the pyrophosphate commits the uridylyltransferase reaction to the direction of glycogen synthesis (Section 10.4).

Glycogen synthase transfers the glucosyl moiety of UDP-glucose to the non-reducing end (Section 3.5) of a glycogen primer. Glycogen synthase is highly specific; it will only produce a new α-(1→4) glycosidic bond. The minimum size for an active primer molecule is four glucose units but the enzyme is more effective with longer polymers. Indeed, the usual primer is a glycogen molecule. The released UDP may be phosphorylated to UTP (at the expense of ATP) which may participate in the formation of another UDP-glucose. Some animal tissues may utilize ADP as a glucosyl carrier but the rate of reaction is lower. Glycogen synthase may repeatedly add glucosyl groups to the primer molecule.

Because of the catalytic constraints of glycogen synthase, branching through α-(1→6) glycosidic bonds occurs by the action of another enzyme, glycogen branching enzyme, which transfers terminal hexa- or septa-saccharide units from growing chains of at least 11 residues to the hydroxyl group

FIGURE 11.8   Branching of glycogen

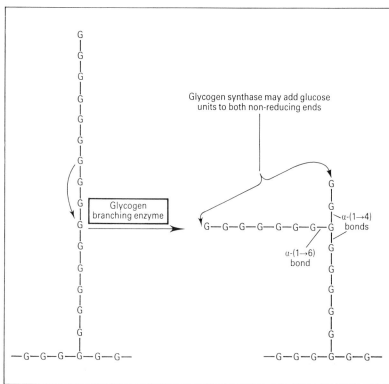

of glucose residues in internal positions (Figure 11.8). Branch points are not created closer than every fourth residue. Since similar chemical linkages are involved, the free-energy change is very small. Branching increases the number of non-reducing ends which may be simultaneously elongated or degraded by glycogen synthase or phosphorylase respectively. In plant tissues, starch is synthesized by an analogous pathway which employs starch synthase and ADP-glucose (Section 14.6).

Glycogen degradation (called glycogenolysis) proceeds by the action of the enzyme, glycogen phosphorylase (Figure 11.7). The reaction involves the cleavage of the α-(1→4) glycosidic linkage between the terminal glucose residue of a branch and its neighbour by phosphorolysis. The products of the reaction are glucose 1-phosphate which retains the α-configuration and a glycogen molecule which is one glucose residue smaller. Glucose 1-phosphate is rearranged into glucose 6-phosphate. Glycogen phosphorylase may sequentially remove residues from the non-reducing ends of glycogen chains until it approaches a branching point. Like glycogen synthase, glycogen phosphorylase cannot negotiate α-(1→6) glucosidic linkages which require an enzyme system called the glycogen debranching system. The debranching system of mammals and yeast contains two enzymic activities: 4-α-glucanotransferase and

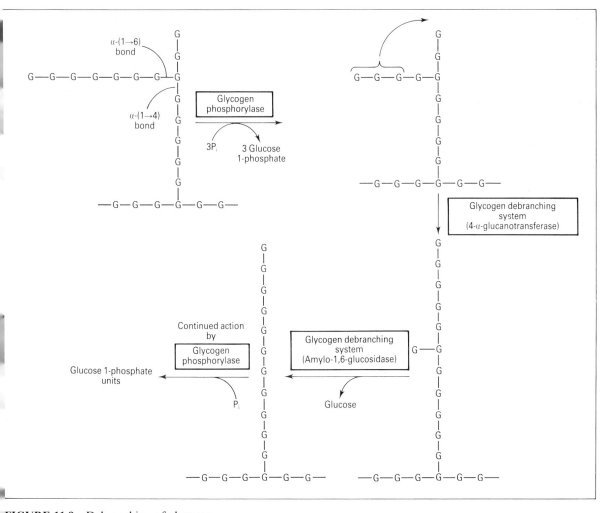

FIGURE 11.9   Debranching of glycogen

amylo-1,6-glucosidase (Figure 11.9). The activity of glycogen phosphorylase ceases at the fourth residue from an α-(1→6) linkage. The 4-α-glucano-transferase transfers a trisaccharide unit to the end of another chain. The solitary glucose remaining at the branch is removed by the amylo-1,6-glucosidase activity. Glycogen phosphorylase resumes its activity.

The fate of glucose 6-phosphate and glucose depends on the nature of the tissue. In skeletal muscle cells, the non-phosphorylated glucose which accounts for about 10% of the cleavage products (branches occur every 8–12 glucose residues) may be phosphorylated into glucose 6-phosphate. Glucose 6-phosphate from either route may be utilized in energy production through glycolysis.

The liver utilizes glucose-6-phosphatase to remove the phosphate from glucose 6-phosphate. Non-phosphorylated glucose from liver glycogen can traverse the plasma membrane and be transported via the blood circulation to other tissues. Glucose-6-phosphatase is absent from skeletal muscle and brain and so glucose is retained by these tissues as glucose 6-phosphate which cannot permeate the plasma membrane.

11.6 The role of gluconeogenesis

After a meal, glycogenesis from C_3 compounds, especially lactate, by the liver is normally of sufficient magnitude to maintain blood glucose concentrations for at least 12 h. As glycogen stores are utilized, gluconeogenesis promotes the continuance of the supply of glucose to the blood circulation. This is of paramount importance since certain tissues, including brain, erythrocytes and renal medulla, utilize glucose as their primary source of energy although their gluconeogenic capacity is almost negligible. They depend upon the liver (the major site of gluconeogenesis) and the renal cortex to support their glucose catabolism during periods of glycogen depletion.

Following periods of strenuous muscular ac-tivity, gluconeogenesis aids the restoration of glycogen levels in skeletal muscle. Rapid provision of ATP by glycolysis in highly active muscle results in the formation of lactate (Section 11.3). The lactate together with some pyruvate diffuses through the permeable plasma membrane into the blood circulation. These substances are sequestered by the liver and, in the cytosol of hepatocytes, the lactate is oxidized to pyruvate which is converted by the gluconeogenic pathway into glucose. The resultant glucose may diffuse into the blood circulation and be absorbed by skeletal muscle cells to replenish their depleted glycogen stores. This sequence of events, called the Cori cycle (Figure 11.10), oper-ates between tissues in which glucose is not com-

FIGURE 11.10   The Cori cycle

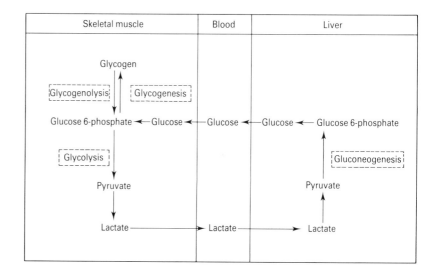

pletely oxidized and the liver.

Dietary proteins are a source of amino acids which can serve as important precursors for gluconeogenesis. During a fast or starvation, a major contribution is made by alanine which is released along with other amino acids from skeletal muscle. Since labile proteins rich in alanine are not present in muscle, the released alanine appears to result from the activity of alanine aminotransferase (Section 16.1) which produces alanine from pyruvate. This is the basis of the alanine cycle which also operates between skeletal muscle and the liver. The alanine cycle functions only when peripheral tissues reoxidize glycolytic NADH through the oxidative phosphorylation pathway. In the presence of oxygen, pyruvate is not utilized in lactate production and is available for the amino transfer reaction.

The enzymic hydrolysis of triacylglycerols in adipose tissue yields glycerol and fatty acids (Section 15.1). Glycerol may be employed as a source of glucose or energy by entry into the gluconeogenic or glycolytic pathways respectively through the common intermediate, glycerone phosphate. The fatty acids may undergo β-oxidation (Section 15.2) to acetyl-CoA which cannot significantly contribute to gluconeogenesis. However, fatty acids which are branched or have an odd number of carbon atoms also yield some propionyl-CoA which may be metabolized to succinyl-CoA, a tricarboxylate cycle intermediate (Section 15.2). Additional production of tricarboxylate intermediates, e.g. from glutamine (Section 16.3), makes the cycle available as a source of gluconeogenic precursors which may enter the pathway through the reversal of anaplerotic pathways (Section 12.6).

11.7 The reactions of gluconeogenesis

The synthesis of glucose from pyruvate is not simply a reversal of glycolysis despite the participation of all glycolytic intermediates (Figure 11.11). Seven reactions which are freely reversible are shared by both pathways. Three glycolytic reactions (hexokinase, 6-phosphofructokinase and pyruvate kinase) are essentially irreversible in the cell because of their standard free energies of hydrolysis. In gluconeogenesis, more favourable alternative reactions, termed the bypass reactions, are exploited.

Lactate and alanine enter as pyruvate following the activities of lactate dehydrogenase (Figure 11.4) and alanine aminotransferase (Section 16.3). The first of the bypass reactions, the objective of which is to overcome the unfavourable energetics of a reversal of the pyruvate kinase reaction, seems a tortuous route (Figure 11.11). The reaction sequence relies on two important enzymes: pyruvate carboxylase and phosphoenolpyruvate carboxykinase. Since pyruvate carboxylase is located exclusively in the mitochondrion, pyruvate must cross the inner mitochondrial membrane (Section 12.2). Oxaloacetate produced by pyruvate carboxylase cannot traverse the inner membrane and is reduced by malate dehydrogenase into L-malate. This step is the reversal of the tricarboxylate cycle reaction (Section 12.4). Malate may, of

course, be formed by the sequential action of cycle enzymes following increased levels of cycle intermediate pools, e.g. 2-oxoglutarate and succinyl-CoA. Malate may be translocated out of the mitochondrion in exchange for phosphate by the malate–phosphate antiport system. Oxaloacetate is re-formed from the malate by the cytosolic isoenzyme of malate dehydrogenase. Oxaloacetate is the substrate for phosphoenolpyruvate carboxykinase which produces phosphoenolpyruvate; the enzyme specifically requires GTP to act as phosphate group donor. GTP may be formed from ATP through the action of nucleoside-diphosphate kinase (Section 10.4).

From phosphoenolpyruvate, the gluconeogenic pathway proceeds through the reversal of glycolytic reactions as far as the formation of fructose 1,6-bisphosphate. ATP must be supplied for the phosphoglycerate kinase reaction whilst NADH and phosphate are necessary for the glyceraldehyde-3-phosphate dehydrogenase reaction. When lactate is the source of cytosolic pyruvate as in liver, this NADH is generated by the lactate dehydrogenase reaction. However, if pyruvate arises from other sources, e.g. alanine, the NADH is made available through the cytosolic malate dehydrogenase reaction of the first bypass. Glycerol released from triacylglycerol storage undergoes phosphorylation in gluconeogenic tissues to form 8 *sn*-glycerol 3-phosphate which is then oxidized to glycerone phosphate.

Following fructose-bisphosphate aldolase activity, the second bypass reaction circumvents the irreversible glycolytic reaction catalysed by 6-phosphofructokinase. Fructose-bisphosphatase irreversibly cleaves a phosphate group from the C-1 position of fructose 1,6-bisphosphate to yield fructose 6-phosphate which is converted into glucose 6-

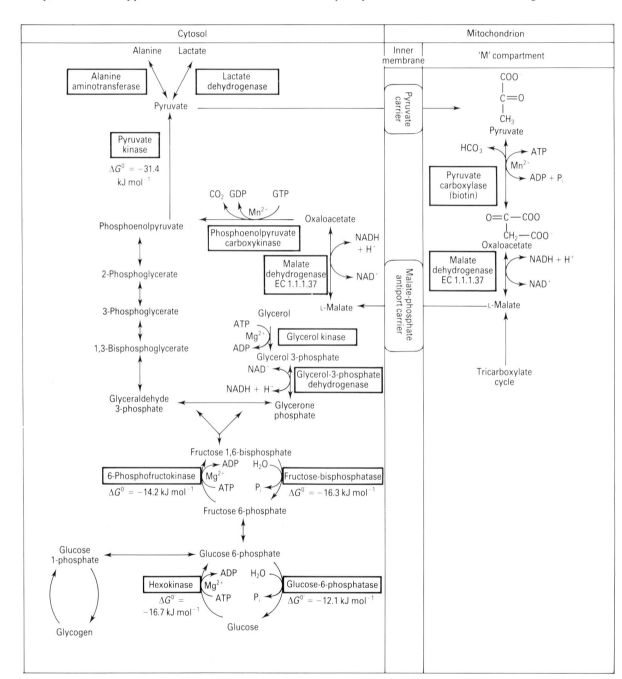

FIGURE 11.11   Pathway for gluconeogenesis from lactate, alanine and glycerol

phosphate by isomerization. Glucose 6-phosphate may be processed to glycogen and thereby employed to replenish depleted glycogen stores. Glucose, however, may be required to maintain blood glucose levels in which case the third bypass reaction, the removal of the phosphate group, is achieved by glucose 6-phosphatase. This enzyme, present in the liver but absent from muscle, permits glucose to be released from the liver in the blood circulation (Section 11.5).

11.8 The role of the pentose phosphate pathway

The pentose phosphate pathway is also known as the hexose monophosphate shunt and the phosphogluconate pathway because of the variety of intermediates formed by the pathway under different conditons. The pathway which occurs in a wide variety of organisms including animals, plants and microorganisms is classifiable as secondary metabolism (Section 10.5) due to the relatively small quantity of glucose catabolized by this route. In mammalian tissues, the pathway yields a number of important products, in particular, reduced nicotinamide adenine dinucleotide phosphate (NADPH) and pentose sugars.

Although structurally similar (Figure 5.3a), the biological roles of NADH and NADPH are different. Reduced NAD is of importance in catabolism especially the generation of ATP through oxidative phosphorylation (Chapter 13) whilst the primary metabolic function of reduced NADP is as reducing power in certain biosyntheses, e.g. to reduce double bonds to single bonds in the synthesis of saturated fatty acids. Appreciable quantities of fatty acids are synthesized in adipose (fat) tissue, liver and mammary glands. Steroid biosynthesis is particularly active in the adrenal cortex, testes and ovaries. Since reducing power in the form of NADPH is required for these biosynthetic pathways, the pentose phosphate pathway is highly active in these tissues. Tissues which are less active in NADPH-dependent reductive biosyntheses generally exhibit markedly less pathway activity, e.g. skeletal muscle.

Erythrocytes (red blood cells) require NADPH for a different reason, i.e. to protect indirectly against: (i) the oxidation of the sulphydryl groups of haemoglobin (Section 4.7) with concomitant impairment of its performance in oxygen transport and (ii) cell lysis due to the oxidation of unsaturated lipids of the cell membrane.

Neutrophilic polymorphonuclear leukocytes (a class of white blood cells) provide the first line of defence against bacterial infection. Upon phagocytosis (Section 9.3), the invading microorganisms must be destroyed. NADPH supplies the reducing power for the NADPH oxidase-catalysed reduction of molecular O_2, the reaction which initiates the generation of the potent bactericidal oxygen radicals, hydroxyl radical and singlet oxygen (which contains one electron less than molecular oxygen).

The reducing power of NADPH plays an important role in certain biological hydroxylation reactions. A series of cytochrome *P*-450 enzymes catalyse these hydroxylations (Figure 11.12). Their locations in eukaryotic cells are predominantly in the endoplasmic reticulum (Section 9.6) and also in the mitochondrion (Section 9.5). In contrast to cytochrome a_3 of the respiratory chain which can also reduce oxygen and react with carbon monoxide, reduced cytochromes *P*-450 when complexed with CO exhibit maximum absorption of light at 450 nm, hence their name. The enzymic activity of cytochromes *P*-450 is called a monooxygenase activity since one atom of the molecular O_2 is employed in the formation of a hydroxyl group, the other being reduced by NADPH + H$^+$ to water. Cytochrome *P*-450 enzymes participate in a variety of reactions involving numerous different substrates, e.g. the biosynthesis of steroid hormones (Section 15.8), the hydroxylation of drugs and other foreign substances (xenobiotics) largely by the liver during detoxification processes.

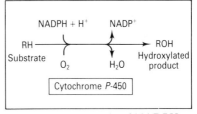

FIGURE 11.12 Role of NADPH in hydroxylation reactions catalysed by cytochrome *P*-450 enzymes

Pentose sugars are required for the synthesis of nucleic acids. Ribose 5-phosphate is utilized in the synthesis of purine and pyrimidine deoxyribo- and ribo-nucleotides. Since neonatal and fetal thymuses are highly active in nucleic acid synthesis, these tissues have an active pentose phosphate pathway to furnish ribose 5-phosphate. Ribose moieties also feature in the structure of major coenzymes such as $NAD(P)^+$, coenzyme A and FAD (Figure 5.3). The degradation of nucleic acids and nucleotides produces ribose 1-phosphate which is converted by phosphopentomutase into ribose 5-phosphate. The non-oxidative phase (Section 11.10) of the pathway provides a route into the glycolytic pathway for its utilization in energy production. Since NADPH and NADH are interconvertible through the action of $NAD(P)^+$ transhydrogenase, the pentose phosphate pathway under aerobic conditions can contribute electrons for energy production.

11.9 The reactions of the pentose phosphate pathway

The pentose phosphate pathway can be sectioned into two phases: the oxidative phase and the non-oxidative phase. During the oxidative phase (Figure 11.13), glucose 6-phosphate is oxidized by the removal of electrons which are accepted by the coenzyme, $NADP^+$, and decarboxylated to yield ribose 5-phosphate. The first reaction involves oxidation by the $NADP^+$-specific enzyme glucose-6-phosphate dehydrogenase with concomitant reduction of $NADP^+$ to produce 6-phosphoglucono-1,5-lactone. The lactone, although unstable and liable to revert to the open-chain form (Section 3.3), is rapidly hydrolysed by a specific lactonase to yield 6-phosphogluconate which undergoes oxidative decarboxylation. $NADP^+$ again participates as electron acceptor. Both the removal of firstly electrons and secondly the carboxylate group are catalysed by the same enzyme, phosphogluconate dehydrogenase (decarboxylating). The product, ribulose 5-phosphate, is isomerized into the corresponding aldose phosphate.

In some other tissues (Section 11.8), the pathway

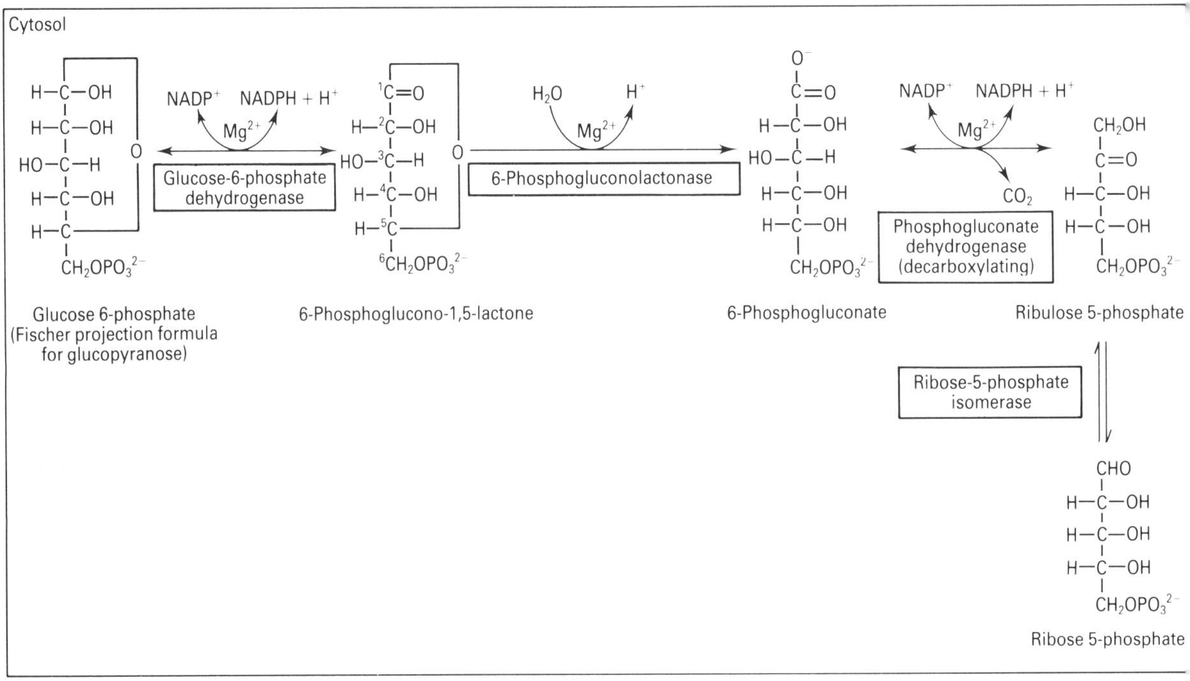

FIGURE 11.13   The oxidative phase of the pentose phosphate pathway

is terminated at this point with the utilization of ribose 5-phosphate in nucleotide synthesis. During the oxidative phase of the pathway, the processing of one molecule of D-glucose generates one D-ribose 5-phosphate, one CO_2 and two NADPH. This pathway occurs in the cell cytosol, the same intracellular compartment as fatty acid synthesis (Section 15.4).

Although the oxidative phase is firmly established in active tissues, the sequence of events during the non-oxidative phase in the liver remains a contentious issue. The pathway will be considered as it occurs within the adipose (fat) tissue (i.e. the F-type pathway). An alternative scheme for the liver (the L-type pathway) has been proposed.

Tissues which are more active in the synthesis of lipids than nucleotides require NADPH rather than ribose moieties. In such tissues, e.g. adipose tissue, the ribose 5-phosphate enters a series of sugar interconversion reactions which connect the pentose phosphate pathway with glycolysis and gluconeogenesis. These interconversion reactions constitute the non-oxidative phase of the pathway (Figure 11.14) and since oxidation is not involved, NADPH is not produced. Two enzymes catalyse the important reactions: transketolase which contains thiamin diphosphate (Figure 12.3a) as its prosthetic group and transaldolase. Both enzymes function in the transfer of carbon units: transketolase transfers two-carbon units and transaldolase transfers three-carbon units. The transfer always occurs from a ketose donor to an aldose acceptor. The interconversion sequence requires the oxidative phase to operate three times, i.e. three molecules of glucose 6-phosphate yield three molecules of ribulose 5-phosphate.

The first of the interconversions features xylulose 5-phosphate and ribose 5-phosphate. Because transketolase has the specific requirement that the hydroxyl group at C-3 must be in the xylulose configuration, xylulose 5-phosphate is produced from ribulose 5-phosphate by epimerization involving the enzyme, ribulose-phosphate 3-epimerase. Epimers are sugars which differ only in the configuration of the hydroxyl group on one specific chiral carbon atom (Section 3.2), in this case C-3, hence the name of the enzyme. Carbon atoms 1 and 2 of xylulose 5-phosphate are transferred to ribose 5-phosphate to synthesize sedoheptulose 7-phosphate which, under the influence of transaldo-

lase, serves as a three-carbon unit donor for the conversion of glyceraldehyde 3-phosphate (the other product) into fructose 6-phosphate. The remainder of the carbon chain of sedoheptulose 7-phosphate forms erythrose 4-phosphate.

The six-carbon product of the transaldolase reaction enters the cytosolic pool of fructose 6-phosphate and may be utilized in energy production through the glycolytic pathway. Alternatively, it may be isomerized into glucose 6-phosphate and reprocessed through the oxidative phase of the pathway.

A second transketolase reaction converts the erythrose 4-phosphate into another molecule of fructose 6-phosphate. Because of the specificity of the enzyme, a second xylulose 5-phosphate contributes two carbon atoms to yield the ketose phosphate and glyceraldehyde 3-phosphate. Thus, three molecules of ribulose 5-phosphate are required for complete interconversion from the pentose to glycolytic intermediates which are two molecules of fructose 6-phosphate and one molecule of glyceraldehyde 3-phosphate. The possible fates of fructose 6-phosphate are mentioned above but only glycolytic degradation in relation to carbohydrate metabolism appears to be available to glyceraldehyde 3-phosphate. However, if the oxidative phase of the pathway functions another three times, two molecules of glyceraldehyde 3-phosphate would be produced, one of which could be converted by triose phosphate isomerase to glycerone phosphate (Section 11.2). Glucose 6-phosphate could be synthesized through gluconeogenic reactions (Figure 11.11). The pentose phosphate pathway can therefore operate as a cycle which in effect processes one molecule of glucose 6-phosphate to six CO_2 with an appreciable yield of reduced NADP (Table 11.1).

In tissues in which the availability of ribose 5-phosphate for nucleotide synthesis predominates, this demand may be satisfied through the reversal of the sugar interconversion reactions. In other words, glycolysis may be employed to generate fructose 6-phosphate and glyceraldehyde 3-phosphate from which transketolase and transaldolase produce ribose 5-phosphate. By this route, five molecules of glucose 6-phosphate can yield six molecules of ribose 5-phosphate at the expense of five ATP (6-phosphofructokinase reaction).

144

FIGURE 11.14 The non-oxidative
phase of the pentose phosphate
pathway in adipose tissue

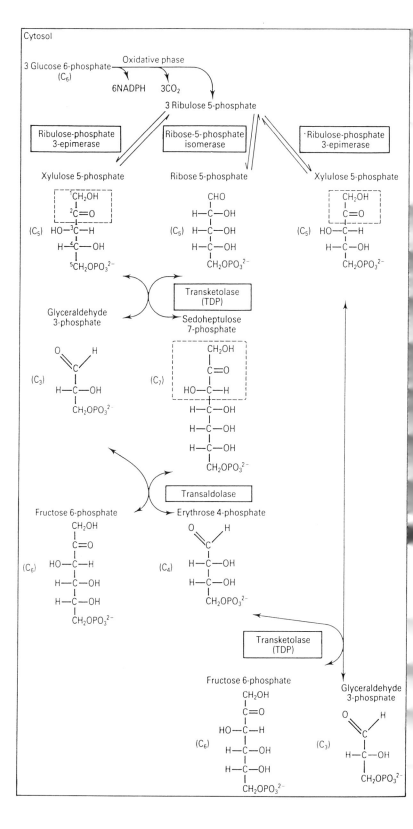

TABLE 11.1   The operation of the pentose phosphate pathway as a cycle

Stage number	Reaction sequence	Equation
Stage 1	Oxidative phase	6 Glucose 6-phosphate→6 ribulose 5-phosphate + 12 NADP⁺ + 6 H₂O + 6 CO₂ + 12 NADPH + 12H⁺
Stage 2	Non-oxidative phase	6 Ribulose 5-phosphate→4 fructose 6-phosphate + 2 glyceraldehyde 3-phosphate
Stage 3	Gluconeogenesis	2 Glyceraldehyde 3-phosphate→1 glucose 6-phosphate + 1 H₂O + 1 phosphate
Stage 4	Isomerization	4 Fructose 6-phosphate→4 glucose 6-phosphate
	Sum of stages	6 Glucose 6-phosphate→5 glucose 6-phosphate + 12 NADP⁺ + 7 H₂O + 6 CO₂ + 12 NADPH + 12H⁺ + 1 phosphate
	Net reaction	1 Glucose 6-phosphate→6 CO₂ + 12 NADPH + 12H⁺ + 1 phosphate + 12 NADP⁺ + 7 H₂O

11.10 The energetics of carbohydrate metabolism

The pathways of carbohydrate metabolism conform to the principles of thermodynamics (Chapter 10). Each pathway is overall exergonic. For example, as calculated from thermodynamic data, the degradation of glucose to two lactate molecules proceeds with the release of free energy according to the equation:

$$\text{Glucose} \rightarrow 2 \text{ lactate} + 2\text{H}^+;$$
$$\Delta G^{0\prime} = -196.6 \text{ kJ mol}^{-1}$$

In mammalian skeletal muscle cells, the degradation occurs according to the following equation:

$$\text{Glucose} + 2\text{ADP} + 2 \text{ phosphate} \rightarrow$$
$$2 \text{ lactate} + 2\text{H}^+ + 2\text{ATP} + 2\text{H}_2\text{O};$$
$$\Delta G^{0\prime} = -135.6 \text{ kJ mol}^{-1}$$

Thus, during glycolysis, part of the energy released is conserved by the substrate-level phosphorylation reactions which synthesize ATP. The greater proportion of energy is dissipated as heat.

Table 11.2 indicates the standard free-energy changes for the individual reactions of glycolysis. Over half of the reactions are endergonic, i.e. $\Delta G^{0\prime} = +\text{ve}$. However, when the actual free-energy changes, ΔG, are calculated employing available data on intracellular concentrations of metabolites, only three reactions, i.e. the triose-phosphate isomerase, phosphoglycerate kinase and phosphoglycerate mutase reactions, are energy requiring but by such small amounts that their energetic deficiencies can be accommodated by the mechanism of coupling reactions (Section 10.3). Accurate assessments of ΔG necessitate that the reaction achieves a steady state. However, metabolic flow through pathways (Section 10.6) implies that none of the intermediate reactions are at equilibrium so

TABLE 11.2   The standard and actual free energy changes during the reactions of glycolysis

Enzyme	Free energy change (kJ mol⁻¹)	
	Standard; $\Delta G^{0\prime}$	Actual; ΔG
Hexokinase	− 16.7	− 33.4
Glucose 6-phosphate isomerase	+ 1.7	− 2.5
6-Phosphofructokinase	− 14.2	− 22.2
Fructose-bisphosphate aldolase	+ 23.8	− 1.3
Triose-phosphate isomerase	+ 7.5	+ 2.5
Glyceraldehyde-3-phosphate dehydrogenase	+ 6.3	− 1.7
Phosphoglycerate kinase	− 18.8	+ 1.3
Phosphoglycerate mutase	+ 4.6	+ 0.8
Enolase	+ 1.7	− 3.3
Pyruvate kinase	− 31.4	− 16.7

that ΔG values must also be considered as of limited value although serving as a basis for rationalization.

The net yield of ATP from the anaerobic catabolism of glucose can be calculated as shown in Table 11.3. Glycolysis yields two molecules of ATP per molecule of glucose consumed.

Glycogen is a highly efficient way of storing glucose. Only one equivalent of ATP (i.e. UTP) is utilized in the elongation of a glycogen chain by one glucose residue. Phosphorolysis cleaves glycogen to glucose 1-phosphate which is readily converted into glucose 6-phosphate. Each glucose released by the debranching system is phosphorylated into glucose 6-phosphate at the expense of one ATP. Under anaerobic conditions, each glucose 6-phosphate will yield three molecules of ATP.

Diversion of glucose 6-phosphate into the pentose phosphate pathway reduces the direct ATP yield during oxidation to pyruvate since three glucose 6-phosphate molecules generate only eight molecules of ATP.

In gluconeogenesis, pyruvate kinase is circumvented by a multistep route which under standard conditions requires only 0.84 kJ mol^{-1}. On con-

sideration of actual intracellular conditions, the reaction is exergonic ($\Delta G \approx -25$ kJ mol^{-1}). Dephosphorylation reactions catalysed by fructose-bisphosphatase and glucose-6-phosphatase provide exergonic reactions which reverse exergonic glycolytic reactions by a different mechanism. However, it should be noted that ATP participates in the phosphorylation reaction whereas the hydrolytic cleavage of the phosphate group releases energy in the opposite reaction (Figure 11.11).

Gluconeogenesis from pyruvate is an energy-requiring process. The pyruvate kinase bypass utilizes ATP in the pyruvate carboxylase step and GTP (equivalent to ATP) in the PEP carboxykinase step. Reversal of the phosphoglycerate kinase and glyceraldehyde-3-phosphate dehydrogenase reactions consumes ATP and NADH respectively. To attain glyceraldehyde 3-phosphate from pyruvate requires three ATP. Two glyceraldehyde 3-phosphate are needed to produce one glucose. The synthesis of glucose from pyruvate therefore requires six ATP. Glycolysis only yields two ATP, thus gluconeogenesis must be considered as energetically expensive, a feature of fundamental importance in the starving individual.

TABLE 11.3   The role of ATP in glycolysis

Stage	Enzymic reaction	ATP change per molecule of glucose	
		Utilization	Production
Stage 1: priming	Hexokinase	1	—
	6-Phosphofructokinase	1	—
Stage 2: splitting	—	—	—
Stage 3: energy conservation	Phosphoglycerate kinase	—	1 × 2*
	Pyruvate kinase	—	1 × 2*
Totals		2	4
Net yield of ATP = 4 − 2 = 2 molecules			

*Stages 1 and 2 degrade each glucose molecule into 2 molecules of glyceraldehyde 3-phosphate so that stage 3 occurs twice per glucose molecule

11.11 The regulation of carbohydrate metabolism

The principal aspects of the regulation of glycogen metabolism, i.e. the interconversions between forms of glycogen synthase and between forms of glycogen phosphorylase, have been discussed in Sections 10.6 and 10.7. The glycolytic pathway contains three non-equilibrium reactions, those

catalysed by hexokinase, 6-phosphofructokinase and pyruvate kinase. These reactions are bypassed in gluconeogenesis by alternative reactions.

Hexokinase activity promotes the intracellular retention of glucose and thereby controls its rate of entry into carbohydrate metabolism whereas glucose 6-phosphatase activity permits the release of glucose from hepatic tissue. This substrate cycle (Section 10.6) is therefore functional in the regulation of blood glucose concentrations. Hexokinase type I, II and III isoenzymes may phosphorylate glucose, mannose, fructose and glucosamine whereas type IV is restricted to glucose and mannose. Types I, II and III have similar kinetic properties with low K_m values (approximately 10^{-5} mol dm^{-3}) for glucose. Type IV, found almost exclusively in mammalian and human liver, demonstrates a K_m of approximately 10^{-2} mol dm^{-3} for glucose and therefore requires much higher glucose levels for maximum activity. This feature is useful in the control of high blood glucose levels which may damage tissue proteins by the non-enzymic attachment of glucose to them. The reaction product, glucose 6-phosphate, inhibits only types I, II and III isoenzymes to prevent depletion of intracellular inorganic phosphate required for other cellular reactions.

Glycolytic 6-phosphofructokinase together with fructose-bisphosphatase catalyse the reactions of a substrate cycle in mammalian gluconeogenic tissues. 6-Phosphofructokinase functions under the influence of a number of positive and negative effectors (Table 11.4) depending upon the tissue under consideration. Intracellular [ATP]/[ADP] ratios contribute to the intracellular energy status and the control of the activity of the enzyme. A high ratio results in ATP binding to a regulatory site with concomitant reduction in product formation. A low ratio implies an energy requirement, therefore the operation of the glycolytic pathway is desirable and 6-phosphofructokinase becomes more active. High levels of NADH, citrate and long-chain fatty acids imply that the energy needs of the cell may be satisfied by the utilization of oxidative phosphorylation with reduced coenzymes supplied through the tricarboxylate cycle (Section 12.4) and β-oxidation (Section 15.2) pathway respectively. Fructose-bisphosphatase is inhibited by

AMP and fructose 2,6-bisphosphate. AMP serves to amplify the net flux through the glycolytic pathway (Section 10.6).

The 6-phosphofructokinase/fructose-bisphosphatase cycle is subject to extracellular influences. Investigations into the mechanism of action of glucagon on liver gluconeogenesis led to the discovery in 1980 of fructose 2,6-bisphosphate, a major effector of both enzymes which is present at extremely low intracellular concentrations (nmol per g wet weight of tissue). In liver, fructose 2,6-bisphosphate activates 6-phosphofructokinase and inhibits fructose-bisphosphatase to amplify the glycolytic flux. The presence of fructose 2,6-bisphosphate in all mammalian cells suggests that its main role is to control 6-phosphofructokinase and thereby glycolysis. Fructose 2,6-bisphosphate is synthesized by 6-phosphofructo-2-kinase from fructose 6-phosphate and ATP and degraded by fructose-2,6-bisphosphatase to fructose 6-phosphate and orthophosphate. Both reactions constitute a substrate cycle in which 6-phosphofructo-2-kinase is activated by orthophosphate but inhibited by citrate, phosphoenolpyruvate and sn-glycerol 3-phosphate while fructose-2,6-bisphosphatase is stimulated by P_i, sn-glycerol 3-phosphate and nucleoside triphosphates and inhibited by fructose 6-phosphate. Both enzymes are also controlled by the phosphorylation/dephosphorylation reactions of their interrelated enzyme interconversion cycles (Section 10.6).

Pyruvate kinase, in general, is inhibited by high concentrations of ATP, alanine, acetyl-CoA and long-chain fatty acids. Thus the affinity of the enzyme for its substrate is lowered when energy requirements can be satisfied by other means. Conversely at low [ATP], the affinity of pyruvate kinase for phosphoenolpyruvate (PEP) increases to support the substrate-level phosphorylation of ADP even at low [PEP] because of its inherent instability. The liver isoenzyme is activated by fructose 1,6-bisphosphate so that pyruvate kinase activity is coordinated with variations in

TABLE 11.4 Principal allosteric effectors of 6-phosphofructokinase

Positive effectors	Negative effectors
Fructose 1,6-bisphosphate	ATP
Fructose 2,6-bisphosphate	NADH
ADP	Citrate
AMP	Long-chain fatty acids
Phosphate	H$^+$
K$^+$	Ca^{2+}

6-phosphofructokinase activity. Pyruvate kinase is subject to hormonally controlled (e.g. glucagon) interconversion between *a* and *b* forms, the *b* form being phosphorylated. The gluconeogenic bypass route is allosterically controlled at pyruvate carboxylase by positive effectors, acetyl-CoA and ATP, and the negative effector, ADP.

There are, however, additional complications to consider. Glycolytic enzymes, e.g. 6-phosphofructokinase, fructose-bisphosphate aldolase, glyceraldehyde-3-phosphate dehydrogenase, may bind to cytoskeletal structures and cellular membranes. Particle-bound enzymes differ in enzyme kinetics from soluble-phase enzymes. 6-Phosphofructokinase relinquishes its conformational flexibility which is accompanied by a switch from allosteric (Section 6.4) to Michaelis–Menten kinetics (Section 6.2). Unlike soluble-phase 6-phosphofructokinase, the membrane-bound enzyme is not inhibited by ATP and the plot of its velocity versus fructose 6-phosphate is non-sigmoidal. Moreover, under various physiological conditions, the degree of binding of glycolytic enzymes and their isoenzymic forms may markedly differ. In addition, such binding interactions effectively compartmentalize the glycolytic enzymes within the cytoplasm. Also because of the problems of compartmentalization, the actual available concentrations of effectors in mammalian cells are unknown.

The regulation of the pentose phosphate pathway has not been as fully studied as that of glycolysis. The rate of the pathway appears to be controlled by glucose-6-phosphate dehydrogenase. The major regulatory factor governing this essentially irreversible reaction is the cytosolic ratio of [NADP$^+$]/[NADPH].

When the ratio lies markedly in favour of NADPH, the reduced coenzyme competes with NADP$^+$ for its binding site on the enzyme and inhibits the reaction. Higher NADP$^+$ concentrations enhance the metabolism of glucose 6-phosphate through the pathway. In addition, ATP acts as a competitive inhibitor (Section 6.3) of the enzyme. The control of the non-oxidative phase has not been elucidated.

Suggested further reading

NEWSHOLME, E. A. and LEECH, A. R. (1983) *Biochemistry for the Medical Sciences*, Wiley, Chichester

WOOD, T. (1985) *The Pentose Phosphate Pathway*, Academic Press, New York

WORTH, H. G. J. and CURNOW, D. H. (1980) *Metabolic Pathways in Medicine*, Arnold, London

catabolic ~ conversion of
Catoms of Acetyl CoA → CO2
generation of reduced H carriers

TCA

anaero-
aero-
respiration / fermentation

photosynthesis

CHAPTER 12

The tricarboxylate cycle

12.1 Role in metabolism

Small quantities of ATP are yielded when carbohydrate substrates are degraded to pyruvate (Section 11.10). Under anaerobic conditions, pyruvate is frequently converted into another substance to effect the regeneration of NAD^+ (Section 11.3). Much of the energy contained within the initial monosaccharide structure is retained in the end product of the fermentation. Under aerobic conditions, however, a higher ATP yield can be achieved by the complete degradation of substrate to carbon dioxide and water. This degradation in eukaryotes occurs within the mitochondrial matrix through the reactions of: (i) the tricarboxylate cycle in which the carbon atoms of the acetyl group of acetyl-CoA derived from pyruvate are oxidized to CO_2, and (ii) oxidative phosphorylation, in which coenzymes reduced during cycle reactions are oxidized indirectly by molecular oxygen and are thus regenerated with a further yield of ATP and the formation of water (Chapter 13). The overall process is called respiration to differentiate from fermentation which occurs in the absence of oxygen. Acetyl-CoA is not exclusively produced from pyruvate within the mitochondrion but is also the oxidation product of the catabolism of fatty acids and some amino acids. Although the degradation of other amino acids yields tricarboxylate cycle intermediates, the major substrate of the cycle is acetyl-CoA derived primarily from the breakdown of carbohydrate and fatty acids.

The role of the tricarboxylate cycle is not confined to the degradation of acetyl-CoA. The cycle is a central metabolic pathway involved in both catabolic and anabolic processes (Figure 12.1). The major catabolic function of the cycle involves the conversion of the carbon atoms of acetyl-CoA to CO_2 and the generation of reduced hydrogen carriers. A number of cycle intermediates may be used in biosynthetic pathways. Oxaloacetate and 2-oxoglutarate may be converted into aspartate and glutamate respectively by amino transfer reactions (Section 16.1) and thereby be employed as sources of these amino acids for protein synthesis. Through the action of glutamate dehydrogenase (Section 16.1), 2-oxoglutarate serves as an important source of glutamate in animals, plants and microorganisms. Since protein synthesis is a cytoplasmic event, these amino acids must be transported across the inner mitochondrial membrane by a specific carrier. During protein degradation, the same reactions in reverse permit the entry of these amino acids into the cycle. Citrate serves as a source of acetyl-CoA for the biosynthesis of fatty acids and cholesterol which occur in the cytosol (Section 15.4). Citrate may be translocated out of the mitochondrion whereas acetyl-CoA cannot leave the matrix. Subsequent synthesis of steroids necessitates the transport of cholesterol into the 'M' compartment (Section 15.7). In animals and microorganisms, succinyl-CoA serves as a starting material for the synthesis of protoporphyrin IX which forms the basis of haem, the oxygen-binding component of haemoglobin and the electron-binding component of the cytochromes of the electron-transport system. Cycle intermediates may be also employed in the synthesis of glucose by gluconeogenesis (Section 11.6). In plants, chlorophyll which is photo-oxidized during photosynthesis (Section 14.2) is derived from protoporphyrin IX produced not from succinyl-CoA but from 2-oxoglutarate using a different pathway.

149

FIGURE 12.1   Role of the tricarboxylate cycle in catabolism and anabolism

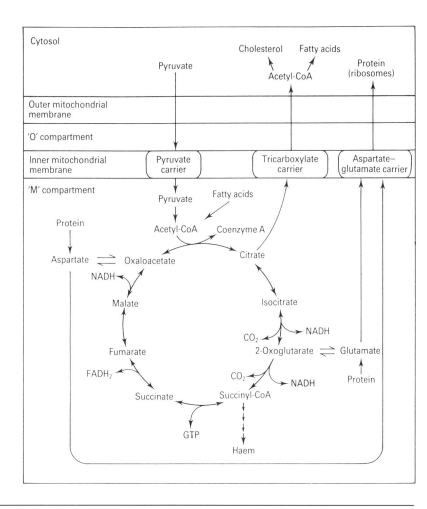

12.2 Entry of pyruvate into the mitochondrion

Aerobic utilization of pyruvate in eukaryotes necessitates its entry into the mitochondrial matrix where the reactions of the tricarboxylate cycle are considered to occur although some of the enzymes are bound or may bind to the inner membrane. The translocation is achieved by either non-carrier-mediated diffusion or the pyruvate–hydroxyl ion antiport system which, through conformational change, exchanges the pyruvate for a hydroxyl ion thereby maintaining the pH balance across the membrane.

12.3 The oxidative decarboxylation of pyruvate

Upon entry into the mitochondrial matrix, pyruvate may be converted into acetyl-CoA by the action of a multienzyme complex called the pyruvate dehydrogenase system. The overall non-equilibrium reaction (Figure 12.2a) is exergonic to an extent which appears capable of supporting the substrate-level phosphorylation of ADP. However, ATP synthesis does not occur. The large negative $\Delta G^{0\prime}$ renders the reaction essentially irreversible under physiological conditions so that acetyl-CoA

FIGURE 12.2 Oxidative decarboxylation of pyruvate. (a) Overall reaction. (b) Mechanism of action of the pyruvate dehydrogenase system

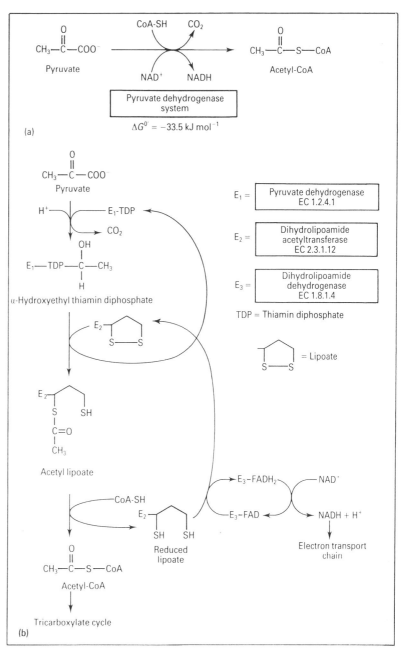

from fatty acid oxidation (Section 15.3) cannot be employed to produce carbohydrate via this route. The mammalian enzyme system consists of three enzymes, located in the mitochondrial matrix. These exist as a complex of molecular weight approximately 8 million which is comprised of 20–30 molecules of pyruvate dehydrogenase, 60 molecules of dihydrolipoamide acetyltransferase and 5–6 molecules of dihydrolipoamide dehydrogenase and control enzymes depending on source. The microbial complex is different in structure. The systems employ five different coenzymes, some as prosthetic groups: thiamin diphosphate (TDP) (Figure 12.3a), lipoate (Figure 12.3b), nicotinamide adenine dinucleotide, coenzyme A and flavin adenine dinucleotide (Figure 5.3). The multienzyme complex retains the product of one reaction and transfers it to the active site of another enzyme by the movement of a flexible group. This improves catalytic efficiency by increasing the chances of

FIGURE 12.3 Structure of two coenzymes involved in the pyruvate dehydrogenase system. (a) Thiamin diphosphate (TDP). (b) Lipoate

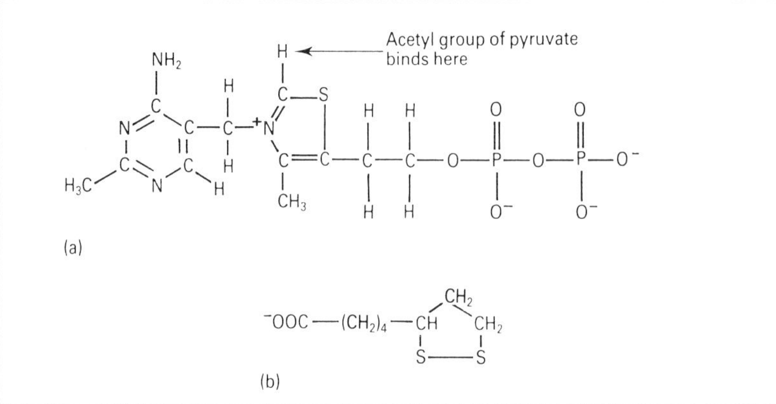

contact with the next active site and by providing immunity from other reactions. Regulation of the series of reactions is simplified since only one of the participating enzymes, i.e. pyruvate dehydrogenase, is subject to control.

Pyruvate (Figure 12.2b) is initially decarboxylated by the enzyme, pyruvate dehydrogenase, the cofactor of which is TDP. To the thiazole ring of TDP is bound a hydroxyethyl group which pyruvate dehydrogenase utilizes in the reduction and acetylation of the flexible lipoate (containing four methylene groups) prosthetic group of dihydro-lipoamide acetyltransferase. The pyruvate dehydrogenase may then repeat the process with another pyruvate molecule. Next coenzyme A accepts the acetyl group to yield reduced lipoate and acetyl-CoA. The latter may enter the tricarboxylate cycle. The remaining two stages in the mechanism relate to the oxidation of the reduced lipoate involving the FAD prosthetic group of another enzyme, dihydrolipoamide dehydrogenase which is regenerated to its oxidized state at the expense of free NAD^+. The reduced NAD may be utilized in oxidative phosphorylation.

12.4 The reactions of the tricarboxylate cycle

The acetyl groups of acetyl-CoA enter the tricarboxylate (TCA) cycle (Figure 12.4) by condensation with oxaloacetate to form citrate. The reaction, catalysed by citrate synthase, occurs in two stages: the formation of a citryl-CoA enzyme-bound intermediate which is hydrolysed to yield citrate and coenzyme A (Figure 12.5a). The cleavage of the thioester bond of citryl-CoA accounts for the high negative $\Delta G^{0'}$ value and the irreversibility of the reaction. Intracellular levels of acetyl-CoA and oxaloacetate, together with the concentrations of some cycle intermediates, modulate the activity of citrate synthase and are important influences on cycle flux.

Citrate is converted into another tricarboxylate, isocitrate, because the position of the hydroxyl group prevents its direct oxidation. Aconitate hydratase, the enzyme that catalyses this reaction, contains an iron–sulphur centre (Section 13.2) and functions by stereospecific removal of the elements of water to produce an enzyme-bound intermediate called *cis*-aconitate to which the proton and hydroxyl ion are added back to form isocitrate (Figure 12.5b). Energetically, the reaction proceeds because of coupling to citrate production.

The next reaction, catalysed by allosteric isocitrate dehydrogenase, also occurs in two stages: isocitrate is oxidized to the corresponding keto acid and then decarboxylated (Figure 12.5c). The formation of the enzyme-bound intermediate, oxalosuccinate, involves the reduction of NAD^+ and the release of a proton which is utilized in the formation of 2-oxoglutarate. During the first turn of the cycle, the C–C covalent bond of the introduced acetyl group remains intact and is retained within the structure of oxaloacetate. Subsequent turns of the cycle effect cleavage of this bond by isocitrate dehydrogenase with the loss of one

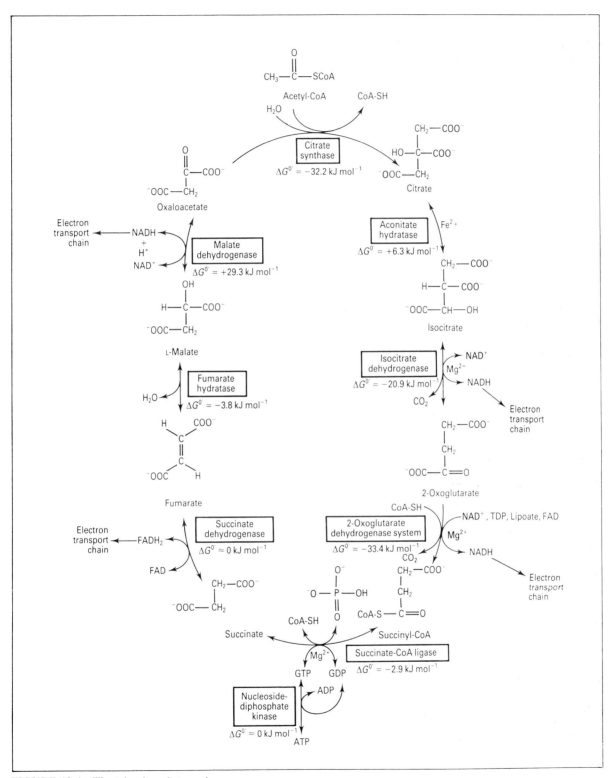

FIGURE 12.4 The tricarboxylate cycle

FIGURE 12.5   Intermediates of cycle reactions. (a) Citrate synthase reaction. (b) Aconitate hydratase reaction. (c) Isocitrate dehydrogenase reaction

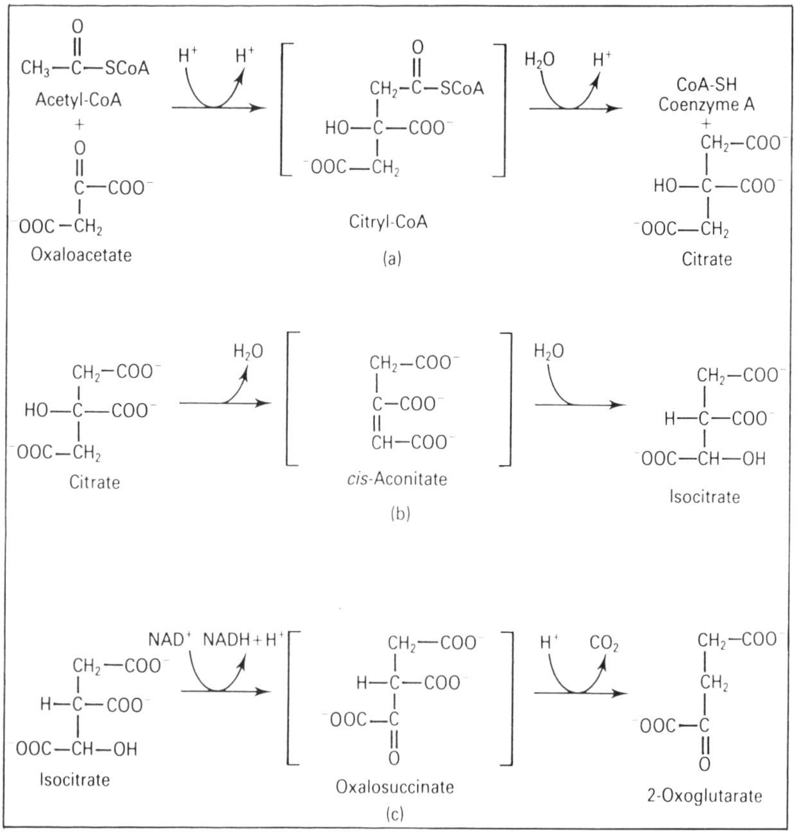

carbon atom as CO_2. There are two different enzymes called isocitrate dehydrogenase, EC 1.1.1.41 which is NAD linked and EC 1.1.1.42 which is NADP linked. The NADP-linked enzyme, the only form present in most microorganisms, can decarboxylate oxalosuccinate added to an *in vitro* assay whereas EC 1.1.1.41 cannot.

2-Oxoglutarate is also subjected to oxidative decarboxylation but not by the same mechanism as employed by isocitrate dehydrogenase. Instead, the reaction proceeds by a mechanism identical to that employed by the pyruvate dehydrogenase system. The 2-oxoglutarate dehydrogenase system, a complex of three enzymes which includes dihydrolipoamide dehydrogenase, has the same cofactor requirements. The reaction mechanism is as shown in Figure 12.2 if E_1 = oxoglutarate dehydrogenase (EC 1.2.4.2), E_2 = dihydrolipoamide succinyltransferase (EC 2.3.1.61) and formulae are modified as appropriate.

Hydrolysis of the thioester bond of succinyl-CoA would release a quantity of free energy in excess of that required for ATP synthesis. The cleavage of the bond is therefore coupled to an energy-conservation reaction. The reaction is therefore an example of substrate-level phosphorylation (Section 10.4). The excess amount of free energy is so small that the reaction is reversible. The name of the enzyme, succinate-CoA ligase, recognizes the involvement of a nucleotide in the reaction (Section 5.3). In mammalian systems, GDP is phosphorylated and the GTP formed may be readily converted into ATP by the action of nucleoside-diphosphate kinase. This reaction is not an integral part of the cycle. In the systems of some bacteria and higher plants, ADP is directly phosphorylated by a different succinate-CoA ligase.

The remainder of the cycle is concerned with the regeneration of oxaloacetate (with which acetyl groups condense in the initial reaction) from succinate. The structures of oxaloacetate and succinate are very similar (Figure 12.4). Three reactions, an oxidation, a hydration and another oxidation, are required to convert a methylene group of succinate into a carbonyl group, a fundamental biochemical principle which is seen during the pathway for the β-oxidation of fatty acids (Section 15.2).

Succinate is oxidized during a reaction catalysed

by succinate dehydrogenase (Section 6.3). The use of inhibitors of this reaction provided important information during the elucidation of the cycle. Succinate dehydrogenase differs from other tricarboxylate cycle enzymes in that it is an integral component of the inner mitochondrial membrane (Complex II, Section 13.2) and contains both a FAD as prosthetic group and iron–sulphur centres. It is imperative that FAD is the hydrogen acceptor in this reaction since the free-energy change is too small to accomplish the reduction of NAD^+. Succinate dehydrogenase provides a direct link between the cycle and the electron-transport sys-

tem. The enzyme is stereospecific and removes the hydrogen atoms from succinate to produce only the *trans* isomer, fumarate.

During the next reaction, fumarate is hydrated by another stereospecific enzyme, fumarate hydratase, to form L-malate which is oxidized to oxaloacetate by an NAD^+-linked malate dehydrogenase (EC 1.1.1.37). Although the $\Delta G^{0\prime}$ value implies that the reverse reaction is thermodynamically more favourable, oxaloacetate formation is promoted by its role in the highly exergonic initial reaction of the cycle.

12.5 The energetics of the cycle

Degradation of glucose to pyruvate is accompanied by a standard free-energy change of $-171.5\,kJ\,mol^{-1}$ of which $61\,kJ\,mol^{-1}$ is conserved as ATP. Under standard conditions, complete oxidation of glucose to CO_2 and H_2O through aerobic glycolysis, the tricarboxylate cycle and oxidative phosphorylation releases $2870\,kJ\,mol^{-1}$. Approximately 94% of the energy contained within the chemical bonds of glucose is retained within the pyruvate molecule as it gains access to the mitochondrion for oxidation. The potential for energy conservation is indeed high! However, within the tricarboxylate cycle, only one substrate-level phosphorylation occurs (succinate-CoA ligase).

A vast amount of the energy resides within the reduced coenzymes generated during the oxidation reactions involving isocitrate dehydrogenase, the 2-oxoglutarate dehydrogenase system, succinate dehydrogenase and malate dehydrogenase. The pyruvate dehydrogenase system and the glycolytic glyceraldehyde-3-phosphate dehydrogenase also contribute to the mitochondrial pool of reduced coenzymes. Electrons are transferred to the electron-transport assemblies of the inner mitochondrial membrane and a proportion of the energy released during their transfer across the redox carriers is conserved during oxidative phosphorylation (Chapter 13). The net energy production during aerobic degradation of pyruvate and glucose is shown in Table 12.1.

TABLE 12.1   The net yield of ATP during complete oxidation of pyruvate and glucose

Location	Reaction sequence	Product	ATP yield per pyruvate	ATP yield per glucose	
				In liver, kidney, cardiac muscle	In skeletal muscle, brain
Mitochondrion	Tricarboxylate cycle	1 GTP	1	2	2
		3 NADH*	9	18	18
		1 FADH†	2	4	4
	Pyruvate dehydrogenase system	1 NADH	3	6	6
Cytosol	Glycolysis	2 ATP	—	2	2
		2 NADH‡	—	6‡	4‡
Total	—	—	15	38	36

* Each NADH on delivery of its electrons to the beginning of the electron-transport chain produces three ATP through oxidative phosphorylation
† Each $FADH_2$ of complex II of the electron-transport chain produces two ATP through oxidative phosphorylation
‡ Each NADH produced in the cytosol must circumvent the permeability barrier of the inner mitochondrial membrane by the use of shuttle mechanisms (Section 11.3). The malate–aspartate shuttle yields mitochondrial NADH capable of producing three ATP whereas each $FADH_2$ produced by the glycerol-phosphate shuttle provides only two ATP

Each pyruvate molecule will ultimately produce 15 molecules of ATP. Since every glucose molecule is degraded to two molecules of pyruvate, the mitochondrial processes listed account for 30 ATP per glucose molecule. Glycolysis contributes two ATP but, under aerobic conditions, reduced coenzymes participate in oxidative phosphorylation to produce another four or six ATP per glucose molecule depending upon their mode of entry into the mitochondrion. The complete oxidation of glucose 6-phosphate produced during glycogenolysis (Section 11.10) by skeletal muscle cells will yield 37 ATP since only one priming phosphorylation reaction is necessary (Section 11.2). A simple calculation

$$\frac{\text{Energy conserved}}{\text{Energy available}} = \frac{38 \times 30.5 \text{ kJ mol}^{-1}}{2870 \text{ kJ mol}^{-1}}$$

$$= \frac{1159}{2870} = 0.404$$

reveals that approximately 40% of the available energy contained within the glucose molecule is conserved as ATP or GTP.

12.6 Anaplerosis

The tricarboxylate cycle is not concerned only with catabolism but may provide precursors for biosynthetic processes (Section 12.1). These functions infer that certain intermediates are withdrawn from the pool of cycle metabolites. To maintain the operation of the cycle, lost intermediates must be replaced. In addition, fluctuations in intracellular conditions may demand enhanced cycle activity which requires the augmentation of the concentrations of intermediates. The process of 'filling up' the pool of cycle intermediates is called, from appropriate Greek roots, anaplerosis. Because of the importance of oxaloacetate in the entry of acetyl groups into the cycle, the major anaplerotic reactions or pathways will ultimately yield oxaloacetate. Figure 12.6 sketches a network of possible reactions.

In mammalian tissues, excluding muscle, the most important anaplerotic reaction employs pyruvate carboxylase which contains a biotin prosthetic group (Figure 5.3b) responsible for the transfer of a carboxyl group. ATP provides the energy to bond covalently the carboxyl group from HCO_3^- to the biotin which transfers it when pyruvate binds to the enzyme. In muscle cells, the major pathway utilizes phosphoenolpyruvate and phosphoenolpyruvate carboxykinase which occurs both in the cytosol and mitochondrial matrix. Two routes are therefore possible in oxaloacetate synthesis: (i) as shown in Figure 12.6 or (ii) phosphoenolpyruvate may traverse the inner membrane and form oxaloacetate by the action of the mitochondrial enzyme.

In plants and bacteria, an enzyme not found in animal tissues, phosphoenolpyruvate carboxylase, may convert phosphoenolpyruvate into oxaloacetate without the requirement of a nucleoside triphosphate or biotin. The enzyme also has an important role in photosynthesis (Section 14.5).

Oxaloacetate may also be produced by amino transfer reactions involving aspartate or indirectly from pyruvate through the concerted action of two malate dehydrogenase enzymes, EC 1.1.1.40 and EC 1.1.1.37. However, the amino transfer reaction is not anaplerotic since it does not accomplish net synthesis of a tricarboxylate cycle intermediate as it employs 2-oxoglutarate. Some glucogenic amino acids (Table 16.4) may contribute to anaplerosis (Section 16.3).

Anaplerotic reactions may also be employed in anabolic functions. Through their reversal, tricarboxylate cycle intermediates may serve as precursors of glucose (Section 11.6). This function is demonstrated in certain species of plants and microorganisms which utilize the glyoxylate cycle (Section 12.8) in the synthesis of carbohydrate from acetyl-CoA produced by the β-oxidation of fatty acids.

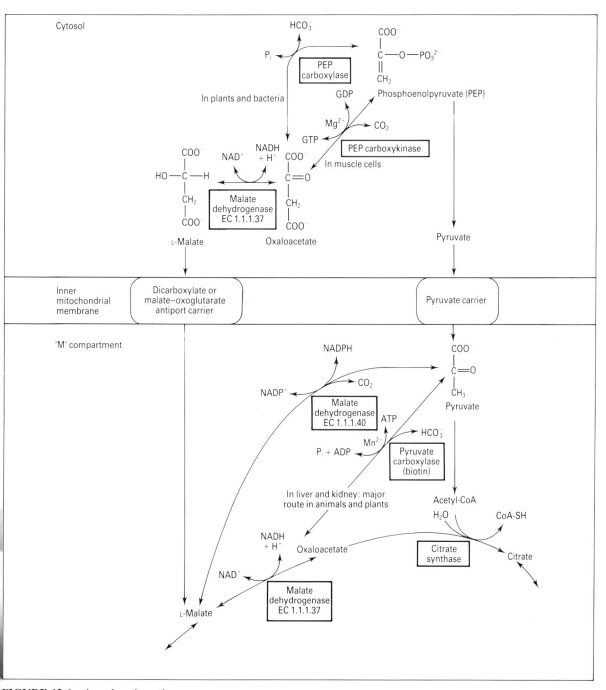

FIGURE 12.6 Anaplerotic pathways

12.7 The regulation of the cycle

The tricarboxylate cycle is regulated in accordance with its function as a supplier of reduced coenzymes for oxidative phosphorylation. The availability of acetyl-CoA is in part controlled by factors modulating the activity of the pyruvate dehydrogenase system which is an important control point in metabolism. The activity of pyruvate dehydrogenase is regulated through an interconversion cycle (Section 10.6) involving pyruvate dehydrogenase kinase and pyruvate dehydrogenase phosphatase which are associated with the enzyme complex. When [ATP] is high, kinase-mediated phosphorylation of the pyruvate dehydrogenase diminishes acetyl-CoA production and consequently ATP production. When [ADP] is high and pyruvate is available, pyruvate dehydrogenase phosphate is dephosphorylated by the specific phosphatase to render the pyruvate dehydrogenase active. Acetyl-CoA and NADH inhibit the reaction by regulation of the activity of the kinase and phosphatase which in turn regulate pyruvate dehydrogenase activity. Since acetyl-CoA requires oxaloacetate for the condensation reaction, acetyl-CoA promotes anaplerosis by acting as a positive effector of pyruvate carboxylase (Section 11.11).

The major factor in the regulation of the cycle flux is the [NAD$^+$]/[NADH] ratio: the [ATP]/[ADP] ratio is apparently less important because mitochondrial ratios exhibit little fluctuation. High NADH concentrations allosterically inhibit three cycle enzymes: citrate synthase, isocitrate dehydrogenase and 2-oxoglutarate dehydrogenase system. Isocitrate dehydrogenase may also be significantly regulated by [ATP]/[ADP] ratios. Cycle intermediates may also effect control on the activity of cycle enzymes. Succinyl-CoA demonstrates product inhibition on the 2-oxoglutarate dehydrogenase system and inhibits citrate synthase. Oxaloacetate inhibits succinate dehydrogenase. Tricarboxylate cycle intermediates may influence the flux of other pathways, e.g. the glycolytic enzymes 6-phosphofructokinase and pyruvate kinase are inhibited by citrate and succinyl-CoA respectively.

Intramitochondrial Ca^{2+} levels are also considered to be important in the regulation of the tricarboxylate cycle. Pyruvate dehydrogenase is activated by increasing Ca^{2+} concentrations through the effect of the ion on the regulatory phosphatase. Isocitrate dehydrogenase (NAD$^+$) and oxoglutarate dehydrogenase are stimulated more directly by Ca^{2+} ions.

12.8 The glyoxylate cycle

In certain species of plants and microorganisms, acetyl-CoA may serve as the substrate of another cycle called the glyoxylate cycle. The glyoxylate cycle is particularly important in species which synthesize carbohydrates from two-carbon substrates, such as ethanol or acetate, and in germinating plant seeds which must synthesize their carbohydrates from stored triacylglycerols.

The main purpose of the glyoxylate cycle (Figure 12.7) which is located in glyoxysomes of plants is the synthesis of succinate from which carbohydrate may be produced. The reaction sequence utilizes organelle-specific isoenzymes of three enzymes of the tricarboxylate cycle: citrate synthase, aconitate hydratase and malate dehydrogenase. These enzymes together with two enzymes unique to organisms capable of growth on two-carbon substrates, isocitrate lyase and malate synthase, constitute the cycle. The glyoxylate cycle may be considered as circumventing the oxidative decarboxylation stages of the tricarboxylate cycle (Figure 12.4) to produce succinate and glyoxylate, the latter progressing through reactions analogous with the tricarboxylate cycle.

Succinate leaves the glyoxysome and enters the mitochondrial matrix where it is converted to malate by enzymes of the tricarboxylate cycle. Malate may traverse the inner membrane to the cytosol where it is converted to glucose by gluconeogenesis (Section 11.7).

In lipid-storing plants, acetyl-CoA is produced by the oxidation of fatty acids. The enzymes of the

FIGURE 12.7   The glyoxylate cycle

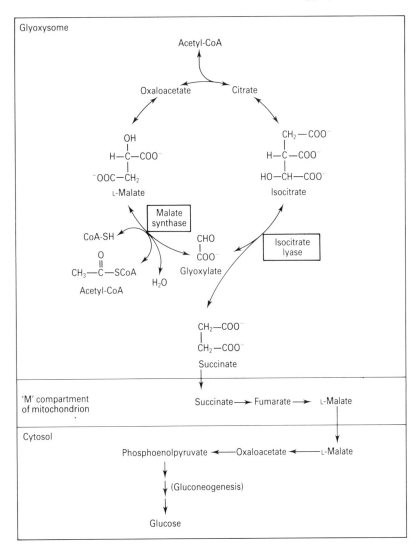

β-oxidation pathway also occur within the glyoxy-some so that acetyl-CoA production is directly linked to the glyoxylate cycle. Such species of plants are capable of converting fat to carbohy-drate in appreciable amounts.

Suggested further reading

LOWENSTEIN, J. M. (ed.) (1969). *Citric Acid Cycle: Control and Compartmentalisation*, Dekker, New York

KAY, J. and WEITZMAN, P. D. J. (eds) (1987) *Krebs' Citric Acid Cycle – Half a Century and Still Turning*, Biochemical Society, Colchester

CHAPTER 13

Mitochondrial oxidative phosphorylation

13.1 The role of oxidative phosphorylation

In the complete oxidation of fuel molecules relatively little ATP is produced directly by substrate-level phosphorylation (Section 12.5). Irrespective of the metabolic fuel (carbohydrates, fatty acids or amino acids), most of the ATP is derived from the electrons released on the reoxidation of coenzymes, NADH or $FADH_2$. During dehydrogenase-catalysed reactions, electrons are removed from substrates and transferred to coenzymic acceptors which in turn deliver the electrons to an organization of numerous proteins, called an electron-transport assembly. These assemblies are located in the inner membrane of mitochondria, in chloroplast thylakoids (Section 9.5) or in the plasma membrane of bacteria. Electrons are passed along the assembly to molecular oxygen, the final acceptor, which is reduced in the presence of protons to water. During their transfer from component to component, a portion of their energy is released and may be conserved by utilization in the phosphorylation of ADP. The reoxidation of the coenzymes by energy-yielding oxidation–reduction (redox) reactions is thus coupled to the phosphorylation of ADP and the overall process is called oxidative phosphorylation.

The role of the electron-transport assemblies is the resynthesis of ATP following its utilization in energy-dependent activities. Consider the daily energy requirements of a 70 kg man in a sedentary occupation to be approximately 10 000 kJ. The standard free energy of hydrolysis, $\Delta G^{0'}$, of MgATP is estimated as $-30.5\,kJ\,mol^{-1}$. Thus this individual hydrolyses the equivalent of about 328 mol or 165 kg of ATP per day whilst his body contains only approximately 50 g of ATP. This calculation suggests that each molecule of ATP is synthesized and hydrolysed over 3000 times each day to provide energy for this individual's activities.

13.2 The structure of electron-transport assemblies

The electron-transport assembly consists of two coupled systems: an electron-transport chain and a system for ADP phosphorylation. By the treatment of the inner mitochondrial membrane with detergents, the hydrophobic protein–protein and protein–lipid interactions may be disrupted and the assembly proteins released from the membrane. The most useful agents have proved to be deoxycholate or cholate which decrease the hydrophobic interactions responsible for the integrity of the membrane. The carboxylate groups of these bile acids (Section 8.10) bestow negative charges on the proteins which create charge repulsions causing the membrane proteins to be released and solubilized in the aqueous environment. The procedural conditions are selected so that the proteins are released without affecting the internal structure of protein complexes. Low concentrations of deoxycholate can solubilize four protein complexes which may be separated by further procedures. A fifth complex is released by a higher deoxycholate concentration in conjunction with salt fractionation.

Each complex (Table 13.1) exhibits a specific enzyme activity. The mitochondrial oxidative phos-phorylation system is composed of these five complexes plus ubiquinone (also called Q) and cytochrome c. Complex V contains the active site for ADP phosphorylation; the others transport electrons and constitute the respiratory chain. FMN and FAD (Figure 5.3e) are the prosthetic groups of NADH dehydrogenase and succinate

TABLE 13.1 The composition of the protein complexes of the electron-transport assemblies of bovine heart mitochondria

Complex	Enzymic function	Electron-transfer components	No. of different polypeptide chains
I	NADH dehydrogenase (ubiquinone)	FMN, 8 FeS*	25
II	Succinate dehydrogenase (uniquinone)	FAD, cytochrome b_{560} 3 FeS, 1 QP†	4
III	Ubiquinol-cytochrome-c reductase	Cytochrome b_{562} Cytochrome b_{566} Cytochrome c_1 1 FeS$_R$‡	10
IV	Cytochrome-c oxidase	Cytochrome a Cytochrome a_3	>11
V	H$^+$-transporting ATP synthase	—	>18

* FeS = iron–sulphur centre
† QP = a specific ubiquinone apoprotein which is required for the binding of ubiquinone
‡ FeS$_R$ = Rieske iron–sulphur binuclear centre, named after its discoverer

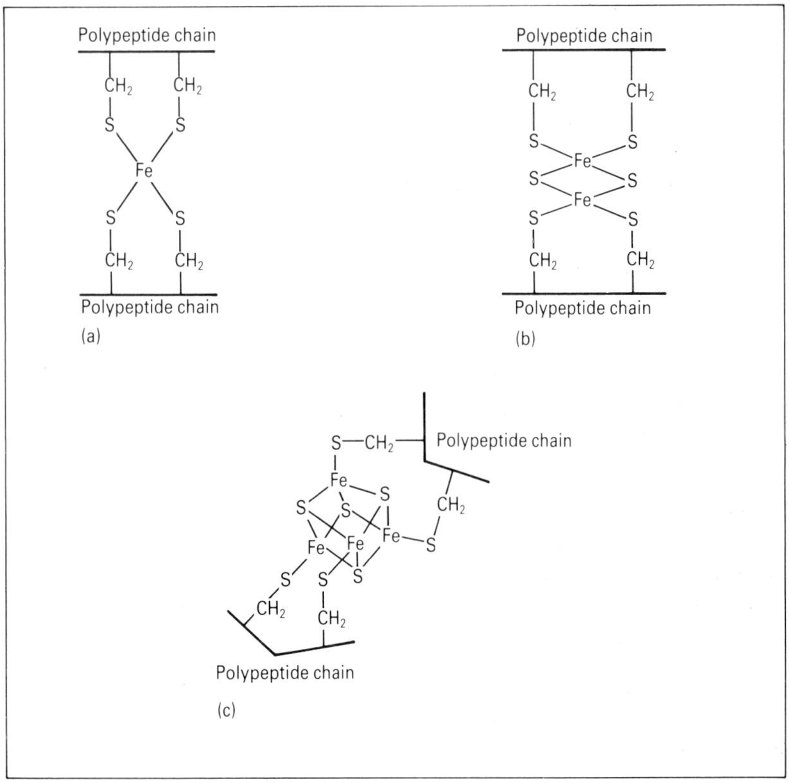

FIGURE 13.1 Iron–sulphur centres. (a) Mononuclear. (b) Binuclear (2Fe-2S). (c) Tetranuclear (4Fe-4S)

dehydrogenase respectively. Complexes I–IV contain iron atoms. In proteins iron may complex with sulphur atoms to form iron–sulphur (FeS) centres. Three types of FeS centres are known (Figure 13.1). A mononuclear centre may be formed by a single iron atom coordinating with the sulphur atoms of four cysteine residues of the FeS protein. A binuclear centre, denoted by 2Fe-2S, contains two iron atoms coordinated with two inorganic and four cysteine sulphur atoms. A tetranuclear centre contains four iron atoms, four inorganic and four cysteine sulphur atoms. The iron atom may exist in the ferrous or ferric state. Complex I contains five binuclear and three tetranuclear centres, Complex II contains two binuclear and one tetranuclear centre and Complex III has one binuclear centre. However, intermediate forms, e.g. 3Fe-4S, may be produced during electron transport.

Alternatively, iron may be complexed as haem, the prosthetic group of the electron-transporting proteins called cytochromes. The structure of the haem of cytochromes b, c and c_1 is identical to that of myoglobin and haemoglobin (Figure 4.15a) but different from cytochrome a in which the substituents at positions 2 and 8 are an isoprenoid chain and a formyl group respectively. The various forms of cytochrome b are denoted by the wavelength of their spectrophotometric absorption maxima when in the reduced state. Complex IV, however, contains two identical haems, called a and a_3, to signify differences in their bonding to the protein. Closely associated physically and functionally with each haem is one copper atom, designated Cu_a or Cu_{a3}, which play an important role in the reduction of molecular oxygen (Section 13.4).

Electron transport operates by sequential oxidation–reduction reactions involving FAD, FMN, ubiquinone (Figure 8.7b), iron–sulphur centres, haems and protein-bound copper atoms. However, each enzyme can only catalyse the transfer of electrons between specific carriers so that electron transport is a highly ordered event with carriers organized in a defined order within the complexes which are precisely positioned within the membrane.

13.3 Oxidation–reduction reactions

The electron-transport system is a series of coupled oxidation–reduction (also called redox) reactions which transfer electrons to molecular oxygen. Carrier 1 (Figure 13.2) in its oxidized form may accept electrons which reduce it. In the reduced state, it may donate the electrons to the oxidized form of carrier 2. In the process of the transfer, carrier 1 becomes reoxidized as carrier 2 becomes reduced. Similarly, reduced carrier 2 may donate electrons to carrier 3 and so on. In each reaction, the electron donor can only release the electrons if there is a suitable acceptor. The electron donor is termed the reductant since it reduces the acceptor and the electron acceptor is termed the oxidant since it oxidizes the donor. In the electron-transport system, each electron carrier oscillates between oxidized and reduced forms which constitute a redox couple.

Electrons can be transferred in various ways. Single electrons may directly reduce transition metals such as Fe^{3+} (ferric ion) to Fe^{2+} (ferrous ion) or Cu^{2+} (cupric ion) to Cu^+ (cuprous ion). Hydrogen atoms and hydride ions (H^-) may serve

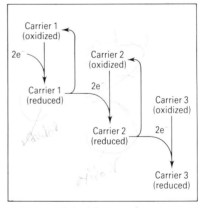

FIGURE 13.2   Nature of oxidation–reduction reactions

as vehicles for electron donation. Since hydrogen atoms contain a single electron, the transfer of a hydrogen atom effects electron transfer. Hydride ions are composed of a hydrogen atom plus an additional electron, therefore its transfer translocates two electrons. The reduction of NAD^+

(Figure 5.3a) involves a hydride ion.

Electron donors and acceptors differ in the efficiency with which they donate or accept electrons. Their ability to transfer electrons is expressed as the standard oxidation–reduction potential (or standard redox potential) denoted by E_0 which is a constant for a redox couple dependent upon temperature, pH and the concentration of the oxidized and reduced species. The measurement of the standard redox potential of redox couples has been by three methods: a spectrophotometric method, a potentiometric method and electron spin resonance. By convention, standard redox potentials (Table 13.2) refer to reactions recorded as oxidant + electron(s)→reductant. Electrons flow from couples of higher potential to those of lower potential in an attempt to equalize the two potentials, a phenomenon termed the electron motive force which is measured in volts (or millivolts). These data are not absolute values since measurements of free carriers differ from that of bound carriers, e.g. FeS_{S-3} exhibits an apparent E'_0

of $+65\,mV$ in Complex II but of $+120\,mV$ in intact mitochondria.

The actual redox potential of any couple may be calculated from the standard redox potential and the concentrations of the oxidized and reduced species. The relationship is given in one form of the Nernst equation:

$$E' = E'_0 + \frac{RT}{nF} \ln \frac{[\text{oxidized species}]}{[\text{reduced species}]}$$

where E' = actual redox potential at pH 7.0, E'_0 = standard redox potential, R = the gas constant = 8.3 J deg^{-1} mol^{-1}, T = the absolute temperature in degrees Kelvin, n = number of electrons transferred, F = the Faraday = 96 500 J V^{-1} and ln = natural logarithm. At 25°C, the equation reduces to

$$E' = E'_0 + \frac{59}{n} \log \frac{[\text{oxidized species}]}{[\text{reduced species}]}$$

when E' and E'_0 are expressed in millivolts.

TABLE 13.2 The estimated standard redox potentials of the respiratory chain carriers

Complex	Carrier	E'_0 (mV)*
	Reference: $2H^+ + 2e^- \rightarrow H_2$	−420
	NAD$^+$	−320
I	FMN	?
	FeS_{N-1a}	−370
	FeS_{N-1b}	−245
	FeS_{N-2}	−20
	FeS_{N-3}	−245
	FeS_{N-4}	−245
	FeS_{N-5}	−270
II	FAD	−180
	Cytochrome b_{560}	−80
	FeS_{S-1}	0
	FeS_{S-2}	−260
	FeS_{S-3}	+65
	Ubiquinone	+65
III	Cytochrome b_{562}	+30
	Cytochrome b_{566}	−30
	FeS_R	+280
	Cytochrome c_1	+230
	Cytochrome c	+230
IV	Cytochrome a	+250
	Cytochrome a_3	+385
	O_2	+820
* Determined at 25°C and pH 7.0		

13.4 The sequence of electron-transport carriers

The sequence of the carriers in the respiratory chain has been deduced from their redox potentials, the use of inhibitors of electron transport (Section 13.7) and enzyme specificities. Since electrons normally flow from more electronegative to more electropositive values, the standard redox potentials of the carriers should become progressively more positive towards oxygen. Figure 13.3 shows the established order of the complexes but within some complexes the order of carrier participation requires elucidation.

NADH, derived from dehydrogenase-catalysed reactions, reduces the FeS centres of Complex I within 10 ms. The carrier sequence including the position of FMN is uncertain. It is considered that FMN interacts with FeS_{N-3} and FeS_{N-2} which reduces ubiquinone to ubiquinol. The reduction of ubiquinone is accompanied by the translocation of at least one proton which appears to involve the FeS centres. Speculation on this event has centred on FeS_{N-2} but controversial centres N-1a and N-5 cannot be discounted.

Complex II transports electrons from succinate (tricarboxylate cycle intermediate) to ubiquinone. Again the roles of the FeS centres are uncertain as is that of cytochrome b_{560}. Complex III catalyses electron transfer from ubiquinol to cytochrome c. The mechanism of Complex III is believed to involve a branching of electron transport in which ubiquinol donates one electron to cytochrome c_1 through FeS_R whilst a second electron cycles through cytochrome b_{566}, cytochrome b_{562} and back to ubiquinol. The branch route is coupled to the translocation of two protons by a mechanism which requires clarification. Cytochrome c_1 transfers electrons to cytochrome c.

Complex IV accepts electrons from cytochrome c and catalyses the reduction of molecular oxygen by four electrons in the presence of four protons. The primary acceptor of the electrons is haem a which appears to be in equilibrium with Cu_a so that Cu_a receives the electron. The electrons are passed to haem a_3 and Cu_{a3} which are the sites of oxygen reduction. The mechanism of oxygen

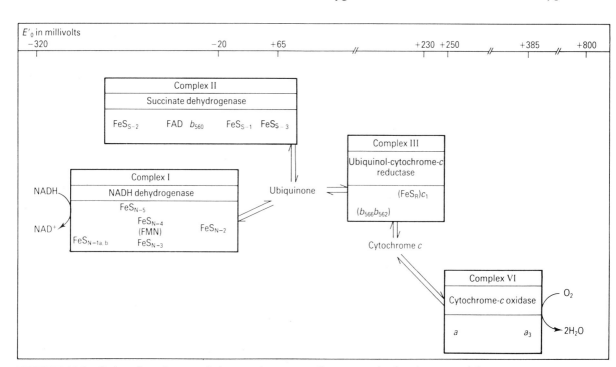

FIGURE 13.3   Order of respiratory chain complexes according to standard redox potentials

reduction is complex involving two-electron and one-electron transfers and remains to be elucidated. It is believed that O_2 reduction is initiated by a two-electron reduction to yield a peroxide intermediate

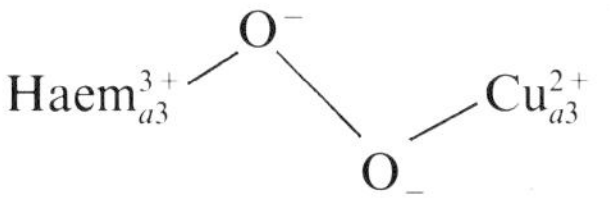

$$Haem_{a3}^{3+} \diagdown \overset{O^-}{\underset{O_-}{}} \diagup Cu_{a3}^{2+}$$

of a catalytic cycle in which further reductions yield two molecules of water.

Electron transfer by cytochrome-c oxidase is associated with a proton-translocation activity which is believed to reside within polypeptide chain III. Therefore, as electrons are transferred by oxidation–reduction reactions in Complexes I, III and IV, migration of protons is induced, events of major significance (Section 13.6).

13.5 The synthesis of ATP

The flow of electrons along the respiratory chain is driven by the reduction in the potential energy which occurs within the electron cloud of each carrier and results in the release of small amounts of free energy. The magnitude of the energy release is dependent upon the difference in the standard redox potentials $\Delta E_0'$, between the two redox couples as exemplified across the respiratory chain in Figure 13.4.

The accompanying changes in free energy between members of the respiratory chain may be similarly calculated. Since under standard conditions, the hydrolysis of ATP yields $30.5\,kJ\,mol^{-1}$, its synthesis from ADP may be considered as requiring $30.5\,kJ\,mol^{-1}$. Therefore, the free-energy changes associated with electron transfer in Complexes I, III and IV are sufficient to enable ATP

synthesis. Free-energy changes between other carriers, e.g. cytochrome c and cytochrome a, are, however, too small to support ADP phosphorylation and this energy is dissipated as heat.

Since 1941, it has been recognized that the consumption of O_2 by aerobic cells is linked to the synthesis of ATP from ADP and orthophosphate. The relationship between phosphate and oxygen consumption has been expressed as the P/O ratio which is defined as the number of molecules of phosphate incorporated into ATP per atom of oxygen utilized. The P/O ratio of the oxidation of NADH derived from dehydrogenase-catalysed reactions by electron transport was interpreted as 3. From this figure, it was deduced that there are three sites of ATP synthesis. The first site was determined to lie between NADH and ubiquinone

FIGURE 13.4 Change in free energy during electron transport over the entire respiratory chain

The change in standard redox potential can be calculated from the equation:

$$\Delta E_0' = E_0' \text{ (electron acceptor)} - E_0' \text{ (electron donor)}$$

For the entire respiratory chain, the acceptor is O_2 and the donor is NADH.

$$\Delta E_0' = +820 - (-320)\,mV \qquad \text{(from Table 15.2)}$$
$$= +1140\,mV$$

The change in standard free energy in a redox reaction is given by the equation:

$$\Delta G^{0'} = -nF\Delta E_0'$$

where $\Delta G^{0'}$ = the standard free energy change in $J\,mol^{-1}$
n = number of electrons transferred
F = the Faraday = $96\,500\,J\,V^{-1}$
$\Delta E_0'$ = change in redox potential in $mV\,mol^{-1}$
$\Delta G^{0'} = -2 \times 96.5 \times 1140\,J\,mV^{-1}\,mV\,mol^{-1}$
$= -220\,020\,J\,mol^{-1} = \underline{-220\,kJ\,mol^{-1}}$

on the basis that the P/O ratio for the oxidation of succinate was 2. Electrons from succinate are passed to ubiquinone and thus bypass the first site of ATP synthesis. The oxidation of substrates by FAD-linked dehydrogenases permit the synthesis of only two ATP. The early observations correlate with the sites of proton translocation identified within the isolated complexes (Section 13.4).

ATP is synthesized by H^+-transporting ATP synthase located in Complex V. The mitochondrial enzyme (Figure 13.5) is composed of at least 18 distinct polypeptides constituting three regions: the catalytic region called F_1, the membrane region called F_o because in prokaryotes this region binds the antibiotic oligomycin, and an interconnecting stalk of two polypeptides, the oligomycin-sensitivity-conferring protein (OSCP) and coupling factor 6 which is necessary for the binding of F_1 to F_o.

The F_1 region contains at least two, possibly three, catalytic sites for the synthesis of ATP. The catalytic sites exhibit cooperativity in that the binding of substrates to the second site substan-tially enhances enzymic activity. The synthesis of ATP from enzyme-bound ADP and orthophos-phate is considered not to require energy. The energy-requiring steps are the binding of the sub-strates and the release of the product. The delivery of the necessary energy is considered in Section 13.6.

Most ATP-requiring reactions occur in the cyto-sol and produce ADP and orthophosphate. Since most ATP is formed by mitochondrial oxidative phosphorylation (in appropriate cells) from ADP and orthophosphate, these molecules must traverse the inner membrane. ATP and ADP are translo-cated by the specific adenine-nucleotide-transport system. This antiport system is widely distributed in the membrane and exchanges one mitochondrial ATP for one cytoplasmic ADP. The carrier selecti-vely binds and transports ADP inwards and ATP outwards. The phosphate enters the mitochondrion via a different antiport system, the phosphate car-rier, which exchanges it for a hydroxyl ion.

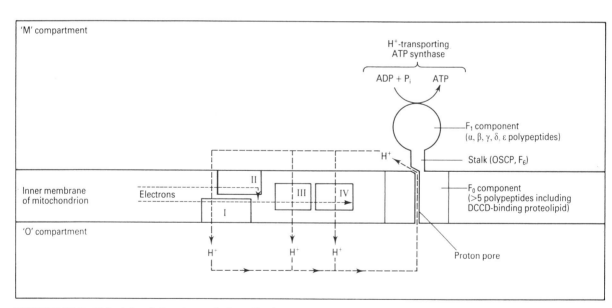

FIGURE 13.5   Principle of chemiosmotic hypothesis

13.6 Mechanisms of coupling electron transport to ATP synthesis

Much investigative effort has been directed towards the elucidation of the coupling of the two aspects of oxidative phosphorylation. Historically, three mechanisms have been proposed: the chemical coupling hypothesis, the chemiosmotic hypothesis and conformational coupling hypothesis. The chemical coupling hypothesis (1953) was modelled on the glycolytic oxidation of glyceraldehyde 3-phosphate to 3-phosphoglycerate (Section 11.2) but it is generally accepted that this hypothesis is incorrect.

The conformational coupling hypothesis (1974) proposed that the free energy released from electrons during transport induced conformational change in the enzyme mediated by certain membrane proteins, to enhance its affinity for substrates. Appositely positioned substrates readily undergo dehydration to form ATP which remains enzyme-bound until pertinent energy-induced conformational change promotes its release. However, the membrane proteins remain unidentified.

The chemiosmotic hypothesis (1961) is currently favoured (Figure 13.5), although recently elements of the conformational coupling hypothesis have been incorporated. The hypothesis proposes that electron transport ejects protons from the mitochondrial matrix into the 'O' compartment where an increasing proton concentration causes a decrease in pH. Since the inner membrane is impermeable to protons, a gradient of protons is established across the membrane. The protons attempt to flow back across the membrane to equilibrate their concentrations on both sides, a phenomenon termed proton motive force by analogy to electron motive force (Section 13.3). It is believed that a specific proton pore exists in the F_o part of the ATP synthase (hence the name, H^+-transporting ATP synthase) which provides access from the 'O' compartment to the 'M' compartment. The proton motive force drives protons through the enzyme structure with a concomitant release of free energy which is utilized in the binding of substrates and subsequent release of ATP from the active site (Section 13.5).

The strength of any hypothesis depends upon its accurate description through experimental evidence. Supportive evidence for the chemiosmotic hypothesis is now considered. The proton motive force may be calculated from the following equation:

$$\Delta p = E_m - 2.3 \frac{RT}{F} {}^i\Delta^o pH$$

where Δp = proton motive force in volts, E_m = membrane potential in volts, R = the gas constant, T = the absolute temperature in degrees Kelvin, F = the Faraday and ${}^i\Delta^o pH$ = the difference in pH from the inside of the membrane to its outside. The equation reduces to:

$$\Delta p = E_m - 59 \, {}^i\Delta^o pH$$

when expressed in millivolts. Note that Δp and E_m are negative values. Experimental investigations have revealed that electron transport may generate a ${}^i\Delta^o pH$ of approximately 1.4 units and a E_m of -140 mV. The proton motive force generated (-223 mV) is sufficient to account for the synthesis of three ATP. Also, appropriate sites for proton translocation have been identified in the respiratory chain (Section 13.4).

Oxidative phosphorylation relies upon an intact inner membrane and a complete proton circuit. Although electron transport may proceed in damaged or modified membranes, the capacity for ATP synthesis may be destroyed. Membranes perforated by detergents permit leakage of protons into the matrix which abolishes both the gradient and ATP formation. Uncouplers and certain ionophores produce similar effects (Section 13.7). Certain agents, such as NN'-dicyclohexylcarbodiimide (DCCD) and oligomycin, are believed to block the proton pore and thereby destroy the continuity of the circuit with the result that ATP formation is prevented. In addition, the affinity of the enzyme for ATP is reduced in the presence of either agent. It has been suggested that conformational changes induced by their binding to F_o are transmitted to the active sites in the F_1. On this basis, it has been proposed that the proton flow causes protonation of key amino acid residues with concomitant conformational changes in F_o which are relayed to the active sites to displace bound ATP.

13.7 Inhibitors of oxidative phosphorylation

Oxidative phosphorylation may be inhibited at different stages by a variety of agents (Table 13.3) which have proved invaluable in its experimental investigation. Electron transport may be inhibited at a number of locations. Rotenone and amytal abrogate ATP synthesis driven by NADH-derived electrons but that initiated by $FADH_2$ continues. The sites of action of electron-transport inhibitors were identified by the 'crossover technique' in which the carriers before the blockage become more reduced and those beyond more oxidized.

Oxidative phosphorylation may be inhibited by agents which do not impair electron transport but prevent phosphorylation by abrogation of the transmembrane proton gradient. Such agents, e.g. 2,4-dinitrophenol and carbonyl cyanide-p-trifluoromethoxyphenylhydrazone, are called uncouplers because they separate the two functional aspects of oxidative phosphorylation. Ionophores, e.g. valinomycin and nigericin, are also lipid-soluble substances which promote the transfer of cations across the membrane. They may function by insertion into the membrane to create a pore or as mobile carriers which diffuse through the membrane. Oligomycin B and DCCD inhibit oxidative phosphorylation by blocking the proton pore of the ATP synthase.

TABLE 13.3 Some inhibitors of oxidative phosphorylation

Site of inhibition	Agent	Comment
Electron transport	Rotenone | Amytal |	Prevent reduction of ubiquinone and simultaneous oxidation of Complex I FeS centres
	Antimycin A	Inhibits transfer of electron from cytochrome b_{562} to ubiquinone
	Hydrogen cyanide Hydrogen sulphide Azide	Bind to Fe^{3+} of cytochrome a and a_3
	Carbon monoxide	Binds to Fe^{2+} of cytochrome a and a_3
Inner membrane	2,4-Dinitrophenol Carbonyl cyanide- p-trifluoromethoxy- phenylhydrazone	Are anionic at pH 7.0, may protonate to become lipophilic and soluble in membrane. Protons are transported through membrane and H^+ gradient is abolished
	Valinomycin	Renders membrane permeable to K^+ which may abolish E_m
	Nigericin	Abolishes H^+ gradient by K^+-H^+ exchange
ATP synthase	Oligomycin	Binds to OSCP in stalk and blocks H^+ pore
	DCCD	Reacts with DCCD-binding proteolipid of F_0 component and blocks H^+ pore
Adenine nucleotide carrier	Atractyloside	Binds to external conformation to preclude ADP interaction
	Bongkrekic acid	Binds to internal conformation to preclude ATP interaction
Phosphate carrier	Mercurial reagents	Bind to sulphydryl groups

Suggested further reading

NICHOLLS, D. G. (1982) *Bioenergetics: An Introduction to the Chemiosmotic Theory*, Academic Press, London and
TZAGALOFF, A. (1982) *Mitochondria*, Plenum, New York

CHAPTER 14

Photosynthesis

14.1 The role of photosynthesis

Another process in which electron transport is of major importance is photosynthesis. Photosynthesis is conducted by green plants, algae and certain bacteria which utilize the electromagnetic energy of sunlight to generate ATP and NADPH. Subsequently the energy and reducing power contained within these compounds is responsible for the reduction of carbon dioxide to form carbohydrate, a process termed the fixation of carbon dioxide.

The capture of sunlight releases electrons and protons from water in green plants, algae and cyanobacteria so that oxygen is produced as a by-product. Certain sulphur bacteria utilize various sulphur substrates, e.g. H_2S, as the electron donor and therefore make no contribution to the replenishment of atmospheric oxygen.

The energy can be recovered from the carbohydrates by oxidative processes in both plants and animals. Although green parts of the plant perform photosynthesis in the presence of light, they also respire (photorespiration) but to a much lesser extent so that there is net absorption of CO_2 and net production of O_2. In darkness, the same tissues exhibit respiration, i.e. O_2 is utilized and CO_2 is released. Non-green tissues demonstrate only respiration irrespective of light intensity. Some of the carbohydrate is metabolized by the plant to provide necessary molecules, e.g. amino acids (Section 16.1). Animals obtain much of their energy by the oxygen-dependent recovery of energy from plant-derived carbohydrates (Section 12.5) so that photosynthesis performs the dual roles of energy and oxygen provider.

The annual synthesis of carbohydrate by carbon fixation performed by all photosynthetic organisms is estimated at approximately 2×10^{14} kg. Only about 0.2–0.3% of the total radiant energy reaching the surface of the earth participates in photosynthesis, the remainder being absorbed by the oceans and landmasses or reflected and emitted as heat.

14.2 The thylakoid photosystems

In plant cells, the electromagnetic energy is captured by specialized organelles called chloroplasts (Section 9.5) which are exclusive to the green tissues. The major light-absorbing and therefore colour-conferring molecules in the chloroplast thylakoid membranes (Figure 9.8) are the chlorophylls (Figure 14.1a) which like haem molecules (Figure 4.15a) are substituted tetrapyrroles. The chlorophylls, however, also contain a fifth pentanone ring. The five-membered ring is termed a phaeo-porphyrin (phaeo- indicating of plant origin) and contains an extensive conjugated bond system (Section 1.2) which permits light absorption and electronic excitation. The propionate substituent of reduced ring IV is esterified with a polyisoprenoid alcohol called phytol which is responsible for the

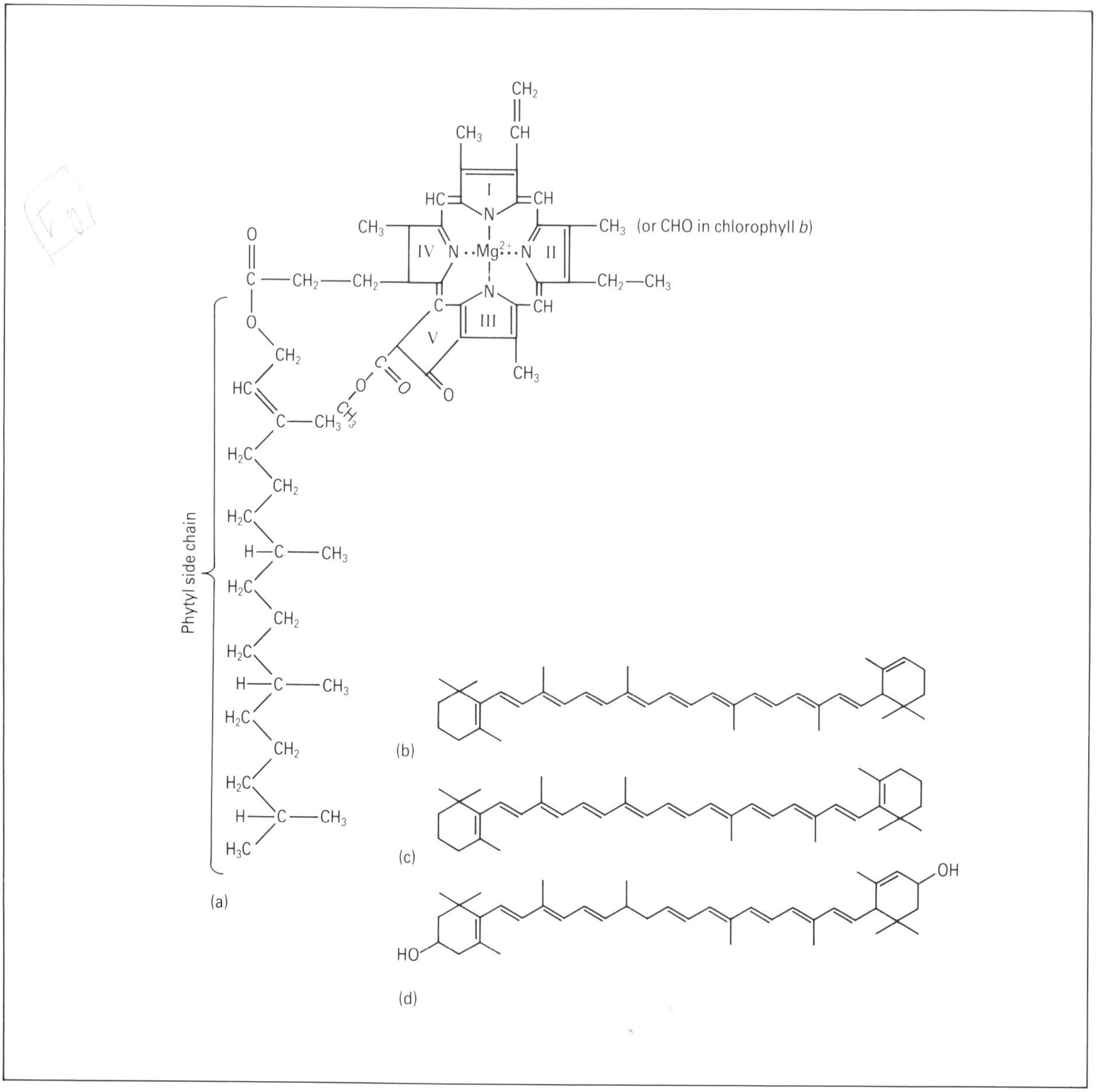

FIGURE 14.1   Structures of some components of photosystems. (a) Chlorophyll *a(b)*. (b) α-Carotene.
(c) β-Carotene. (d) Lutein

anchorage and orientation of the molecule in the membrane. The four nitrogen atoms of the tetra-pyrrole are chelated with magnesium so that chlorophyll is a magnesium porphyrin.

Two types of chlorophyll are found in higher plants, chlorophyll *a* and chlorophyll *b*, which differ in a substituent on ring II while algae contain four chlorophylls (*a, c, d, e*). Photosynthetic

bacteria contain bacteriochlorophyll *a* and *b* which are not organized within an organelle but are associated with the invaginations of the bacterial cell membrane. Different chlorophylls absorb light at different wavelengths (Figure 14.2). Chlorophyll *a* and *b* function most effectively in the blue region and the red region of the visible spectrum at wavelengths of 400–500 and 600–700 nm but weakly

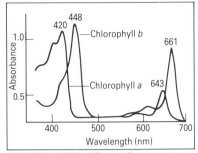

FIGURE 14.2 Absorption spectra of extracted chlorophyll *a* and chlorophyll *b*. (*Photosynthesis*, C. Foyer, © 1984 Wiley. Reprinted by permission of John Wiley and Sons, Inc.)

between 500 and 600 nm. The thylakoid membranes contain other light-absorbing molecules collectively called accessory pigments which include at least four members of the carotenoids, i.e. α- and β-carotene (Figure 14.1b, c), lutein (Figure 14.1d), violaxanthin and neoxanthin, and the phycobiliproteins.

On illumination of *Chlorella*, a green alga, at wavelengths above 680 nm at which only chlorophyll *a* may absorb light, Emerson and coworkers in 1943 observed a progressive decline in photosynthesis as measured by oxygen evolution. This phenomenon was termed the red drop effect. By the simultaneous use of additional wavelengths below 680 nm, photosynthesis was enhanced by over 30% beyond the sum of the rates obtained by separate monochromatic illumination. This observation,

termed the enhancement phenomenon, illustrates the unequal absorption of light by different photosystems. These observations led to the proposal that photosynthesis involves two photosystems (PS I and PS II), one of which may be triggered by wavelengths longer than 680 nm but both can respond to light of shorter wavelengths.

The photosystems are the major elements of light-harvesting complexes (LHC, Section 9.5) in which the chlorophylls are bound to the membrane by two anionic binding proteins; a major polypeptide may associate with both PS I and PS II and two distinct polypeptides may bind only one of the photosystems. Of the total number of chlorophyll molecules in a photosystem, a few are located in unique environments in which they trap absorbed energy and initiate photochemical activity. These traps are the reaction centres of PS I and PS II and are referred to as P_{700} and P_{680} respectively because of their absorption maxima. P_{700} contains either a single or an aggregation of two chlorophyll *a* molecules in association with a specific protein. P_{680} is similarly a monomer or dimer of chlorophyll *a* but is associated with at least two proteins.

The reaction centres participate in the photochemical reactions called the light reactions in which ATP, NADPH and oxygen are generated. The synthesis of carbohydrate involves a second series of light-independent reactions called the dark reactions which are catalysed by stromal and cytosolic enzymes but require the availability of ATP and NADPH.

14.3 The light reactions: electronic excitation

The absorption of electromagnetic energy by an atom or molecule results in electronic excitation. Each electron possesses a quantity of energy, determined by the location and speed of its normal orbit around the atomic nucleus, called its ground state. The absorption of sufficient energy causes the electron to be elevated to an orbital at a higher energy level or to accelerate within its orbit. Electromagnetic energy is contained within discrete entities called quanta or photons which oscillate in wavelike motions. According to Einstein's Law of the Photochemical Equivalent (1905), each participating molecule in a photochemical reaction

absorbs one photon which contains sufficient energy to promote electronic excitation of the absorbing molecule. Light of wavelength 661 nm is calculated to have an energy content of 180 kJ per einstein (Figure 14.3). Similar calculations show that the shorter the wavelength, the more energy contained by its photons. Absorption of the photon only occurs if its energy content is sufficient to transfer the electron to a higher energy level, otherwise the molecule is unaffected.

In their ground state, electrons frequently orbit in pairs with each member of the pair spinning in opposite directions. Upon photon-induced

FIGURE 14.3 Calculation of the amount of energy available in light of a given wavelength

The energy, ε, of each photon is related to the number of oscillations per second, called frequency, v:

ie. $\varepsilon = hv$ where h = Planck's constant = 6.63×10^{-37} kJ s

1 mol of photons is called an einstein,

$\therefore$ the energy per einstein, $E = N\varepsilon = Nhv$

where N = number of photons per einstein
= Avogadro's number = 6.02×10^{23}

Since $v = \dfrac{c}{\lambda}$ where c = the velocity of light = 3×10^{10} cm s^{-1} in a vacuum

and λ = wavelength in cm

then $E = \dfrac{Nhc}{\lambda}$

Substitute values for N, h and c:

$$E = \frac{6.02 \times 10^{23} \times 6.63 \times 10^{-37} \times 3 \times 10^{10}}{\lambda} \text{ kJ s cm s}^{-1} \text{ einstein}^{-1}$$

$$= \frac{1.19 \times 10^{-2}}{\lambda} \text{ kJ cm einstein}^{-1}$$

The energy absorbed by 1 mol of chlorophyll a at 661 nm:

$$E = \frac{1.19 \times 10^{-2} \text{ kJ cm einstein}^{-1}}{661 \times 10^{-7} \text{ cm}}$$

$$= 1.8 \times 10^{2} \text{ kJ einstein}^{-1}$$

$$E = 180 \text{ kJ einstein}^{-1} \text{ (mol}^{-1}\text{)}.$$

electronic excitation, an electron is elevated to a higher unoccupied orbital without directional change of spin (called the singlet state) or the spin may reverse to that of its former partner (called the triplet state). Within the singlet state, a number of energy levels are available and a wavelength of 430 nm raises chlorophyll electrons to a higher singlet state than a wavelength of 680 nm. Upon excitation, the electron may return to its ground state by emitting energy as light of a longer wavelength (fluorescence), heat or, through the exchange of the excited electron for one of lower energy. The last mechanism is employed to drive photosynthesis.

The photosystems contain different accessory pigments (Section 14.2), the electrons of which may respond to different wavelengths of light. As they relapse to their ground state, the energy released is transmitted to excite chlorophyll a molecules. The accessory pigments are therefore called light-harvesting or antenna molecules.

An excited electron is less influenced by the atomic nucleus than a ground state electron and is readily transferable to an acceptor molecule which is thereby reduced. The initial reaction in photosynthesis is therefore a light-dependent one-electron redox reaction (Section 13.3). To prevent the reversal of the reaction and promote the utilization of this redox energy, the phenomenon of charge separation occurs. Within 1–5 picoseconds (10^{-12} s) of the attainment of the singlet state, the organization of the components of the thylakoid membranes permits an adjacent acceptor to obtain electrons from chlorophyll a. The resultant chlorophyll cation acts as a strong oxidant that can appropriate an electron from a suitable donor and return to ground state. In the ground state, a chlorophyll a molecule donates an electron from its highest occupied low-energy orbital to a low unoccupied higher-energy orbital and so is neither a strong reductant nor a strong oxidant. In the excited state, however, electron donation occurs from a higher-energy orbital with subsequent acquisition of an electron to occupy the vacancy in the lower-energy orbital. In the excited state chlorophyll can perform both as a strong oxidant and strong reductant. These events may be summarized as:

D.Chlorophyll.A$\rightleftharpoons$D.Chlorophyll*.A
$\rightleftharpoons$D.Chlorophyll$^+$.A$^-$$\rightleftharpoons$D$^+$.Chlorophyll.A$^-$

where D = donor, chlorophyll* = excited chlorophyll and A = acceptor. The reduced acceptor

molecule (A$^-$) may rapidly transfer the electron sequentially to other membrane components which serve as electron transport carriers. Although both excited singlet and triplet states may act as electron sources for redox reactions, the reaction centres apparently utilize only the excited singlet-state electrons from antenna molecules. In plants, algae and cyanobacteria, water is the primary electron donor and the final acceptor is NADP$^+$ which is reduced to NADPH.

14.4 The light reactions: electron transport

By plotting the redox potentials of the electron carriers (Table 14.1) the pathway of the water-derived electrons may be followed. This is referred to as the Z-scheme (Figure 14.4), first proposed by Hill and Bendall in 1960. Although alternative models have been proffered the Z-scheme remains fundamental to our understanding of photosynthetic electron transport. The interaction of a photon with the reaction centre of PS II initiates a chain of redox reactions. The first recognized electron acceptor of PS II is a bound molecule of meta-stable phaeophytin a (unchelated chlorophyll a) which instantly donates the electrons to one of two protein-bound plastoquinone (Figure 8.7c) molecules which has been identified as the primary

stable electron acceptor. The flow of electrons between the plastoquinones is inhibited by the herbicides, DCMU [3-(3,4-dichlorophenyl)-1,1-dimethylurea] and atrazine, which interact with the plastoquinone-associated protein. Single electrons are transferred from the first to the second molecule of plastoquinone until the latter is fully reduced (two electrons required) to plastoquinol. From the bound plastoquinols, the electrons are collected by a pool of free plastoquinones which may be reduced by electrons from a number of reaction centres.

Because the two photosystems are segregated (Section 9.5) mobile electron carriers are believed to diffuse along the membrane from PS II to PS I.

TABLE 14.1   The estimated redox potentials of electron-transport carriers in thylakoid membranes

Carrier	E'_0 (mV)*
H_2O	+820
Mn-containing complex	N.A.†
Z	N.A.
P_{680}	N.A.
Phaeophytin	−610
Plastoquinone (bound)	N.A.
Plastoquinone (pool)	+118
Cytochrome b_6 (b_{563})	−120
Cytochrome f (c_{552})	+360
Rieske iron–sulphur centre	+290
Plastocyanin	+370
P_{700}	+450
A_0	−730
A_1	N.A.
FeS_{1-3}	−590 to −550
Ferredoxin	−430
NADPH	−320

* Determined at 25°C and pH 7.0
† N.A. = not available

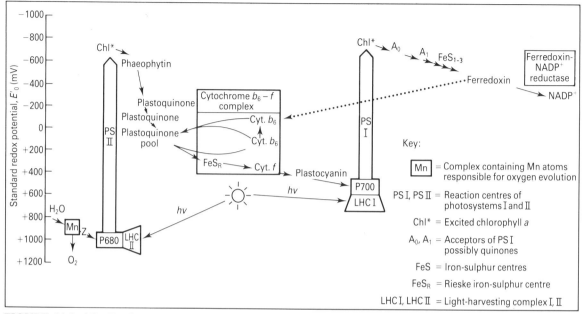

FIGURE 14.4   The Z-scheme of linear electron transport in thylakoid membranes

Hill & Bendall (1960)

This process appears to occur in two stages: the first involves the lipid-soluble free plastoquinols and the second, plastocyanin, a water-soluble copper protein. Free plastoquinols migrate to effect the reduction of a membrane cytochrome b_6–f complex which contains two cytochrome b_{563} (b_6), one cytochrome c_{552} (f) and one Rieske iron–sulphur protein. In an analogous manner to Complex III of the mitochondrial inner membrane (Section 13.4), electron transport is believed to branch, with an electron reducing the Rieske FeS centre whilst a second electron cycles back to the plastoquinone pool through cytochrome b_6. This branch route is coupled to the translocation of two protons to the intrathylakoid space. From the FeS centre, electrons proceed to cytochrome f and then to reduce the second mobile carrier, plastocyanin. Plastocyanin acts as the primary electron donor to PS I on the photon-dependent excitation of its reaction centre. The excited chlorophyll a of PS I donates its singlet-state electron to as yet unidentified acceptors which are possibly quinones. The redox electron transfers proceed through a series of tetranuclear FeS proteins (Figure 13.1) to free ferredoxin. Ferredoxin is a binuclear FeS protein which delivers the electrons for the reduction of NADP$^+$ to NADPH by the enzyme, ferredoxin–NADP$^+$ reductase.

The above process is referred to as a linear elec-

tron-transport system. In bacteria, the photosynthetic electron-transport system is cyclic. However, in plants and algae, when NADPH concentrations are high, electrons can be passed from ferredoxin to cytochrome b_6 of the cytochrome b_6–f complex and then to the plastoquinone pool. This cyclic flow may occur to some extent even during optimum conditions.

The ultimate source of electrons is water. The excitation of PS II generates a strong oxidant which may return to its ground state by the appropriation of an electron from its immediate unidentified donor called Z. Z is re-reduced by an electron derived from water which is oxidized to oxygen by a manganese-containing complex sometimes called the oxygen-evolving complex. The number of Mn atoms in this complex is uncertain, two or five to eight have been suggested. They may exist in a variety of oxidation states. The production of one molecule of oxygen requires the removal of a total of four electrons from two water molecules:

$$2H_2O \rightarrow 4H^+ + 4e^- + O_2$$

Precisely how this is achieved remains unresolved but it has been postulated that single electrons are removed sequentially as a single manganese is elevated through higher oxidation states. A pair of released electrons may reduce one molecule of Z.

The synthesis of ATP during photosynthesis, called photophosphorylation, is presently accounted for in terms of the chemiosmotic hypothesis (Section 13.6). The proton gradient is established across the thylakoid membrane by the electron-driven translocation of protons from the stroma into the intrathylakoid space. Proton translocation may be effected at three stages during electron transport: the oxygen-evolving manganese complex, the cytochrome b_6–f complex and the ferredoxin–$NADP^+$ reductase reaction. Re-entry of the protons into stroma occurs via the proton pore of H^+-transporting ATP synthase, the F_1 catalytic unit of which is located on the stromal side of the thylakoid membrane. Newly synthesized ATP is therefore released into the stroma.

14.5 The dark reactions: the Calvin cycle

Carbon dioxide is fixed by a series of light-independent reactions, called the dark reactions, which utilize the NADPH and ATP generated by light-dependent electron transport within the thylakoid membranes. The enzymes of the dark reactions reside mainly within the chloroplast stroma but it should be noted that sucrose synthesis from triose phosphate is a cytosolic process.

The key enzyme in carbon fixation is ribulose-bisphosphate carboxylase, the substrates for which are D-ribulose 1,5-bisphosphate and CO_2 (not HCO_3^-). This copper-containing enzyme which does not require biotin (Section 12.6) features in a pathway called the Calvin cycle (Figure 14.5). This reductive pentose phosphate pathway performs both carbon fixation and the regeneration of ribulose 1,5-bisphosphate to maintain the reductive process. By employing radioactive $^{14}CO_2$ in experiments with *Chlorella*, an easily cultured unicellular green alga, Calvin and coworkers, in the late 1940s, identified the first product of carbon fixation as 3-phosphoglycerate. Further experimentation determined that 3-phosphoglycerate is formed from ribulose 1,5-bisphosphate.

The stoichiometry of the Calvin cycle is important. For every three ribulose 1,5-bisphosphate utilized, six molecules of 3-phosphoglycerate are synthesized and are phosphorylated to 1,3-bisphosphoglycerate at the expense of ATP synthesized during the light reactions. Six molecules of 1,3-bisphosphoglycerate are reduced to glyceraldehyde 3-phosphate by a specific stromal enzyme utilizing light-generated NADPH. Only one molecule of glyceraldehyde 3-phosphate, however, is utilized in carbohydrate synthesis. The other five molecules are required for the regeneration of ribulose 1,5-bisphosphate through a series of sugar interconversions resembling but not identical with those of the non-oxidative phase of the pentose phosphate pathway (Section 11.9).

Briefly, two of the five glyceraldehyde 3-phosphates are isomerized to glycerone phosphate, one of which reacts with a third glyceraldehyde 3-phosphate under the influence of fructose-bisphosphate aldolase (Section 11.2) to yield fructose 1,6-bisphosphate which is dephosphorylated to fructose 6-phosphate (Section 11.7). Transketolase catalyses a two-carbon unit transfer between fructose 6-phosphate and a fourth glyceraldehyde 3-phosphate to yield erythrose 4-phosphate and xylulose 5-phosphate. An aldol condensation of erythrose 4-phosphate with the second glycerone phosphate, catalysed by fructose-bisphosphate aldolase, produces sedoheptulose 1,7-bisphosphate which on dephosphorylation yields sedoheptulose 7-phosphate. A second transketolase reaction utilizes sedoheptulose 7-phosphate and a fifth glyceraldehyde 3-phosphate to produce xylulose 5-phosphate and ribose 5-phosphate. The epimerization of both xylulose 5-phosphates and the isomerization of ribose 5-phosphate (Section 11.9) produces ribulose 5-phosphates which are phosphorylated to regenerate three ribulose 1,5-bisphosphate molecules.

Modifications of the Calvin cycle have been identified. In sugar cane and corn, using $^{14}CO_2$, it was discovered that the initial product of carbon fixation was not 3-phosphoglycerate but malate. This type of photosynthesis is termed C_4 photosynthesis since malate has four carbon atoms, as opposed to C_3 photosynthesis described above. Since C_4 plants are hot-climate plants, they are adapted to conserve water, the loss of which is reduced by limitation of stomatal opening through which gaseous interchange between the air spaces of the leaf and the external atmosphere occurs. To

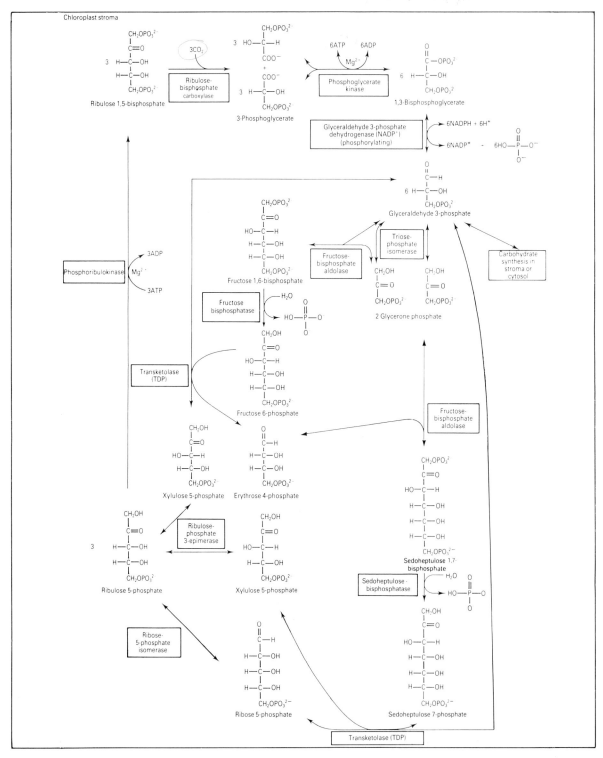

FIGURE 14.5 The Calvin cycle (reductive pentose phosphate pathway)

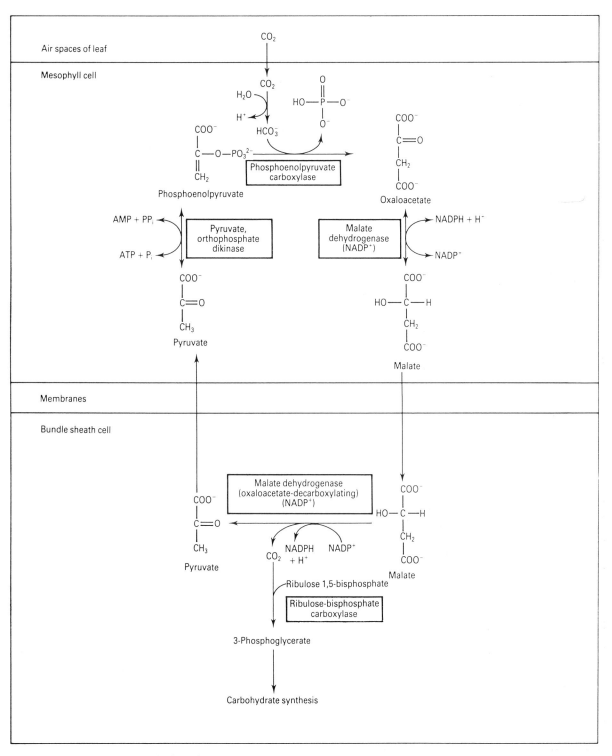

FIGURE 14.6 The Hatch–Slack pathway

provide for photosynthesis, these plants possess an additional pathway elucidated by Hatch and Slack in 1970 (Figure 14.6). This pathway provides a mechanism for the accumulation of large quantities of CO_2 as malate from which CO_2 can be procured by decarboxylation as required. To facilitate this provision, C_4 plants have an unusual leaf anatomy in which the veins are surrounded by bundle sheath cells which are, in turn, encompassed by mesophyll cells. Both cells are photosynthetic but cooperate to enhance photosynthesis in the bundle sheath cells.

A further modification (referred to as crassulacean acid metabolism) is conducted by the family, Crassulaceae, mainly found in South Africa. These plants live in extremely arid conditions. To prevent dehydration, their stomata remain closed during daylight hours but open after dark to absorb CO_2 which is fixed by the carboxylation of phosphoenolpyruvate to malate. Large quantities of malate can be stored in the large cellular vacuoles until the following day when decarboxylation of malate releases CO_2 for photosynthesis.

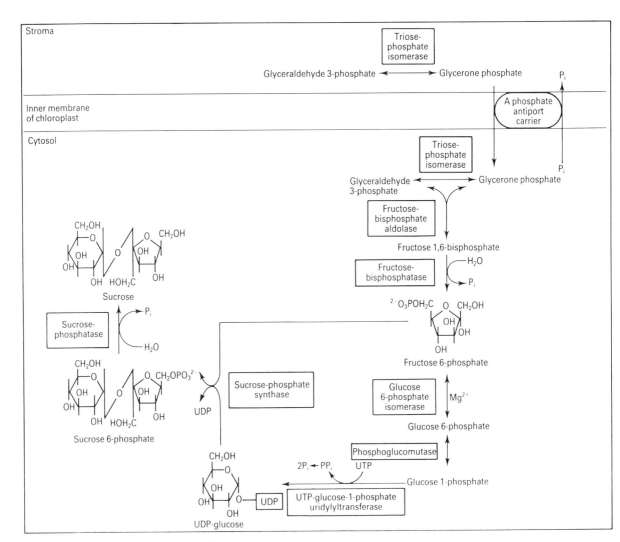

FIGURE 14.7   Synthesis of sucrose in leaves

14.6 The dark reactions: carbohydrate synthesis

The major end products in leaves are starch and sucrose both of which are synthesized from the sixth glyceraldehyde 3-phosphate intermediate of the Calvin cycle (Section 14.5). Starch synthesis occurs within the chloroplast stroma. Glyceraldehyde 3-phosphate is converted to glucose 6-phosphate (Section 11.7) which is utilized in a pathway analogous to that of glycogen synthesis (Section 11.5). The glucosyl carrier, however, is not UDP-glucose but ADP-glucose produced by glucose-1-phosphate adenylyltransferase. The polymerizing enzyme is starch synthase.

Since sucrose synthesis (Figure 14.7) occurs in the cytosol, glyceraldehyde 3-phosphate is isomerized to glycerone phosphate which is translocated out of the stroma by a phosphate antiport carrier in exchange for phosphate. This phosphate has an important role in the regulation of photosynthesis. Glycerone phosphate is converted to glucose 6-phosphate as in gluconeogenesis. Further conversion to UDP-glucose occurs as in glycogen synthesis (Section 11.5). UDP-glucose and fructose 6-phosphate serve as substrates for sucrose-phosphate synthase which produces sucrose 6-phosphate. Dephosphorylation by sucrose-phosphatase yields sucrose.

Suggested further reading

FOYER, C. H. (1984) *Photosynthesis*, Wiley, New York
HOOBER, J. K. (1984) *Chloroplasts*, Plenum, New York

CHAPTER 15

The metabolism of lipids

15.1 Fatty acids as energy sources

Although fatty acids (Section 8.2) are important as constituents of more complex molecules, e.g. phosphoacylglycerols (Section 8.5) and as precursors of eicosanoids (Section 8.8), they are major sources of energy for cells. In humans and mammals, small amounts of fatty acids are stored within most cells and larger amounts are generally found in specialized storage tissues, e.g. adipose tissue. The major storage form of fatty acids is triacylglycerols (Section 8.4) which are anhydrous and can yield more energy per unit weight than hydrated storage carbohydrates. For this reason, during periods of excess food consumption, energy is stored as fat. Fatty acids supply about 40% of the calorific requirements of man on a normal diet. This figure may increase to almost l00% during periods of fasting and starvation. Fatty acids constitute the major energy supply during the migration of birds and hibernation of animals.

The main route of energy provision from fatty acids is the β-oxidation pathway in which carbon atom C-3 (β-carbon) is oxidized. In man, other pathways also exist. The α-oxidation pathway which involves the oxidation of the C-2 atom is important in the degradation of ingested branched fatty acids and brain lipids to prepare such fatty acids for entry into the β-oxidation route. The ω (omega)-pathway involves the oxidation of the terminal methyl group primarily of C_6 to C_{10} fatty acids. The dicarboxylate product enters the β-oxidation pathway.

The fatty acids for β-oxidation are derived from storage triacylglycerols or the turnover of membrane lipids. The mobilization of fatty acids from adipocytes occurs when the diet or glycogen reserves are insufficient to satisfy the calorific requirements of tissues. Hormonally controlled lipases systematically hydrolyse the ester bonds of triacylglycerols to release fatty acids and glycerol. This lipolysis is mediated by cAMP following the interaction of, e.g. adrenaline or glucagon, with their specific receptors in the adipocyte plasma membrane (Section 10.7).

The glycerol by conversion to glycerone phosphate can enter the glycolytic pathway or be released into the blood circulation from which it is sequestered by the liver and kidneys for gluconeogenesis (Section 11.7). The fatty acids diffuse through the plasma membranes and are transported in the blood circulation as a serum albumin–acylate complex to the tissues requiring fatty acids for oxidation where the fatty acids dissociate from the complex and enter the tissue cells by diffusion. This aspect of fatty acid transport is governed by the ratio of the concentration of albumin-bound fatty acid to the intracellular concentration of fatty acid. The fatty acids delivered to the tissue cells undergo cytosolic activation by long-chain-fatty-acid-CoA ligase before entry into the mitochondrion for oxidation.

15.2 The *β*-oxidation pathway

The fatty acid in its ionized form is activated in the cytosol by an acylate-CoA ligase located on the outer surface of the eukaryotic outer mitochon-drial membrane (Figure 15.1). There are three such enzymes known: long-chain-fatty-acid-CoA ligase which acts on C_6 to C_{20} substrates; butyrate-CoA

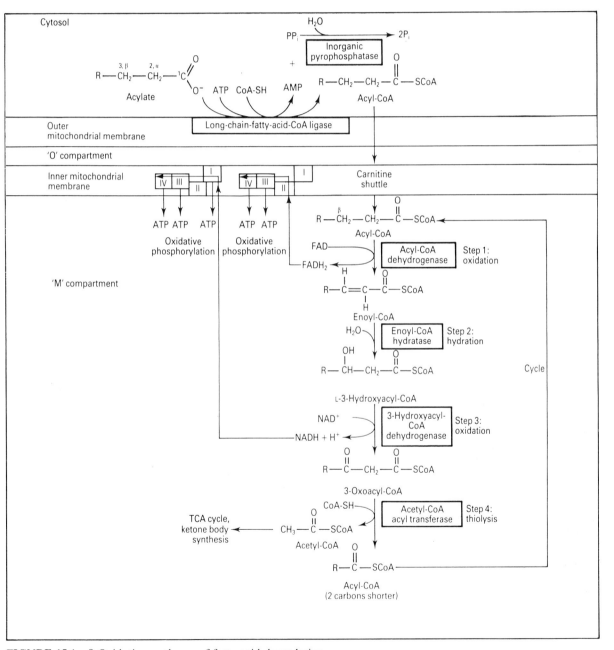

FIGURE 15.1   β-Oxidation pathway of fatty acid degradation

ligase which acts on C_4 to C_{12} substrates and ace-tate-CoA ligase which activates acetate. The reaction is freely reversible and so to drive the reaction in the desired direction, the pyrophosphate is hydrolysed by inorganic pyrophosphatase (Section 10.4).

Long-chain acyl-CoA molecules, e.g. palmitoyl-CoA, gain entry to the mitochondrial matrix where the discrete enzymes of the β-oxidation cycle are located by utilizing the carnitine shuttle (Figure 15.2). Carnitine palmitoyltransferase, located on the outside of the inner membrane, bonds the acyl group of palmitoyl-CoA to carnitine. The palmitoylcarnitine thus formed crosses the inner membrane and is reconverted into palmitoyl-CoA and carnitine by another isoenzyme of carnitine palmitoyltransferase located on the inside of the membrane. The carnitine is acetylated by the action of

carnitine acetyltransferase to enable its passage through the membrane as acetylcarnitine. Deacetylation releases the carnitine molecule. By controlling the rate of entry of palmitoyl-CoA into the mitochondrial matrix, carnitine palmitoyltransferase regulates the rate of the β-oxidation pathway.

In the mitochondrial matrix, the acyl-CoA is successively oxidized, hydrated, oxidized (Section 12.4) and thiolysed in a cycle of reactions. The $FADH_2$ produced by acyl-CoA dehydrogenase passes its electrons to Complex II of the electron-transport chain and is employed in the production of two ATP by oxidative phosphorylation. The NADH passes its electrons to Complex I and produces three ATP by oxidative phosphorylation (Section 13.5). Each cycle produces acetyl-CoA and an acyl-CoA which is two carbons shorter than the acyl-CoA entering step 1. The shortened

FIGURE 15.2 Transportation of palmitoyl-CoA into the mitochondrion for fatty acid oxidation

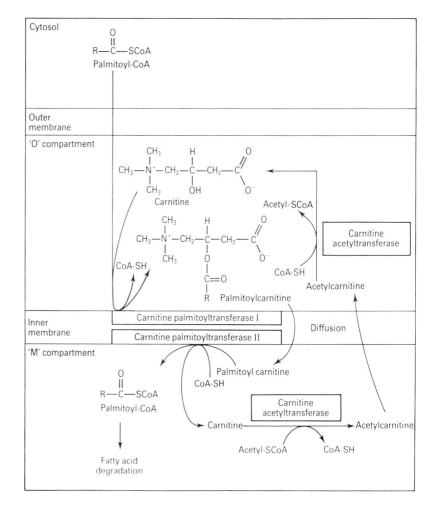

acyl-CoA re-enters the cycle at step 1. If the initial fatty acid contained an even number of carbon atoms, this cycling continues until C_4 acyl-CoA (butyryl-CoA) enters step 1 and produces one $FADH_2$, one NADH and two acetyl-CoA molecules. However, the last cycle from a fatty acid containing an odd number of carbons (mainly originating from the individual's diet) starts from C_5 acyl-CoA and produces one $FADH_2$, one NADH, one acetyl-CoA and one terminal propionyl-CoA. The acetyl-CoA enters the TCA cycle to produce GTP and reduced coenzymes for use in oxidative phosphorylation, the two carbons of the acetyl group being oxidized to CO_2.

Palmitoyl-CoA would be processed by steps 1 to 4 of the cycle seven times (Table 15.1). The maximum yield of energy as ATP from the β-oxidation of a fatty acid can be calculated as shown in Table 15.2. One molecule of palmitate will yield 129 molecules of ATP. Compare this yield with that from complete oxidation of glucose (Table 12.1). For energy yield from other even-numbered saturated fatty acids, adjust the number of cycles and recalculate.

The fate of the propionyl-CoA is entry into the TCA cycle as succinyl-CoA (Figure 15.3). Propionyl-CoA is carboxylated to form the D-stereoisomer of methylmalonyl-CoA. However, succinyl-CoA can only be produced by methylmalonyl-CoA mutase if the substrate is in the L-form. Therefore, the D-configuration is converted into L-methylmalonyl-CoA by the appropriate epimerase. L-Methylmalonyl-CoA is rearranged internally by the specific mutase to yield succinyl-CoA. Methylmalonyl-CoA mutase requires as coenzyme a form of the vitamin cobalamin. Study of the formulae of methylmalonyl-CoA and succinyl-CoA may suggest that it is the carboxylate group which is repositioned. However, the rearrangement proceeds by the transfer of the bulky coenzyme A group. When calculating the energy yield from an odd-numbered saturated fatty acid, the propionyl-CoA

TABLE 15.1   The sequential degradation of a fatty acid by the β-oxidation pathway

Palmitate as substrate	No. of cycles
CH_3—CH_2—CH_2—CH_2—CH_2—CH_2—CH_2—CH_2—CH_2—CH_2—CH_2—CH_2—CH_2—CH_2—CH_2— COSCoA	

						Acetyl-CoA	First cycle
					Acetyl-CoA		Second cycle
				Acetyl-CoA			Third cycle
		Acetyl-CoA					Fourth cycle
	Acetyl-CoA						Fifth cycle
Acetyl-CoA							Sixth cycle
Acetyl-CoA Acetyl-CoA							Seventh cycle

For any fatty acid, the number of cycles can be calculated by the formula:

$$\text{Number of cycles} = \frac{\text{Number of carbon atoms in the fatty acid} - 2}{2}$$

TABLE 15.2   The net yield of ATP during complete oxidation of a fatty acid by the β-oxidation pathway

Fatty acid	Step no. (Figure 18.3)	Number of cycles	Number of molecules of ATP gained per cycle via oxidative phosphorylation	Number of molecules of ATP gained per molecule of fatty acid
Palmitate	1	7	FADH ≡ 2	14
	3	7	NADH ≡ 3	21
	4	7	Acetyl-CoA ≡ 12	84
	4	Terminal	Acetyl-CoA ≡ 12	12
	Total of ATP molecules gained			131
	Number of ATP equivalents used during activation			2*
	Net yield of ATP molecules			129

* Although only one ATP is actually used in the cytosolic activation, the product is AMP. The regeneration of ATP from this AMP would require two phosphorylation reactions and so the number of ATPs used is quoted as two equivalents

FIGURE 15.3 Fate of propionyl-CoA produced by β-oxidation of fatty acids with an odd number of carbons

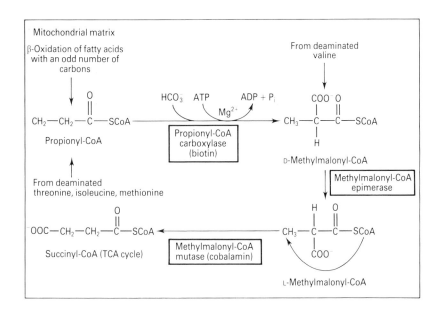

is equivalent to five ATP. The catabolism of some amino acids also utilizes this pathway.

Degradation of unsaturated fatty acids is primarily by the β-oxidation pathway. However, the presence of double bonds necessitates additional steps. β-Oxidation proceeds until a *cis* double bond occurs in the Δ^3 position (between C-3 and C-4). The enzyme acyl-CoA dehydrogenase cannot utilize a compound with such a configuration as a substrate and so an additional enzyme, dodecenoyl-CoA Δ-isomerase is required to convert the

double bond into a Δ^2 *trans* bond which can be utilized by enoyl-CoA hydratase, and the normal pathway for β-oxidation continues.

Degradation of polyunsaturated fatty acids is likewise by the β-oxidation step but in addition to the need for dodecenoyl-CoA Δ-isomerase, a further enzymic step (3-hydroxyacyl-CoA epimerase) is required to convert the D-product of enoyl-CoA hydratase into its L-stereoisomer. Thereafter, β-oxidation resumes.

15.3 Ketone body metabolism

The utilization of acetyl-CoA by the tricarboxylate cycle is dependent upon the availability of an appropriate intramitochondrial concentration of oxaloacetate which is maintained by anaplerotic reactions (Section 12.6). The intracellular concentration of oxaloacetate therefore depends upon the levels of certain glycolytic intermediates. If carbohydrate metabolism is depressed and fatty acid degradation predominant such as during starvation, fasting or diabetes mellitus, acetyl-CoA cannot enter the tricarboxylate cycle and is utilized by a reaction sequence leading to ketone body formation. There are three so-called ketone bodies:

acetoacetate, D-3-hydroxybutyrate (not a ketone, but derived from acetoacetate) and acetone.

The major site of ketone body production (Figure 15.4) is the liver. Two acetyl-CoA molecules condense to form acetoacetyl-CoA. The enzyme catalysing this reaction is acetyl-CoA acyltransferase and the step is therefore a reversal of step 4 of the β-oxidation pathway (Figure 15.1). Although the equilibrium is unfavourable for the formation of acetoacetyl-CoA, the reaction proceeds by coupling (Section 10.3) to the next step which involves the hydrolysis of the thioester linkage of another acetyl-CoA. When fatty acid oxi-

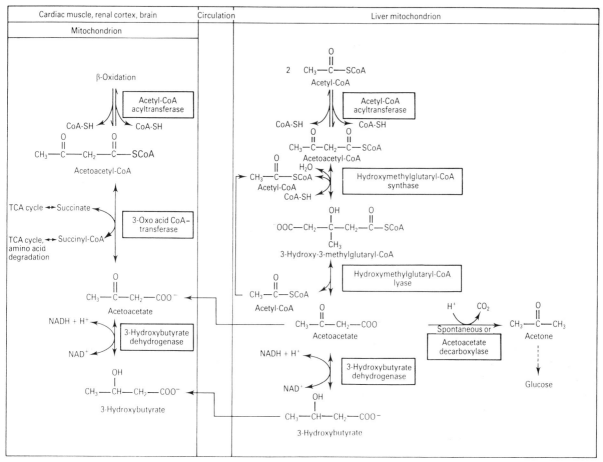

FIGURE 15.4 Synthesis and utilization of ketone bodies

dation proceeds under conditions of insufficient oxaloacetate, step 4 of the final cycle and thus reversal would be bypassed leading directly to the formation of 3-hydroxy-3-methylglutaryl-CoA (HMG-CoA). (Glutarate has the formula: $^-OOC-CH_2-CH_2-CH_2-COO^-$.) The formation of HMG-CoA involves the addition of an acetate group from acetyl-CoA and water to one end of the acetoacetyl-CoA whilst the following step, the cleavage of HMG-CoA, involves the removal of an acetyl-CoA from the other end to yield acetoacetate. 3-Hydroxybutyrate is formed by the reduction of acetoacetate. The final concentrations of 3-hydroxybutyrate and acetoacetate are dependent on the [NADH]/[NAD$^+$] ratio in the mitochondrion. Acetone is produced either by slow spontaneous decarboxylation of acetoacetate or by the action of acetoacetate decarboxylase. 3-Hydroxy-

butyrate and acetoacetate do not undergo further metabolism by the liver. They diffuse from the hepatocytes into the extracellular fluid and into the blood circulation which transports them to 3-oxo-acid CoA-transferase-containing tissues which can utilize them as sources of energy. In these tissues, 3-hydroxybutyrate is converted back into acetoacetate. Acetoacetate is converted into acetoacetyl-CoA by 3-oxoacid CoA-transferase which requires succinyl-CoA as the source of coenzyme. A. Acetoacetyl-CoA enters step of 4 of β-oxidation to yield two acetyl-CoA. Cardiac muscle and the renal cortex preferentially use these ketone bodies rather than glucose. The brain prefers glucose to satisfy its high energy demands but during starvation etc. may adapt to use acetoacetate as an energy source.

Acetone may diffuse into the blood circulation and, being volatile, may be lost during respiratory gaseous exchange in the lungs. Acetone may, however, participate in gluconeogenesis satisfying up to 10% of the gluconeogenic demands of humans fasted for 2l days. Two routes in rat liver have been proposed: the methylglyoxal pathway and the propanediol pathway. These studies suggest that a pathway does exist for the conversion of fat to carbohydrate in the mammalian liver. It had been previously considered that while the glyoxylate pathway (Section 12.8) enabled such transformation in plants and certain microorganisms, such a facility was absent from animal tissues.

15.4 The synthesis of fatty acids

The synthesis of fatty acids takes place in the cytosol but the precursor acetyl-CoA is produced in the 'M' compartment. Acetyl-CoA cannot pass through the inner membrane of the mitochondrion but the acetyl group is transferred across the membrane as citrate by the citrate–malate antiport carrier (Figure 15.5). Acetyl-CoA, produced from this citrate in the cytosol by the action of ATP citrate lyase, is utilized in the biosynthesis of fatty acids. The oxaloacetate can be utilized to transfer another acetyl group of an acetyl-CoA following resynthesis from malate within the matrix.

Acetyl-CoA is carboxylated in the cytosol into malonyl-CoA by acetyl-CoA carboxylase (Figure 15.6) which contains the biotin (Figure 5.3b) prosthetic group essential for most carboxylation

FIGURE 15.5 Transportation of acetyl-CoA from the mitochondrion for fatty acid synthesis

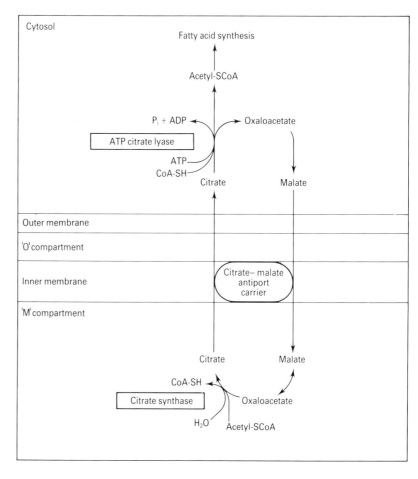

187

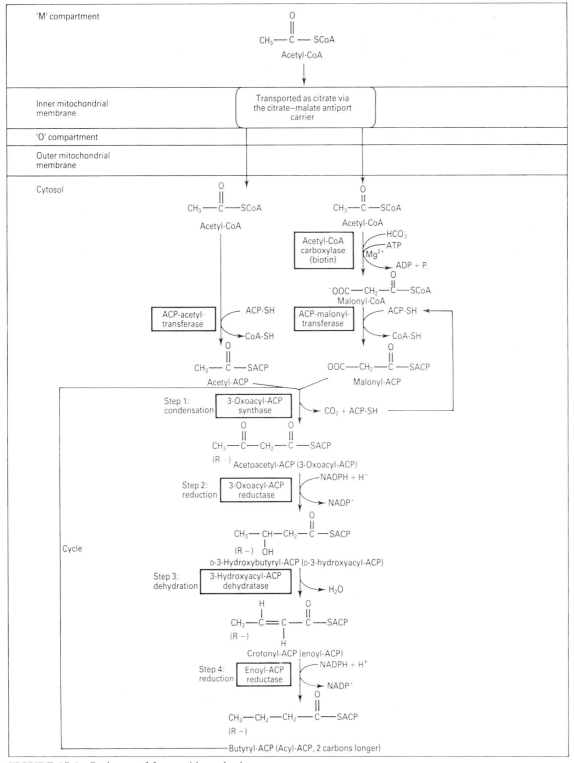

FIGURE 15.6 Pathway of fatty acid synthesis

reactions. This reaction is important since it commits the acetyl-CoA to the route of fatty acid synthesis. Although HCO_3^- is required for fatty acid synthesis, its carbon atom is not a constituent of the product.

The activity of acetyl-CoA carboxylase is modulated allosterically (Section 6.4) by citrate as the positive modulator and palmitoyl-CoA as a negative modulator. The level of citrate is high when both acetyl-CoA and ATP are plentiful and available for use in fatty acid synthesis. High palmitoyl-CoA levels indicate an excess of fatty acids and that fatty acid synthesis is not desirable in the cell at that time. Palmitoyl-CoA reinforces its action on acetyl-CoA carboxylase by inhibiting citrate transport from the mitochondrion and NADPH generation by the pentose phosphate pathway.

Malonyl-CoA is converted into malonyl-ACP (acyl-carrier protein) by a highly specific enzyme, ACP-malonyltransferase. Reactants participate in the synthetic pathway, only when linked to the ACP. Malonyl-ACP donates a two-carbon unit to elongate the acyl group attached to ACP. Initially, malonyl-ACP condenses with acetyl-ACP formed from acetyl-CoA by the action of ACP-acetyltransferase. The enzyme is less specific than ACP-malonyltransferases and can also bond propionyl groups from propionyl-CoA to ACP to form propionyl-ACP in the synthesis of fatty acids with an odd number of carbons. During the condensation reaction, CO_2 is released to drive the formation of acetoacetyl-ACP, a reaction which otherwise would be thermodynamically unfavourable. The free energy provided by ATP in the carboxylation step is therefore employed to synthesize acetoacetyl-ACP from acetyl-ACP and malonyl-ACP.

The pathway continues by a reduction, employing NADPH as reducing agent. The NADPH is provided mainly by the pentose phosphate pathway. The product of this reaction is D-3-hydroxybutyryl-ACP (D-3-hydroxyacyl-ACP). Following a dehydration catalysed by various enzymes depending upon the length of the substrate, and a further reduction employing NADPH, butyryl-ACP is produced. This compound is two carbons longer than the acetyl-ACP which participated in the condensation reaction. The butyryl-ACP re-enters the cycle at the condensation reaction (step 1) and condenses with malonyl-ACP. This cycling con-

tinues until palmitoyl-ACP is produced. After the first cycle, it is more convenient to use general names (in brackets) for the intermediates. The addition of a two-carbon unit requires two NADPH.

The enzymes of the mammalian synthetic cycle are a structurally organized multifunctional complex comprising fatty acid synthase, the major product of which is palmitate. The role of the 4'-phosphopantotheinyl group of ACP is similar to that of lipoate in the pyruvate dehydrogenase system (Section 12.3), that is to swing the product of one reaction to another active site (Figure 15.7). Stearate may be synthesized by this system or by the further addition of an acetyl group derived from malonyl-CoA to palmitoyl-ACP by an elongation system present in the endoplasmic reticulum or mitochondria. These elongation systems are responsible for the synthesis of saturated fatty acids with larger numbers of carbon atoms.

The energetics of fatty acid synthesis is complicated since, although ATP is apparently used only in the production of malonyl-CoA from acetyl-CoA (Figure 15.6), ATP is also required to recover the acetyl-CoA from citrate after transport across the inner membrane of the mitochondrion (Figure 15.5) and in the production of NADPH by the pentose phosphate pathway if glucose is the source of glucose 6-phosphate, but to a lesser extent if glycogenolysis (Section 11.5) provides the glucose 6-phosphate.

Unsaturated fatty acids are synthesized from saturated fatty acids by the action of desaturases (Figure 15.8) located in the endoplasmic reticulum. Four desaturases designated Δ^9-, Δ^6-, Δ^5-, Δ^4-acyl-CoA desaturase are capable of synthesizing all known naturally occurring polyunsaturated fatty acids. When the substrate is a saturated fatty acid, the first double bond is inserted between C-9 and C-10. When the substrate is already unsaturated, subsequent double bonds are inserted between the double bond nearest the carboxyl group and the carboxyl group itself. This means that animal tissues cannot synthesize linoleate with a double bond at Δ^{12} and linolenate with double bonds at Δ^{12} and Δ^{15} (Table 8.1). Linoleate and linolenate must be supplied in the mammalian diet usually from plants and are therefore called essential fatty acids.

FIGURE 15.7   Role of the flexible 4′-phosphopantotheinyl group of ACP in catalysis by the fatty acid synthase system

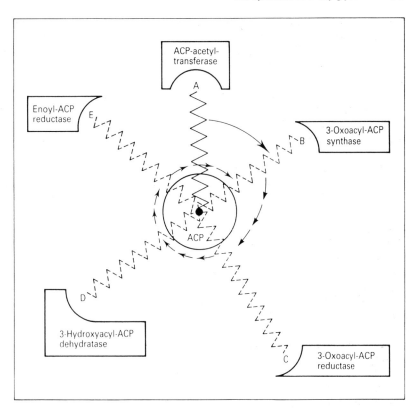

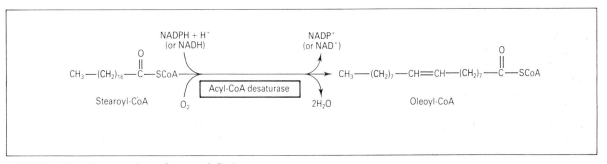

FIGURE 15.8   Desaturation of stearoyl-CoA

15.5 The synthesis of triacylglycerols

Triacylglycerols are the storage molecules for fatty acids (Section 8.4) from which the fatty acids may be released prior to oxidative catabolism in eukaryotic organisms (Section 15.1). The key intermediates in their synthesis are a phosphatidate and 1,2-diacylglycerol, the latter being synthesized from the former. There are two pathways for the synthesis of phosphatidate in mammalian cells, one involving glycerol 3-phosphate, the other involving the direct acylation of glycerone phosphate (Figure 15.9). Glycerol 3-phosphate is produced in adipose tissue by the reduction of the glycolytic

190

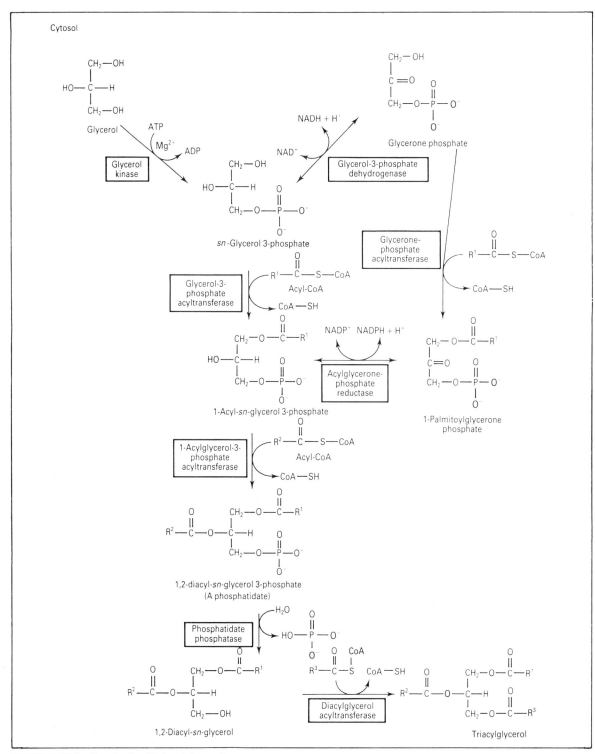

FIGURE 15.9 Synthesis of triacylglycerol

intermediate, glycerone phosphate by glycerol-3-phosphate dehydrogenase and in the liver and intestine by the phosphorylation of glycerol catalysed by glycerol kinase. Fatty acids activated by long-chain-fatty acid-CoA ligase (Section 15.2) are transferred firstly by glycerol-3-phosphate acyltransferase which converts a substrate of chain length greater than 10 carbon atoms to 1-acylglycerol 3-phosphate and secondly by 1-acylglycerol-3-phosphate acyltransferase, which is specific for an acyl-CoA containing one or two double bonds, to yield phosphatidate with an unsaturated fatty acid in the *sn*-2 position. An alternative route to phosphatidate involving the acylation of glycerone phosphate has been identified in rat adipocytes, rat hepatocytes and yeast but its relative importance is uncertain.

Phosphatidate is dephosphorylated to yield 1,2-diacylglycerol which is subsequently esterified at the *sn*-3 position to yield a triacylglycerol. Although the entire reaction sequence occurs in the cell cytosol, most of the enzymes are associated with the cytosolic surface of the membranes of the endoplasmic reticulum.

15.6 The synthesis of eicosanoids

The precursors of the prostaglandin series PG_1, PG_2 and PG_3 (Section 8.8) are an eicosatrienoate ($C_{20:3}$), lacking the Δ^5 double bond of arachidonate, arachidonate and an eicosapentaenoate ($C_{20:5}$) with an additional Δ^{17} double bond. The synthesis of the PG_2 series (Figure 15.10) occurs in most mammalian tissues and commences with arachidonate, released from membranous phosphoacylglycerols (Sections 8.5, 10.7) by the action of phospholipase A_2 (Figure 10.7b). Arachidonate undergoes double dioxygenation and cyclization to yield PGG_2 which is subsequently reduced to PGH_2. The two reactions are catalysed by a single enzyme known as cyclo-oxygenase located in the endoplasmic reticulum. The therapeutic benefits of the drug aspirin are derived from its inhibitory action on cyclo-oxygenase. Prostaglandin H_2 is the substrate for various synthases which yield prostaglandins D_2, $F_{2\alpha}$, E_2 and I_2 and thromboxanes A_2 and B_2 (Section 8.8).

Prostaglandin E synthase (also called prostaglandin-H_2 E-isomerase), which requires glutathione, also acts on PGG_2 albeit more slowly. Prostaglandin $F_{2\alpha}$ may also be synthesized by the action of prostaglandin F synthase on PGD_2 or by a minor route involving prostaglandin-E_2 9-keto-reductase on PGE_2. Different cells and tissues produce different quantities of the prostaglandins. For example, cardiac muscle produces equivalent amounts of PGE_2, $PGF_{2\alpha}$ and PGI_2 whereas PGI_2 is the principal product in the endothelial cells of blood vessels where it functions to prevent coagulation.

Leukotrienes (Section 8.8) are synthesized from arachidonate (Figure 15.10) in polymorphonuclear leucocytes and mast cells. A single oxygen molecule is added to the C-5 position of arachidonate accompanied by a double bond shift to the Δ^6 position to yield a 5-hydroperoxy derivative. This initial reaction is catalysed by the enzyme known as 5-lipoxygenase (15-lipoxygenase yields lipoxins). Subsequent dehydration produces the epoxide-containing leukotriene A_4(LTA_4). Hydrolysis of the allylic epoxide yields LTB_4. The addition of the tripeptide glutathione to the C-6 position of the epoxide together with the formation of a hydroxyl group at the C-5 position produces LTC_4. The enzymic removal of firstly the glutamyl residue and secondly the glycyl residue yields LTD_4 and LTE_4 respectively.

15.7 The synthesis of cholesterol

Cholesterol (Section 8.10) is synthesized from acetyl-CoA in liver and intestinal cells by a metabolic pathway which is located in the cell cytosol. Acetyl-CoA generated in the mitochondrial matrix is transported as citrate into the cytosol (Section 15.4) to serve as the precursor of fatty acid or cholesterol biosynthesis.

Figure 15.11 outlines the sequence of major

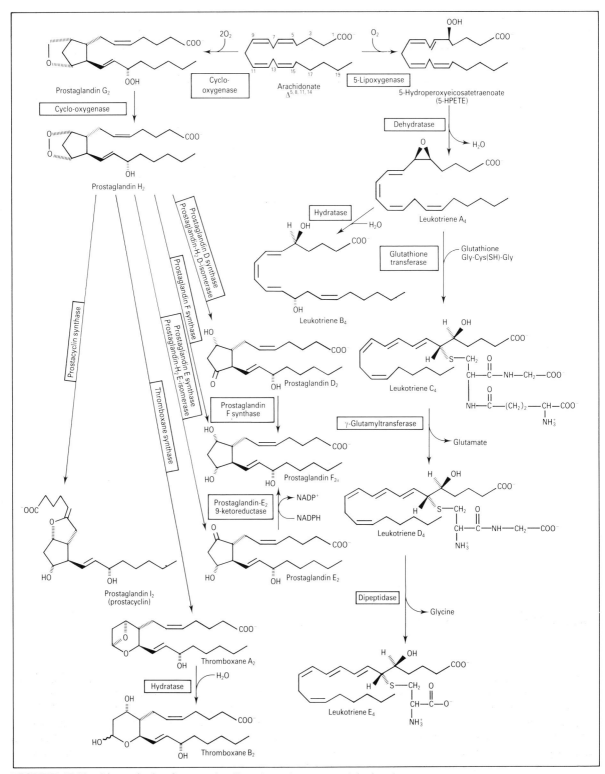

FIGURE 15.10 Biosynthesis of prostaglandins, thromboxanes and leukotrienes

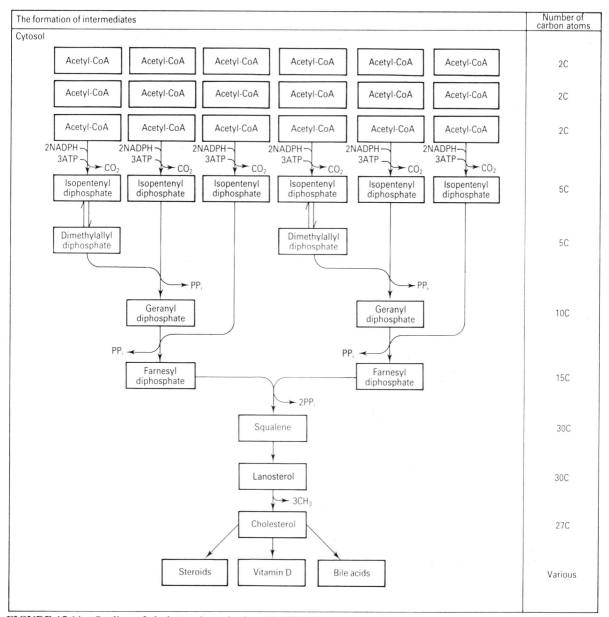

FIGURE 15.11   Outline of cholesterol synthesis and utilization

events as 18 acetyl-CoA molecules are utilized in the synthesis of one molecule of cholesterol. Briefly, three acetyl-CoAs provide the carbons for the synthesis of five-carbon isopentenyl diphosphate which may undergo isomerization to yield dimethylallyl diphosphate. Head-to-tail interaction between isopentenyl diphosphate and dimethylallyl diphosphate yields the 10-carbon geranyl diphosphate to which a further isopentenyl group is added to produce the 15-carbon farnesyl diphosphate. The interaction of two farnesyl diphosphates followed by reduction yields the 30-carbon squalene from which a series of reactions leads to cholesterol.

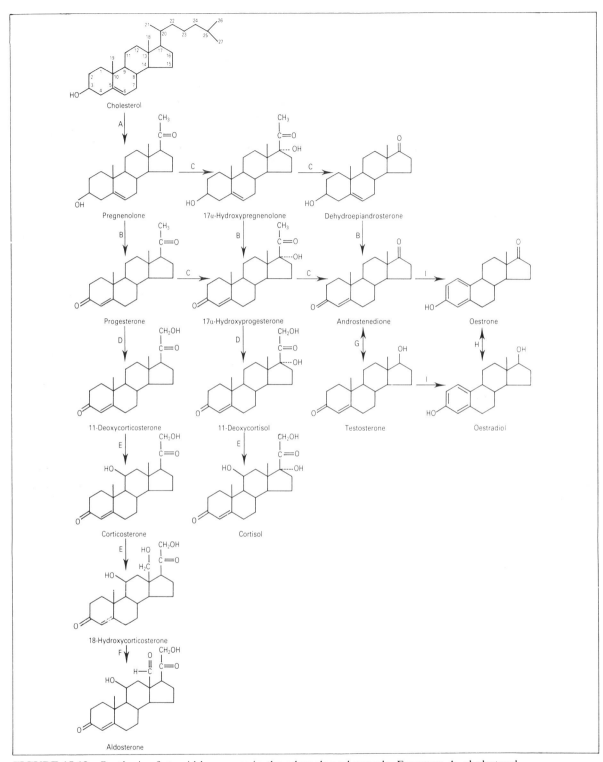

FIGURE 15.12 Synthesis of steroid hormones in the adrenals and gonads. Enzymes: A, cholesterol monooxygenase; B, 3β-hydroxy-Δ⁵-steroid dehydrogenase; C, steroid 17α-monooxygenase; D, steroid 21-mono-oxygenase; E, steroid 11β-monooxygenase; F, steroid 18-dehydrogenase; G, testosterone 17β-dehydrogenase; H, oestradiol 17β-dehydrogenase; I, an aromatase system

15.8 The metabolism of steroid hormones

Steroid hormones are synthesized from cholesterol in a variety of tissues (Section 8.10) by a series of reactions which employ different species of monooxygenases, dehydrogenases and, in the ovary, an aromatase enzyme system. Figure 15.12 outlines the conversion of cholesterol to corticosterone, aldosterone and cortisol in the adrenal cortex whilst gonadal metabolism is represented by the synthesis of testosterone (testes) and oestrogens (ovaries). Cholesterol loses its aliphatic tail by the action of cholesterol monooxygenase located within the mitochondrion to produce pregnenolone. From pregnenolone, aldosterone synthesis involves the conversion of the 3β-hydroxyl group to a ketone group, the isomerization of the Δ^5 double bond to the Δ^4 position, the hydroxylations of the C-21 methyl group and C-11 methylene group, and the oxidation of the C-18 methyl group into an aldehydic group. Cortisol synthesis proceeds via 17α-hydroxyprogesterone which may be synthesized by two routes.

Synthesis of both progesterone and 17α-hydroxyprogesterone occurs in the endoplasmic reticulum from which these intermediates migrate to the mitochondrion, the location of the first reaction and the remainder of the pathways. The monooxygenases involved are all cytochrome P-450 enzymes but different electron-transport pathways transfer the electrons from NADPH to the cytochrome P-450 in the two organelles. The steroidogenesis pathways of the gonads which utilize androstenedione produced in the same manner as in the adrenal cortex, are located within the endoplasmic reticulum.

Cortisol, aldosterone, testosterone and oestradiol are the major secretory products of their respective tissues. They are synthesized in response to the interaction of cell surface receptors with circulatory protein hormones of pituitary (brain) origin called tropic hormones. There is no appreciable storage of steroid hormones in the endocrine glands. The hormones are synthesized as required and secreted into the blood circulation where either cortisol-binding globulin (transcortin) carries cortisol, corticosterone and progesterone or testosterone–oestrogen-binding globulin carries the sex hormones to target tissues. Steroid hormones permeate the plasma membranes of target cells to bind to cytosolic specific receptor proteins (Section 10.7). Many target cells however reduce the Δ^4 double bond of testosterone to yield 5α-dihydrotestosterone which has a higher affinity for the androgen receptor.

The liver is the major site for the inactivation of steroid hormones mainly by stereospecific reduction and/or methylation. These metabolites are conjugated through their hydroxyl groups to sulphate or glucuronate to promote urinary excretion.

Suggested further reading

GERRARD, J. M. (1985) *Prostaglandins and Leukotrienes. Blood and Vascular Cell Function*, Dekker, New York
HALPERN, M. J. (ed) (1985) *Lipid Metabolism and its Pathology*, Plenum, New York

CHAPTER 16

Nitrogen metabolism

16.1 The biosynthesis of amino acids in plants and microorganisms

The incorporation of carbon atoms into biological molecules is dependent upon the fixation of carbon dioxide during photosynthesis (Chapter 14). The nitrogen atoms of amino acids, nucleotides and other nitrogenous biological molecules are also derived from the atmosphere. However, the gaseous form of the element cannot be utilized directly by plants and animals.

Nitrogen fixation, i.e. the process of combining gaseous nitrogen with other elements to form soluble compounds, is conducted in the soil by microorganisms. Some species of nitrogen-fixing bacteria live free in the soil but the most effective species, those of the genus *Rhizobium*, are located in the nodules of the roots of leguminous plants, e.g. clover and soyabean, and of a few non-leguminous

plants, e.g. alder. The species of *Rhizobium* is specific for each species of plant. Cyanobacteria (blue–green algae) perform nitrogen fixation in the oceans and, to some extent, in freshwater. All these microorganisms produce ammonia through the activity of a nitrogenase (Figure 16.1a). The reaction involves three reduced molecules of ferredoxin (Section 14.4) which donate six electrons. The source of this reducing power is NADPH. Twelve to eighteen molecules of ATP supply the necessary energy for the production of ammonia at a rate which is regulated by the inhibitory effect of the product on the association of the two components of the nitrogenase.

Ammonia is also produced by a variety of microorganisms and higher plants from soil nitrates

FIGURE 16.1 Production of ammonia by soil organisms. (a) Nitrogenase reaction. (b) Conversion of nitrate to ammonia

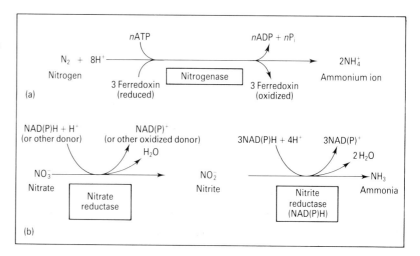

derived from decaying organic matter, natural or artificial fertilizers and the atmosphere. The circulation of nitrogen atoms from the atmosphere into living organisms and their return to the atmosphere by denitrifying bacteria is referred to as the nitrogen cycle. Nitrate can be reduced in two stages involving nitrate and nitrite reductases (Figure 16.1b). Nitrate reductases occur in a variety of organisms. Various forms require NADH, NADPH or either coenzyme as hydrogen donor. These enzymes also contain either FAD or FMN and in some cases a metal such as molybdenum as prosthetic groups. Nitrite reductase catalyses the reduction of nitrite to ammonia employing three NAD(P)H as the source of the necessary six electrons. Because of the occurrence of other nitrite reductases which produce nitric oxide from nitrite utilizing other cofactors, the ammonia-producing enzyme is written as nitrite reductase (NAD(P)H).

Ammonia can be incorporated into organic molecules by the formation of glutamate or glutamine. Therefore, the nitrogen atoms of amino acids and

of other biological molecules are derived from glutamate or the amide group of glutamine. Glutamate is produced from ammonia and 2-oxoglutarate in a reaction catalysed by a NADPH-specific glutamate dehydrogenase found in a variety of plants and microorganisms (Figure 16.2a). The reverse reaction involving NAD^+ may provide 2-oxoglutarate to the tricarboxylate cycle from glutamate (Section 16.3). Glutamate may be converted into glutamine by a second molecule of ammonia, a reaction catalysed by glutamate–ammonia ligase (Figure 16.2b).

In bacteria and plant cells, the 20 amino acids which occur in their proteins may be synthesized from glutamate or glutamine and intermediates of glycolysis, pentose phosphate pathway and tricarboxylate cycle (Table 16.1). In some cases, the synthesis involves a single reaction whilst other pathways may involve as many as 12 reactions. Only the synthesis of tryptophan from phosphoenolpyruvate and erythrose 4-phosphate does not involve at least one amino transfer reaction

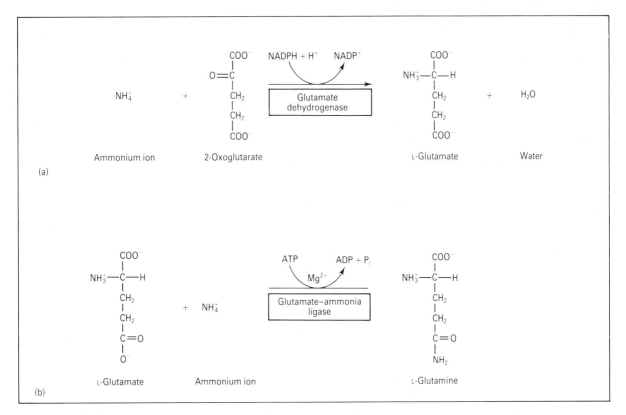

FIGURE 16.2   Incorporation of ammonia into biomolecules. (a) Glutamate dehydrogenase reaction. (b) Glutamate–ammonia ligase reaction

(transamination) although tryptophan aminotransferases do exist. Amino transfer reactions, therefore, play a key role in the metabolism of amino
acids and are catalysed by aminotransferases
(transaminases).

Aminotransferases contain pyridoxal phosphate,
a derivative of the vitamin pyridoxine (B_6), as prosthetic group. During the reaction, outlined in
Figure 16.3a, the prosthetic group is converted into
pyridoxamine phosphate (Figure 16.3b). Pyridoxal

TABLE 16.1   The sources of carbon atoms in the biosynthesis of amino acids in plants and microorganisms

Pathway	Metabolic intermediate	Amino acid products	
		Intermediate	Terminal
Glycolysis	3-Phosphoglycerate	Serine	Cysteine, glycine
	Pyruvate	—	Alanine, valine, leucine
Pentose phosphate pathway	Ribose 5-phosphate	—	Histidine
Glycolysis + pentose phosphate pathway	Phosphoenolpyruvate + erythrose 4-phosphate	Phenylalanine	Tyrosine
		—	Tryptophan, tyrosine*
Tricarboxylate cycle	2-Oxoglutarate	Glutamate	Glutamine, proline, arginine
	Oxaloacetate	Aspartate	Asparagine, methionine, lysine
		Threonine†	Isoleucine

* Tyrosine may be synthesized by different pathways, one of which produces phenylalanine which upon hydroxylation yields tyrosine
† Threonine is synthesized from aspartate

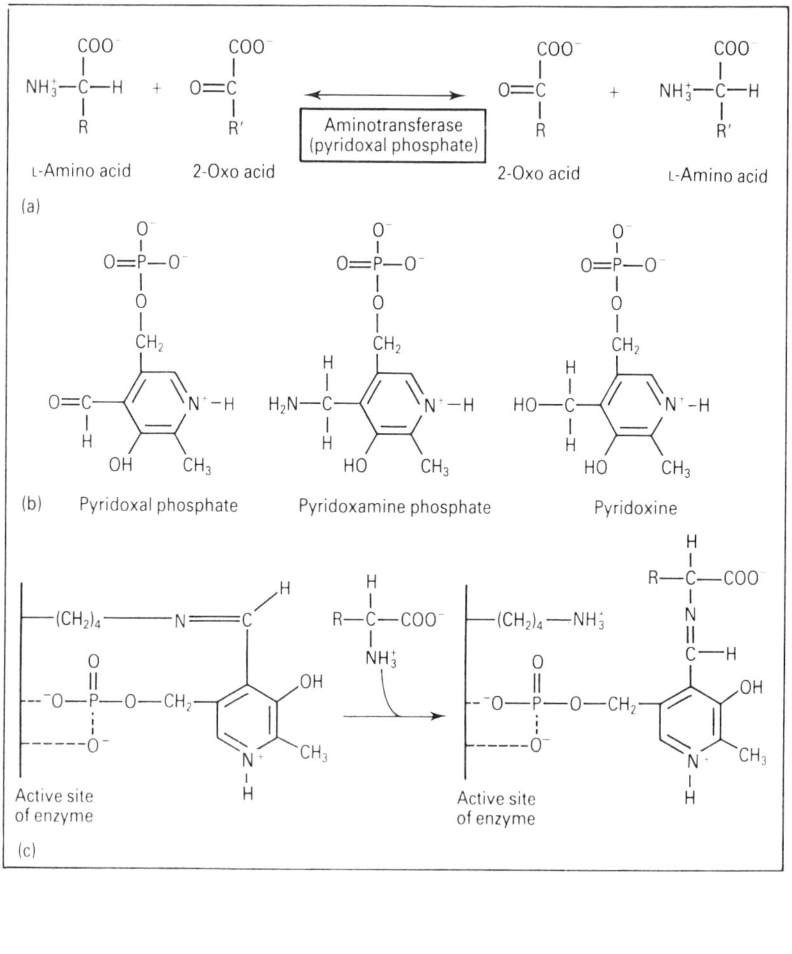

FIGURE 16.3 Aminotransferase reactions. (a) Outline of the reaction. (b) Structures of the prosthetic group and parent compound. (c) Covalent linkage between enzyme and pyridoxal phosphate is replaced by covalent linkage between incoming amino acid and pyridoxal phosphate

phosphate is initially covalently bonded with the ε-amino group of a specific lysyl residue located at the active site of the enzyme (Figure 16.3c). The α-amino group of an amino acid substrate displaces the lysyl residue and forms an aldimine intermediate which is appositely positioned by non-covalent forces. The aldimine intermediate formed by the interaction of the amino acid, e.g. glutamate (Figure 16.4), with the aldehydic group of pyridoxal phosphate undergoes a double-bond shift called tautomerism (Section 7.5) to a ketimine which is subsequently hydrolysed to yield the corresponding 2-oxo acid, e.g. 2-oxoglutarate. The glutamate has therefore been successfully de-aminated to 2-oxoglutarate but the amino group is covalently bound to the prosthetic group. The pyridoxamine phosphate intermediate has a transient existence before involvement in the formation of an amino acid by amination of a 2-oxo acid. The amination phase proceeds by a reversal of the deamination mechanism to regenerate pyridoxal phosphate and produce an amino acid corresponding in structure to the 2-oxo acid.

Amino transfer reactions are reversible, have a wide occurrence (Table 16.2) and are important in biosynthesis and degradation in animals and humans. The enzymes are frequently specific for a given amino acid and are named accordingly,

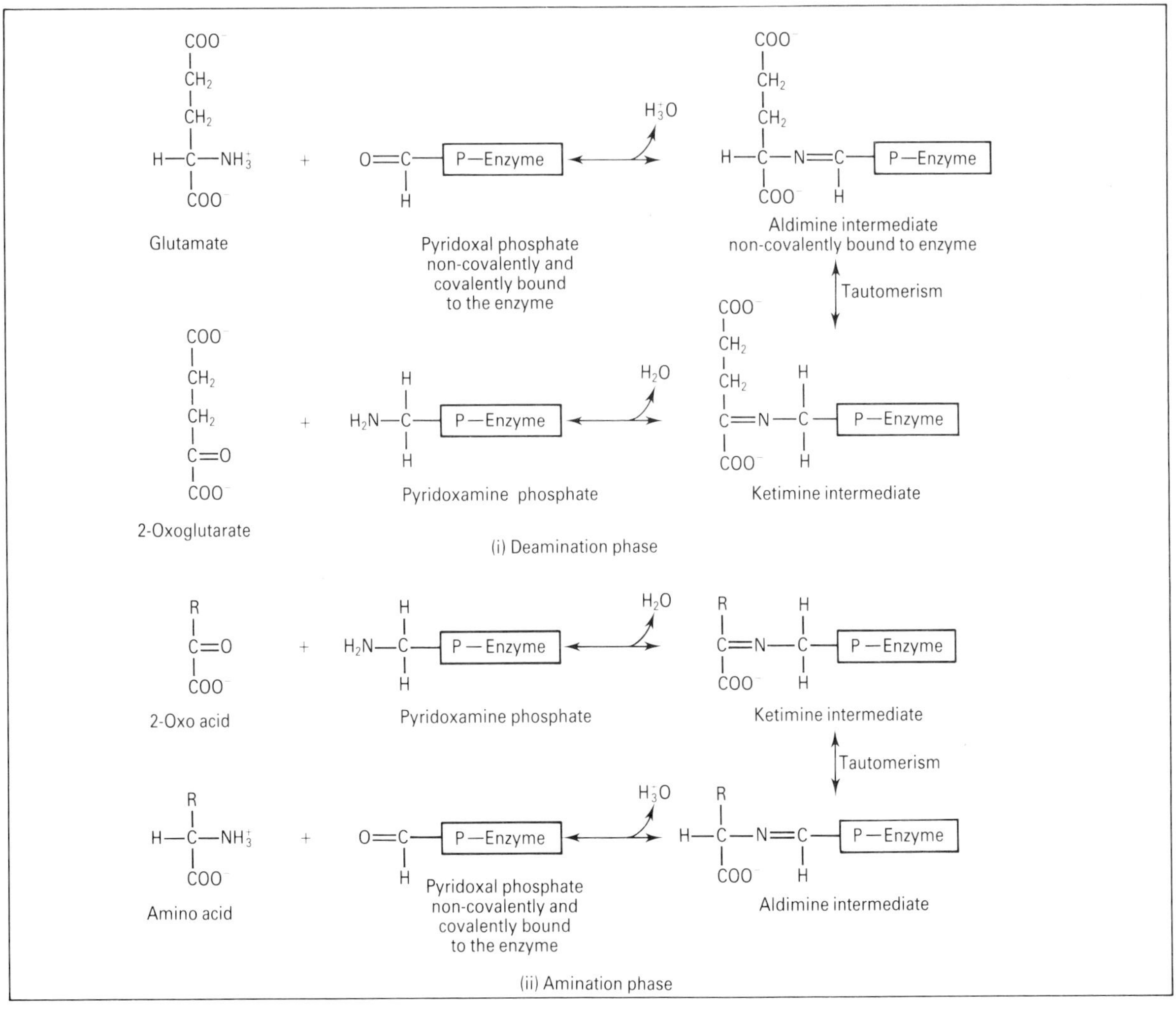

FIGURE 16.4   Double displacement mechanism of amino transfer reactions

TABLE 16.2   Examples of amino transfer reactions

Reaction catalysed	Enzyme	Amino group donor
Oxaloacetate⇌L–aspartate	Aspartate aminotransferase	L–Glutamate
Pyruvate⇌L–alanine	Alanine aminotransferase	L–Glutamate
4-Methyl-2-oxopentanoate⇌L–leucine	Leucine aminotransferase	L–Glutamate
4-Methyl-2-oxopentanoate⇌L–leucine 3-Methyl-2-oxobutanoate⇌L–valine 3-Methyl-2-oxovalerate⇌L–isoleucine	Branched-chain-amino-acid aminotransferase	L–Glutamate
Pyruvate⇌L–alanine	Glutamine–pyruvate aminotransferase	L–Glutamine
3-Methyl-2-oxobutanoate⇌L–valine	Valine–3-methyl-2-oxovalerate aminotransferase	L–Isoleucine

e.g. alanine aminotransferase. Although most aminotransferases employ glutamate as amino group donor, some enzymes utilize other amino acids.

Upon production, amino acids may be incorporated into proteins or contribute to the synthesis of pyrimidines, purines (Section 16.6) and polyamines. The intracellular free amino acid pool also has an osmotic function and concentrations are thus regulated to satisfy both synthetic and osmotic requirements.

16.2 The biosynthesis of amino acids in mammals and humans

Nutritional studies in rats have indicated that mammals cannot synthesize all the amino acids required for protein synthesis. Such studies were conducted by maintenance of growing rats on diets deficient in one amino acid and monitoring for weight gain. In man, approximately 50% of the body protein is replaced every 5–6 months. This turnover involves a controlled balance between degradation and synthesis. Studies in humans employing similarly constructed diets considered short-term maintenance of a positive nitrogen balance, i.e. intake of nitrogen exceeds nitrogen excretion, which suggests that nitrogen is being retained for protein synthesis. A negative nitrogen balance during the experimental period could indicate that tissue proteins are being degraded in an attempt to supply the omitted amino acid for the synthesis of proteins required for major functions. Under normal dietary conditions nitrogen balance is maintained. On the basis of such experimentation, amino acids are classified as 'essential' or 'non-essential', the term 'essential' reflecting the need for supply from dietary sources (Table 16.3).

The non-essential amino acids are those which may be synthesized by the organism. In general, the non-essential amino acids have short synthetic pathways; the longest pathway produces glycine from choline by five reactions. The major site for the synthesis of amino acids in animals and humans is also the principal degradative tissue, i.e. the liver. The liver contains the enzymes necessary to synthesize amino acids either by the same route as in plants or at the expense of other amino acids through amino transfer reactions (Section 16.1).

Essential amino acids cannot be synthesized because the liver is deficient in at least one of the enzymes involved in the analogous plant pathway. Therefore, the carbon skeleton of the essential amino acid but not necessarily the complete amino acid must be supplied in the diet. Proteins from animal sources, e.g. meat, milk and eggs, are very effective in the support of maintenance and growth of rats and man and are classified as 'first-class proteins'. Others, frequently from plant sources, do not contain all the essential components and are called 'second-class proteins'. A second-class protein may lack, or contain inadequate quantities of, one or several amino acids.

TABLE 16.3 Essential and non-essential amino acids for rat and man

Amino acids	
Essential	*Non-essential*
Isoleucine	Alanine
Leucine	Asparagine
Lysine	Aspartate
Methionine	Cysteine
Phenylalanine	Glutamate
Threonine	Glutamine
Tryptophan	Glycine
Valine	Proline
Arginine*	Serine
Histidine*	Tyrosine

*Arginine and histidine are essential amino acids in young animals and children because, although the metabolism of adults can satisfy protein-synthesis requirements, the synthetic pathways do not produce enough amino acid for normal growth.

16.3 The degradation of amino acids

Degradation of amino acids in microorganisms and plants is a rare event but is of major importance in animals and humans. Amino acids which are surplus to the demands of protein synthesis are not excreted like steroids (Section 15.8) but utilized as sources of energy, either directly or indirectly. About 10–15% of human energy requirements are derived from the oxidation of amino acids.

In liver, the major degradative tissue, the initial reaction involves deamination (the removal of α-amino groups) by either amino transfer reactions (Section 16.1) which collect the α-amino groups in a single substance (glutamate) or oxidative or direct deamination. Oxidative deamination of glutamate by glutamate dehydrogenase is extremely important in the formation of urea (Section 16.5). Although readily reversible utilizing NADPH as coenzyme (Figure 16.2a), its primary role in mammals is the NAD^+-dependent deamination of glutamate. Oxidative deamination may also occur by a relatively minor process involving L- and D-amino acid oxidases. Serine and threonine may be directly deaminated by reactions catalysed by serine dehydratase and threonine dehydratase respectively. The ammonium ions may be utilized in the biosynthesis of other nitrogenous compounds, e.g. pyrimidines (Section 16.6), but most will be excreted in a convenient form (Section 16.4).

Deamination yields the carbon skeletons of the amino acids which are independently catabolized into major metabolic intermediates (Table 16.4). The intermediates may participate in the tricarboxylate cycle (Chapter 12) to produce energy mainly through oxidative phosphorylation (Chapter 13). When the demand for energy is low, those carbon skeletons which are potential sources of malate, i.e. those yielding pyruvate or tricarboxylate cycle intermediates, may be employed in gluconeogenesis. Malate, an intermediate in the first bypass reaction of gluconeogenesis (Section 11.7), may be translocated into the cytosol and give rise to phosphoenolpyruvate. The corresponding amino acids are termed glucogenic. Acetyl-CoA and acetoacetyl-CoA produced by other amino acids may be further metabolized to ketone bodies (Section 15.3). Such amino acids are called ketogenic. Isoleucine, tyrosine, phenylalanine and tryptophan are both glucogenic and ketogenic. Lysine and leucine are only ketogenic. Some amino acids may also be decarboxylated to yield biologically active amines, e.g. histamine and dopamine.

In man and mammals, the ammonium ions are converted into urea in the liver. However, peripheral tissues may degrade amino acids. Any release of ammonia into the blood circulation is potentially dangerous because the brain is very sensitive to ammonia which may cause mental retardation, coma or death. Glutamate combines with ammonia to form glutamine (Figure 16.2b), which is electroneutral and can thus pass through plasma membranes. Glutamine acts as a non-toxic vehicle for the delivery of ammonia to the liver which contains within the cytosol, glutaminase

which deaminates glutamine. The glutamate and NH_4^+ may be utilized in the urea cycle to form urea, the excretion product (Section 16.4).

TABLE 16.4   The fate of the carbon skeletons of deaminated amino acids

Carbon skeleton	Major metabolite(s) produced
Alanine Glycine Serine Cysteine	Pyruvate*
Threonine	Pyruvate + succinyl-CoA†
Tryptophan	Pyruvate + acetoacetyl-CoA‡
Arginine Proline Histidine Glutamine Glutamate	2-Oxoglutarate†
Valine Methionine	Succinyl-CoA
Isoleucine	Succinyl-CoA + acetyl-CoA‡
Phenylalanine Tyrosine	Fumarate† + acetoacetyl-CoA
Asparagine Aspartate	Oxaloacetate†
Lysine	Acetoacetyl-CoA
Leucine	Acetyl-CoA + acetoacetyl-CoA

* End product of glycolysis
† Tricarboxylate cycle intermediate
‡ Fatty acid oxidation intermediate

16.4 The disposal of amino nitrogen in the animal kingdom

The form in which amino nitrogen is excreted from the organism is dependent upon the adaptation of the organism to its habitat. Aquatic animals may excrete ammonia directly into their environment since the large volume of water in which they live can effectively dilute and remove this toxic substance. Therefore, fish may excrete NH_3 via their gills and obviate the need for a complex urinary system. Ammonia is transported as glutamine which is deaminated by glutaminase contained within gill tissue.

Terrestrial animals do not have such convenient surroundings and require more elaborate elimination systems. Development of such systems incorporating kidneys, ureter and urinary bladder etc. does not solve the entire problem. The storage capacity of urinary bladders is limited therefore elevated ammonia concentrations could develop. Free ammonia can diffuse through membranes so that ammonia collected in the urine could be passively reabsorbed with toxic effects. Moreover, since

at blood pH, ammonia is in its protonated form, excretion by the kidney necessitates the loss of valuable anions such as chloride and phosphate. For these reasons, it is considered that land-dwelling mammals developed the mechanism to synthesize the highly water-soluble and non-toxic urea molecule.

In the case of birds, flight imposes restrictions upon the weight of the animal. This precludes internal water reservoirs necessary for urea excretion. Birds excrete amino nitrogen as uric acid which requires little water. Since uric acid is also the end product of purine catabolism (Section 16.7), nitrogenous waste is disposed of in a common degradation product.

In terms of amino nitrogen excretion the animal kingdom can be classified into ammonotelic (ammonia), ureotelic (urea) and uricotelic (uric acid) organisms depending on the nature of the discharged substance.

16.5 The urea cycle

Urea is produced as a non-toxic soluble vehicle for the elimination of nitrogen originating from the catabolism of amino acids. Urea is synthesized by a cyclic pathway discovered, in outline, by Krebs and Henseleit in 1932. A major function of the liver is urea biosynthesis but enzymes of the pathway also occur in kidney, skin, brain plus some other cells where their primary purpose is to synthesize arginine.

Figure 16.5 illustrates the reactions and the compartmentalization of the enzymes of the urea cycle. The first reaction in urea biosynthesis is the mitochondrial formation of carbamoyl phosphate, the substrate of the urea cycle. The reaction utilizes an ammonium (NH_4^+) ion, delivered into the mitochondrion as glutamate by the action of both the glutamate–aspartate (Section 11.3) and the glutamate–hydroxyl ion antiport carriers. Oxidative deamination of glutamate by glutamate dehydrogenase releases an NH_4^+ ion.

The carbamoyl group of carbamoyl phosphate is derived from this NH_4^+ and a bicarbonate ion. The reaction which is energetically demanding (two ATP) is catalysed by carbamoyl-phosphate synthase (ammonia). Avoid confusion with a different cytosolic enzyme called carbamoyl-phosphate synthase (glutamine-hydrolysing) which participates in pyrimidine biosynthesis. Carbamoyl-phosphate synthase (ammonia) is an allosteric enzyme which regulates the flux of the urea cycle. Its activity is dependent upon the positive modulator N-acetylglutamate which is synthesized from glutamate and acetyl-CoA by amino-acid acetyltransferase. The cycle is also regulated by diet-induced fluctuations in synthase levels resultant from modulations in the expression of its gene (Section 17.8).

In the first reaction of the cycle the carbamoyl group is transferred from carbamoyl phosphate to ornithine to yield citrulline. Neither of these amino acids are known to occur in proteins. The remainder of the cycle reactions are cytoplasmic so citrulline is transported by a specific uniport carrier across the inner mitochondrial membrane. In the cytosol, argininosuccinate is formed by a condensation reaction which produces a covalent linkage between the carbonyl carbon atom of citrulline and the amino group of aspartate. This reaction, catalysed by argininosuccinate synthase, is readily reversible but is driven forward by the irreversible hydrolysis of the pyrophosphate by-product (Section 10.4). The aspartate is mainly derived from glutamate by the action of aspartate aminotransferase.

Argininosuccinate lyase cleaves argininosuccinate into arginine and fumarate. Fumarate, which conserves the carbon atoms of the aspartate, may be converted by cytosolic molecules of fumarate hydratase (Section 12.4) into malate which is primarily translocated into the mitochondrial pool of tricarboxylate cycle intermediates. Alternatively some cytosolic malate may be reconverted into aspartate via oxaloacetate and an amino transfer reaction. The final reaction of the cycle involves the hydrolysis of arginine by arginase, associated with the endoplasmic reticulum, to yield urea and ornithine. The cycle is completed by the translocation of ornithine to the mitochondrion where its carbamoylation produces another citrulline. The sources of the atoms of the urea molecule are as follows: glutamate is the source of both nitrogen atoms; the carbon atom is derived from the bicarbonate ion resulting from decarboxylation reactions (e.g. in tricarboxylate cycle); the oxygen atom comes from the water participating in the arginase reaction. The cost of urea synthesis is four ATP; two in the synthesis of carbamoyl phosphate and two equivalents in the synthesis of argininosuccinate. In the latter case, although only one ATP is used it is hydrolysed to AMP from which two phosphorylation reactions are required to resynthesize ATP.

Urea readily diffuses across the plasma membrane of liver cells into the blood circulation. Small amounts of urea are secreted in sweat but most is excreted in the urine following filtration by the kidney glomeruli although significant quantities of urea may be passively reabsorbed with water by the proximal tubules on each occasion. Urea is the major nitrogenous constituent of urine when the diet contains normal quantities of protein. Where the diet contains low levels or lacks protein, the decline in urinary urea concentrations reflects the control exercised on carbamoyl-phosphate synthase levels. Defects in the function of carbamoyl-phosphate synthase, ornithine carbamoyltransferase, argininosuccinate synthase and arginase result in hyperammonaemia (elevated blood ammonia concentrations) with concomitant effects on the brain.

204

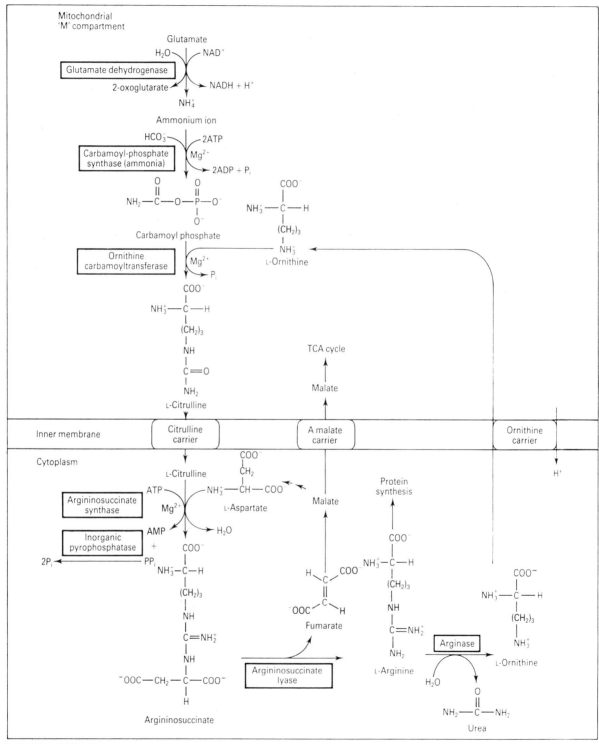

FIGURE 16.5 The urea cycle

16.6 The biosynthesis of heterocyclic compounds

The atoms of the pyrimidine ring are derived from two amino acids, aspartate and glutamine, and carbon dioxide (Figure 16.6a). Biosynthesis does not produce free heterocyclic compounds but nucleotides. The synthetic pathway produces uridine ribonucleotides which also serve as the precursors of other pyrimidine ribonucleotides and deoxyribonucleotides. The cellular pool of free deoxyribonucleotides is normally held at an extremely low level but requires enhancement to support the synthesis of DNA when cells prepare for division.

Three different amino acids, glycine, aspartate and glutamine, carbon dioxide and formyl groups provide the atoms of the purine ring (Figure 16.6b). Although purines contain a pyrimidine ring, the synthetic pathways are distinct with the imidazole ring being initially constructed. Its construction involves one of two formylation reactions in which different folate derivatives donate the formyl group. There are six members of the folate family which can serve as one-carbon atom donors. The first purine nucleotide synthesized is inosine 5′-monophosphate (IMP) which is not found in appreciable concentrations in the cell, either free or as a monomeric unit of nucleic acids. From IMP, divergent pathways lead to GMP and AMP.

Since synthesis of pyrimidine and purine nucleotides *de novo* (anew) is energetically demanding, it may occur using heterocyclic bases from dietary sources or from those released by the turnover of nucleic acids. Such reactions, called salvage pathways (Figure 16.7) since they enable the reutilization of existing bases, facilitate considerable savings in ATP.

FIGURE 16.6   Origins of the atoms of heterocyclic rings. (a) Pyrimidine ring. (b) Purine ring

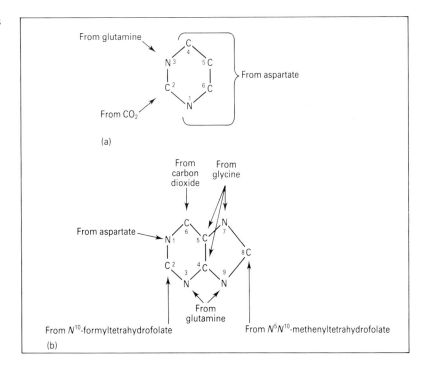

FIGURE 16.7 Some salvage
pathways for heterocyclic bases

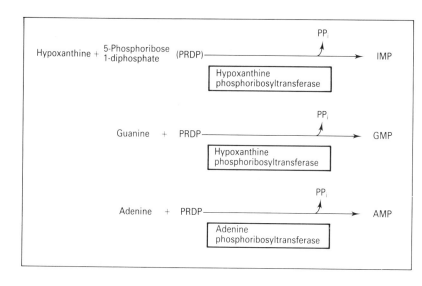

16.7 The hybridoma technique

Biotechnology exploits a salvage pathway in the
production of monoclonal antibodies (Section 4.7).
Mammalian spleen cells (B-lymphocytes) may be
fused with mammalian myeloma cells (cancerous
blood cells which produce large quantities of
immunoglobulins) so that the hybrid cell inherits
characteristics from both cells. The desired characteristics are immortality (not antibody synthesis)
from the cancer cell and antibody production by
the B-lymphocyte. The technique involves mixing
large numbers of both types of cells in the presence
of a fusing agent such as poly(ethylene glycol). A
small number of fusions occur. Hybrid cells are
harvested, monitored for specific antibody production and stored frozen in liquid nitrogen until
additional supplies of monoclonal antibody are
required.

Among the technical problems is the selection of
the hybrid cells from the myeloma cells, both of
which are equally rapid in growth. The biochemical trick, upon which the technique relies, is the
use of mutant non-secreting myeloma cells which
are deficient in hypoxanthine phosphoribosyltrans-
ferase (HPRTase⁻) and a culture medium containing a mixture of hypoxanthine, aminopterin and
thymidine (HAT medium). Aminopterin blocks the
synthesis of both purines and pyrimidines. In the
presence of aminopterin, HPRTase⁻ cells die
because they cannot utilize the pertinent salvage
pathway. Since B-lymphocytes contain HPRTase,
the fused cells survive by utilizing the hypoxanthine and thymidine in the culture medium. The
unfused B-lymphocytes are also unaffected but are
rapidly outgrown by the hybrid cells.

16.8 The degradation of heterocyclic compounds

The turnover of nucleic acids is a continuous process in which synthesis and degradation are carefully regulated. Degradation of RNA and DNA
are effected by a variety of ribonucleases and
deoxyribonucleases respectively. The nucleotides
are converted to nucleosides by the action of

deaminases and phosphatases (nucleotidases).
Removal of the sugar moiety from the nucleoside
is performed by phosphorolysis (phosphorylases)
in which an orthophosphate group cleaves the
glycosidic bond to release ribose (deoxyribose)
1-phosphate. Phosphopentomutase converts

ribose 1-phosphate and deoxyribose 1-phosphate into respective 5-phosphate derivatives. Ribose 5-phosphate may be metabolized by the non-oxidative phase of the pentose phosphate pathway to enter the pool of glycolytic intermediates (Section 11.9). Deoxyribose 5-phosphate is cleaved by deoxyribose-phosphate aldolase into glyceraldehyde 3-phosphate (a glycolytic intermediate) and acetaldehyde from which acetyl-CoA is formed by the action of acetaldehyde dehydrogenase (acetylating). The resultant pyrimidine bases, uracil and thymine, are further degraded by reactions catalysed by the same three enzymes to β-alanine and β-aminoisobutyrate respectively. Although β-alanine is a component of some bio-logical compounds, e.g. coenzyme A, it is mainly excreted in the urine. β-Aminoisobutyrate may be metabolized to succinyl-CoA, a tricarboxylate cycle intermediate, or excreted in the urine.

The resultant purine bases, guanine and hypoxanthine (from AMP and dAMP), may be either salvaged (Section 16.6) or converted to xanthine. The oxidation of xanthine by xanthine oxidase yields urate (uric acid) which is excreted in the urine of man and primates. Other organisms are capable of the synthesis of various enzymes which permit the continuation of the pathway to various end products, e.g. allantoin in mammals, urea and glyoxylate in most fishes (not teleost fishes) and amphibians, and ammonia and CO_2 in crustaceans.

Suggested further reading

BENDER, D. A. (1985) *Amino Acid Metabolism*, Wiley, New York

HURST, D. T. (1980) *An Introduction to the Chemistry and Biochemistry of Pyrimidines, Purines and Pteridines*, Wiley, Chichester

POSTGATE, J. R. (1982) *The Fundamentals of Nitrogen Fixation*, Cambridge University Press, Cambridge

CHAPTER 17

Gene expression

17.1 The central dogma

The concept of the central dogma of molecular biology (Section 1.6), formulated in the late 1950s by Francis Crick may be summarized as DNA (deoxyribonucleic acid)→RNA (ribonucleic acid)→protein.

In all living organisms, nuclear DNA serves as the reservoir of genetic information which is expressed in terms of the structure of proteins manufactured by the cell. The base sequence of the DNA determines the amino acid sequence of pro-

teins which are responsible for all aspects of cellular function. Because of cellular organization, synthesis of protein from the DNA blueprint occurs in two stages: transcription, i.e. the synthesis of a messenger RNA molecule of a structure complementary to the structure of DNA so that the genetic information is transferred to mRNA, and upon delivery of the message to the cytosol, its translation into protein.

17.2   Transcription : initiation and elongation

Through hybridization experiments (Section 7.5), it was shown that the base sequence of mRNA is complementary to sections of one strand of the DNA duplex. At each end of these sections there

are additional sequences which locate the start and end of the transferable information. Thus, relatively short segments of DNA are transcribed as units. Transcription is the process in which RNA is

FIGURE 17.1   Base sequences of prokaryotic (*Escherichia coli*) promoters indicating important regions

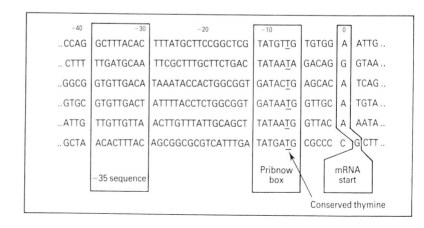

synthesized by enzymes called DNA-directed RNA polymerases (often abbreviated to RNA polymerases). These enzymes use ribonucleoside triphosphates as substrates and DNA as a template. The RNA polymerase of *E. coli* consists of five subunits: two identical α-subunits (molecular weight 36 500) and one each of β (molecular weight 150 600), β′ (molecular weight 155 600) and σ (molecular weight 70 300). The σ subunit readily dissociates from the holoenzyme to leave the core enzyme which has the polymerizing activity.

Transcription may be divided into three phases: initiation, elongation and termination. Transcription commences on the binding of a RNA polymerase at a specific site called a promoter on the DNA molecule. A promoter contains a short deoxyribonucleotide sequence which is recognized by the σ subunit of the RNA polymerase. Two sequences are of major importance (Figure 17.1): a sequence called the Pribnow box and the −35 sequence. Pribnow boxes range from the sixth to the twelfth base preceding the first base transcribed and are variants of the consensus sequence TATAATG. The term consensus sequence implies that determined sequences in various DNAs exhibit only limited variations (one or two bases) from that stated. The underlined T indicates a highly conserved thymine residue employed as a marker during the comparison of different sequences. The −35 sequence ranges from the

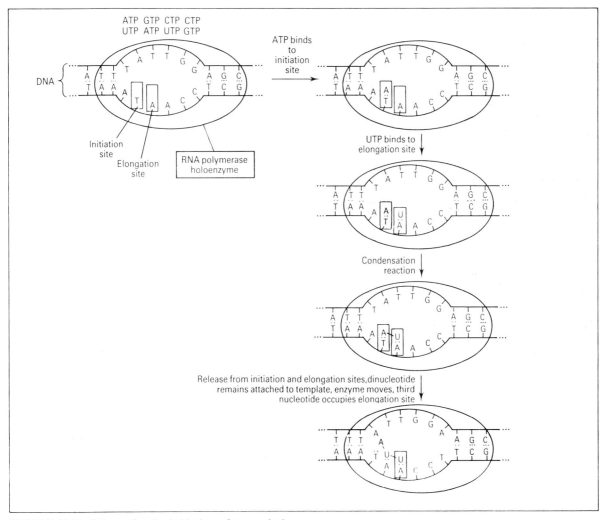

FIGURE 17.2 Scheme for the initiation of transcription

thirtieth to the thirty-eighth base preceding the first base transcribed. To this sequence, the σ subunit binds in a highly specific manner and then the appropriate region of the polymerase interacts with the Pribnow box. On binding to the Pribnow box, the enzyme dissociates from the − 35 sequence. The core enzyme screens a region from bases − 40 to + 20 and initiates local unwinding of the DNA helix which is a prerequisite for transcription. Since the Pribnow box is rich in A and T, this region of the DNA is susceptible to melting

(Section 7.5). This enzyme-bound melted region is termed the open-promoter complex in which the enzyme is strongly bound to one chain of the DNA duplex called the sense or coding strand. This strand is transcribed into RNA. The other strand is not transcribed and is called the antisense strand.

Upon the formation of an open-promoter complex, polyribonucleotide chain formation may commence. RNA polymerase contains two nucleotide-binding sites called the initiation and the elon-

FIGURE 17.3   Condensation of the initial two nucleotides during transcription

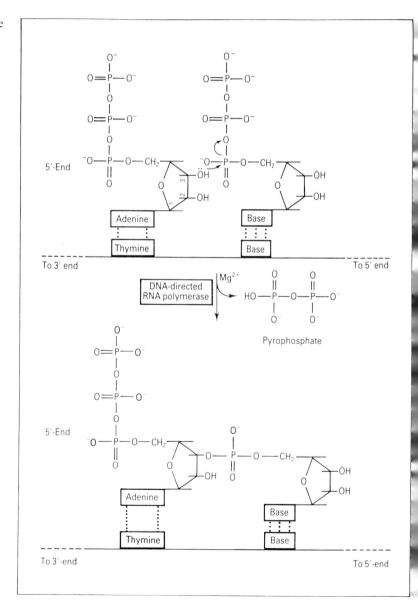

gation sites (Figure 17.2). The initiation site binds mainly purine triphosphates (ATP and GTP) so that adenine is normally the first base in the chain. Frequently the first DNA base transcribed is a thymine in the open-promoter complex which forms a base-pair through hydrogen bonding with the adenine of an incoming ATP. The elongation site contains the next template base to which the appropriate ribonucleoside triphosphate is attracted through its capacity to form the appropriate hydrogen bond arrangement. The two nucleotides undergo a condensation reaction in which the 3'-OH group of the first nucleotide reacts with the 5'-triphosphate group of the nucleotide in the elongation site to form a 3',5'-phosphodiester bond. Pyrophosphate is released (Figure 17.3). This mechanism means that the new RNA chain is synthesized from the 5'-end, i.e. chain growth occurs in the 5'→3' direction and produces a RNA molecule which is of the opposite polarity to the DNA template. The energy for the conden-

sation reaction is provided by the cleavage of the pyrophosphate from the nucleotide. Initiation has been accomplished when the first base is released from the initiation site. The dinucleotide remains attached to the sense strand and the polymerase moves one position along the strand to permit occupancy of the elongation site by a ribonucleotide complementary to the next template base. The process of elongation is now in progress. After some nucleotides have been combined, the σ factor dissociates from the RNA polymerase and the core enzyme catalyses the remaining polymerization reactions. The process of elongation involves the progression of the core enzyme along the sense strand, polymerization of the selected nucleotides, the progressive melting of DNA in front of the elongation site and re-formation of the duplex just behind the enzyme. As the helix re-forms, the hydrogen bonds between the newly synthesized RNA strand and the template are weakened thus facilitating the release of the RNA molecule.

17.3 Transcription: termination

Specific base sequences signal the termination of transcription. The signal may be described as an inverted-repeat sequence which contains an intervening non-repeating segment (Figure 17.4). Transcription cannot terminate at an exclusive sequence since the 3'-end of transcripts initiated from a single promoter may vary in the numbers of consecutive Us and may include other bases. The last transcribed base is always 27–43 bases from the start of the termination sequence. The actual mechanism of termination has not been fully elucidated but it is believed that termination occurs through sequence-promoted pausing of RNA polymerase activity. The first pause may be caused by the inverted-repeat sequence and the second pause by the high G + C region. The pauses may be the consequence of transcript folding. Termination in some cases involves additionally the presence of a termination protein called ρ (rho). On binding tightly to segments containing repeating Cs, ρ acquires an ATPase activity upon which its role depends. The final event in the termination of transcription is the dissociation of the core enzyme from the DNA. On its interaction with any free σ subunit, the holoenzyme is reconstituted and may initiate the transcription of another gene.

Transcription produces RNA molecules. In prokaryotes, rRNAs and tRNAs are synthesized as longer precursors which require post-transcriptional processing including methylation and cleavage by specific endonucleases before they are functional molecules. Polycistronic mRNAs (Section 7.4) do not require further enzymic modification. In eukaryotes, three RNA polymerases have been identified. RNA polymerase I, located in the nucleolus (Section 9.4), synthesizes 5.8S, 18S, and 28S rRNA. RNA polymerase II, found in the nucleoplasm, participates in mRNA synthesis. RNA polymerase III, also identified within the nucleoplasm, functions in tRNA and 5S rRNA synthesis. Post-transcriptional processing similar to that of prokaryotic transcripts produces rRNAs and tRNAs.

Eukaryotic mRNAs are rapidly synthesized from heterogeneous nuclear RNA (hnRNA, Section 7.4) by the removal of sequences which will not undergo translation. At the level of the DNA, these intervening sequences are called introns as opposed to the translated sequences which are called exons. Removal of the introns involves another type of RNA called small nuclear RNA (snRNA) which contains about 100 nucleotides. A complementary segment of snRNA base-pairs with both ends of the intron and adjacent sections of the two exons. The hnRNA is cleaved, the intron excised and, through positioning by snRNA, the exons are spliced to produce an intact translatable mRNA.

FIGURE 17.4 A termination signal with inverted repeat sequences and intervening non-repeat segment highlighted. Transcript folding is also shown

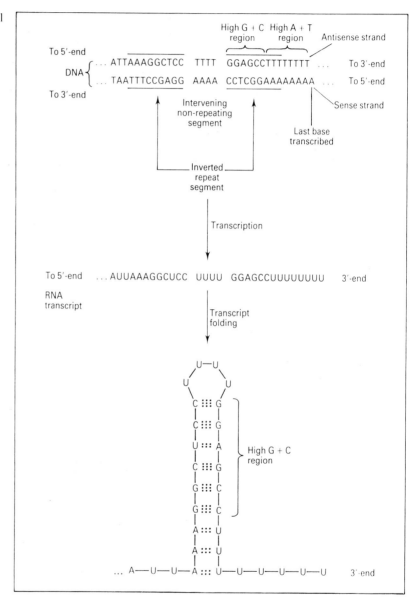

17.4 Translation: the role of amino-acid-tRNA ligases

Translation involves two compartments: the cytosol in which individual amino acids are enzymically attached to their specific tRNAs by amino-acid-tRNA ligases (also called aminoacyl-tRNA synthetases) and the ribosomes in which the amino acids are correctly positioned according to the base sequence of a mRNA template and polymerized into polypeptide chains.

In the cytosol, each of the 20 amino acids occurring in proteins is esterified to the 3'-OH group of its corresponding tRNA(s) by an enzyme which is specific for both the amino acid and the tRNA (Figure 17.5a,b). The reaction occurs in two steps (Figure 17.5c). The first step involves adenylylation of the amino acid in which the carboxyl group of the amino acid and the α-phosphate group of the ATP form an anhydride linkage with the release of pyrophosphate. The aminoacyl–adenylate remains enzyme-bound for the second step in which the aminoacyl moiety forms an ester linkage with the appropriate tRNA. Cleavage of this ester bond, $\Delta G^{0'} = -29.3 \text{ kJ mol}^{-1}$, provides the energy for the ribosomal formation of a peptide bond. The cleavage of pyrophosphate renders the overall reaction irreversible (Section 10.4).

In addition to their ability to load the tRNA with an amino acid, amino-acid-tRNA ligases are capable of recognizing inappropriate attachments, i.e. they have a proofreading function. If an incorrect amino acid has been attached, it may be removed by the hydrolysis of the enzyme-bound aminoacyl–adenylate intermediate. Once the anhydride linkage is cleaved, the amino acid and AMP dissociate from the active site so that the tRNA may be reloaded, hopefully with the correct molecule. The selectivity of these ligases is largely responsible for the maintenance of the fidelity of protein synthesis.

FIGURE 17.5 Loading of tRNA molecules with their corresponding amino acid. (a) General equation. (b) Aspartate reaction. (c) The two-step mechanism

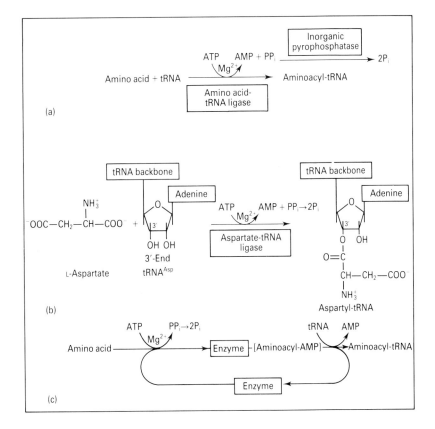

17.5 Translation: the genetic code

The information contained in the base sequence of the mRNA template is interpreted in sequences of three bases called codons; each codon represents one amino acid. Therefore, the unit of information is the codon. Since there are four major bases in mRNA, 4^3 (i.e. 64) different codons are possible. The 64 triplets constitute the genetic code (Table 17.1). All codons have been assigned to amino acids or punctuation signals. Three triplets (UAA, UAG and UGA) are not complemented by anticodons on tRNAs and serve to signal that the polypeptide chain has been completed. Of the other 61 triplets which have complementary tRNAs, two (AUG and GUG) have additional roles in the initiation of protein synthesis. Since there are only 20 amino acids, most amino acids are specified by more than one codon, i.e. the code is degenerate. The genetic code applies to prokaryotes and eukaryotic nuclear and chloroplast mRNAs but not to mitochondrial mRNAs. Therefore the genetic code is quasi-universal!

In numerous cases, the first two letters seem to determine the amino acid to be included. The codon is recognized by an anticodon, a nucleotide triplet on the tRNA, through their capacity to hybridize. Using scale models of various base-pairing arrangements, it was demonstrated that non-Watson–Crick base-pairing is permissible in the 3'-position of the codon since the steric constraints inherent within the DNA duplex do not apply. The phenomenon is called wobble. The base inosine (I, Figure 7.2a), frequently found in the 5'-position of the anticodon, may pair with A or C or U. G may pair with U. Because of its hydrogen-bonding permutations, I maximizes the number of codons with which the particular tRNA can bind. Wobble therefore reduces the number of specific tRNA molecules needed by the cell.

TABLE 17.1   The genetic code in prokaryotic cells

Amino acid	mRNA codon*
Alanine	GCU, GCC, GCA, GCG
Arginine	CGU, CGC, CGA, CGG, AGA, AGG
Asparagine	AAU, AAC
Aspartic acid	GAU, GAC
Cysteine	UGU, UGC
Glutamic acid	GAA, GAG
Glutamine	CAA, CAG
Glycine	GGU, GGC, GGA, GGG
Histidine	CAU, CAC
Isoleucine	AUU, AUC, AUA
Leucine	CUU, CUC, CUA, CUG, UUA, UUG
Lysine	AAA, AAG
Methionine	AUG
Phenylalanine	UUU, UUC
Proline	CCU, CCC, CCA, CCG
Serine	UCU, UCC, UCA, UCG, AGU, AGC
Threonine	ACU, ACC, ACA, ACG
Tryptophan	UGG
Tyrosine	UAU, UAC
Valine	GUU, GUC, GUA, GUG
Start	AUG, GUG†
Stop	UAA, UAG, UGA

* The mRNA is read from the 5'-end which is indicated by the first letter. The third letter is the 3'-end of the codon
† The use of GUG in initiation is very rare

17.6 Translation: the mechanism of protein biosynthesis

The mechanism of protein biosynthesis occurs in three consecutive phases: initiation, elongation and termination. In prokaryotes and eukaryotes, differences exist in the mechanisms employed. These differences relate to:

1. The factors involved in initiation, elongation and termination (Table 17.2).
2. The sequence of interactions between the small ribosomal subunit, initiator tRNA and mRNA.
3. The structures of mRNAs, ribosomal subunits (Section 7.4) and initiator tRNAs. Nevertheless, in overview, the processes are not dissimilar. Since investigations into prokaryotic protein biosynthesis tend to precede those into eukaryotic systems, this text is restricted to the system in *E. coli*. The components required for each stage of protein biosynthesis in this organism are listed in Table 17.3.

Initiation involves the recognition of the start signal on the mRNA by the small ribosomal subunit and its subsequent association with a large subunit to form an initiation complex (Figure 17.6). Initiator-tRNA is one of two methionine-tRNAs which can recognize the single triplet for methionine, AUG. The other tRNA^{Met} reads internal AUG triplets to insert methionyl residues into the polypeptide chain whereas initiator-tRNA plays an important role only in the initiation of protein synthesis. The methionine loaded on to initiator-tRNA, by methionine-tRNA ligase, is formylated by methionyl-tRNA formyltransferase and so is prevented from translating internal codons. Initiator-tRNA is bound to a 30S ribosomal subunit by the selective action of IF-2 with bound steric effector, GTP. IF-1 stabilizes the binding of IF-2 to the subunit. All initiation factors have been located near the cleft (Figure 7.9a). This small subunit attaches to the starting region of the mRNA through its 16S rRNA, a process mediated by IF-3. IF-3 also functions in keeping the large and small subunits apart. The 3'-end of l6S rRNA is located at the platform and contains a pyrimidine-rich sequence which base-pairs with a complementary purine-rich sequence on the mRNA (called the Shine-Dalgarno sequence or ribosome-binding site) occurring approximately 10 bases before the AUG sequence (Figure 17.7). Therefore,

TABLE 17.2 Factors involved in protein synthesis

Factors	Prokaryotes	Eukaryotes
Initiation factors	IF-1, IF-2, IF-3	eIF-1, eIF-2, eLF-3, eIF-4A, eIF-4B, eIF-4C, eIF-4F, eIF-5, eIF-6, GEF
Elongation factors	EF-Tu.Ts, EF-G	EF-1, EF-2
Termination factors	RF-1, RF-2, RF-3	RF

TABLE 17.3 Components involved in each stage of protein synthesis in *E. coli*

Initiation	Elongation	Termination
Initiator-tRNA	Initiation complex	Termination codon
30S ribosomal subunit	Aminoacyl-tRNAs	Termination factors
Initiation factors	Elongation factors	
Mg^{2+}	Mg^{2+}	
GTP	GTP	
mRNA	Peptidyltransferase (50S subunit)	
Initiation codons		
50S ribosomal subunit		

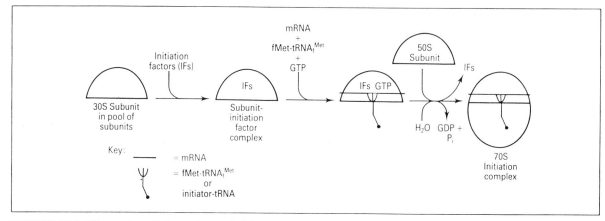

FIGURE 17.6   Formation of the prokaryotic initiation complex

complementary sequence pairing aligns the AUG start codon with the bound initiator-tRNA^Met. The final step in initiation involves the GTP-dependent interaction of this assembly with the 50S ribosomal subunit, permitted by the dissociation of IF-3. On association of the two subunits, IF-1 is liberated simultaneously from the ribosome to be soon followed by IF-2, the release of which requires the hydrolysis of bound GTP. The dissociation of the initiation factors allows the initiation complex to enter the elongation cycle. Once released, the factors may attach to another 30S subunit to initiate the formation of another initiation complex.

The association of ribosomal subunits produces two distinguishable sites (called P for peptidyl-tRNA binding site and A for aminoacyl-tRNA binding site) which function in the addition of amino acids to the formylmethionyl residue. According to the current two-site model (Figure 17.8), the 70S initiation complex contains an occupied site P. The appropriate ternary complex, con-

sisting of an aminoacyl-tRNA (other than initiator-tRNA), elongation factor EF-Tu and GTP, enters site A according to codon–anticodon interactions. Three events occur:

1. The aminoacyl-tRNA binds to the ribosome.
2. GTP is hydrolysed.
3. An EF-Tu–GDP complex and P_i dissociate from the ribosome.

EF-Tu–GDP, being unable to interact with another aminoacyl-tRNA directly, enters a series of reactions to be converted to high-affinity EF-Tu–GTP. These reactions involve another protein called EF-Ts which functions in the promotion of guanine nucleotide exchange. The mechanism is called the EF-Tu–EF-Ts cycle. The aminoacyl-tRNA will remain bound to site A only if the codon and anticodon are complementary otherwise it is released. This mechanism of proofreading contributes to the fidelity of protein synthesis.

The dissociation of the EF-Tu–GDP complex

FIGURE 17.7   Initiation sequences in some bacterial mRNAs

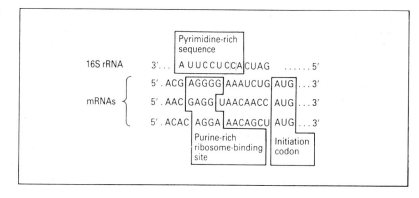

FIGURE 17.8 Elongation cycle according to the two-site model of Watson

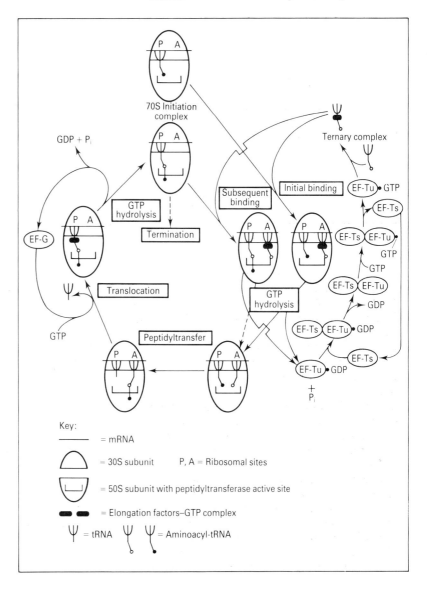

Key:

——————— = mRNA

⌒ = 30S subunit   P, A = Ribosomal sites

⊔ = 50S subunit with peptidyltransferase active site

▬▬ = Elongation factors–GTP complex

Ψ = tRNA   Ψ Ψ = Aminoacyl-tRNA

permits the bound aminoacyl-tRNA to make contact with the active site of the peptidyltransferase, the enzyme responsible for the formation of the peptide bond, which is located in the central protuberance of the large subunit (Figure 7.9b). The cleavage of the ester bond of the peptidyl-tRNA provides the energy for peptide bond formation. Site P is now occupied by a deacylated tRNA and the peptidyl-tRNA is located within site A. During the translocation reaction involving EF-G and GTP, the deacylated tRNA is ejected and the peptidyl tRNA is transferred to the P site. The mRNA

is advanced one codon by the tRNA molecules to which it is hydrogen bonded. EF-G and GDP dissociate from the ribosome following GTP hydrolysis. Site A is once again free and may be occupied by another ternary complex complementary to the unread codon. The elongation cycle continues as described until translocation introduces a stop codon (UAA, UAG or UGA) into site A. Protein synthesis enters the termination phase.

Release factors recognize and bind to these codons. RF-1 interacts specifically with triplets UAA and UAG; RF-2 interacts specifically with

UAA and UGA; RF-3 enhances the activities of RF-1 and RF-2. Codon-bound RF-1 and RF-2 cause a change in the catalytic activity of peptidyl-transferase so that the nascent peptide may be transferred to a molecule of water. This causes the carboxyl end of the growing polypeptide chain to be freed from its anchor, tRNA, and released from the ribosome which dissociates into 30S and 50S subunits. The subunits are held apart by association of IF-3 with the 30S subunit. The mechanism of protein synthesis appears to be highly complex. This degree of complexity is believed to have evolved to achieve the accuracy commensurate with the maintenance of the fidelity of protein synthesis.

A single mRNA may be processed simultaneously by numerous ribosomes to increase the rate of protein synthesis. The structure so formed is called a polyribosome or polysome. Since mRNA molecules are translated in the 5′→3′ direction, the ribosome bound nearest to the 5′-end displays the shortest polypeptide chain.

It is clear that prokaryotic proteins do not contain a formylmethionyl residue at their N-terminus. The products of translation are rarely the final form in which the protein demonstrates its biological activity. Thus the polypeptide chains undergo enzyme-catalysed post-translational modifications, which yield the final products. In eukaryotic cells, certain organelles function in post-translational processing (Section 9.6). In prokaryotes, deformylation of the N-terminal methionine is catalysed by formylmethionine deformylase. Alternatively, aminopeptidases may remove one or more N-terminal residues. In some cases, specific hydrolytic cleavage, i.e. proteolysis, is necessary to permit the spontaneous folding of the polypeptide chains. Protein folding is directed by the information contained within their amino acid sequence which determines bonding capabilities (Section 4.3). Through hydrogen bonds, ionic bonds and hydrophobic interactions, the protein realizes its functional conformation.

17.7 Mutation

Any change in the structure of the DNA will result in an altered primary structure of the protein. Such changes, inducible by a variety of chemical and physical agents or occurring spontaneously, are called mutations. Mutations may be classified by the nature or consequence of the change. The term, point mutation, indicates a variation in only a single base-pair whereas multiple mutation signifies a difference in two or more base-pairs from the natural sequence. A point mutation may be the result of a base substitution, a base insertion or a base deletion although the term is frequently applied to base substitutions. The tertiary structure of the protein may be unaffected by base substitutions if internal bonding arrangements remain unchanged. Insertions or deletions of base-pairs in the DNA may cause frame-shift mutations so called because the subsequent bases are processed in different triplet combinations or reading-frames.

17.8 Control of gene expression

The processes of protein synthesis clearly cannot operate without control otherwise the cell may be flooded with unnecessarily large concentrations of proteins which may disconcert the delicately balanced network of metabolic regulation (Section 10.6). Because of differences in the organization of their nucleic acids, e.g. monocistronic/polycistronic mRNAs (Section 7.4), protein-free/protein-bound DNA (Sections 9.1 and 9.4), the absence/presence of introns (Section 7.2), different mechanisms are employed by prokaryotes and eukaryotes to regulate the synthesis of their proteins. Only regulation of enzyme synthesis in prokaryotes will be briefly considered. Although a variety of potential mechanisms exist, in prokaryotes, mechanisms influencing the rate of transcription rather than the rate of translation are preferred.

Enzyme synthesis may be induced or repressed.

Induction refers to the stimulation of the synthesis of a catabolic enzyme, which is not currently being made by the cell, by the presence of its substrate or a substrate analogue (a substance closely related to the substrate). Repression refers to the inhibition of the synthesis of an enzyme involved in an anabolic pathway when its reaction product reaches a sufficiently high concentration. The two classical examples of induction and repression in *E. coli* are the *lac* operon and the *trp* operon respectively.

An operon or transcriptional unit is comprised of a region of a strand of DNA which contains the genes to be transcribed (called structural genes) and a single regulatory unit consisting of two elements, the promoter and operator sites. The pro-

moter site is the deoxyribonucleotide sequence to which RNA polymerase binds to initiate transcription (Section 17.2). The operator site frequently lies between the promoter site and the structural genes and regulates the rate of transcription. The activity of the operator is governed by a regulator gene located outside the operon (Figure 17.9a).

The *lac* operon will be considered first. When an *E. coli* capable of utilizing lactose as an energy source is grown in a glucose-free culture medium lacking lactose or any other β-galactoside, the intracellular concentrations of enzymes required for lactose utilization are minimal. The enzymes referred to are β-galactosidase, which cleaves lactose to galactose and glucose both of which enter

FIGURE 17.9   The *lac* operon of *E. coli*. (a) Organization of the *lac* operon showing bound RNA polymerase. (b) Inhibition of enzyme synthesis in the absence of lactose. (c) Stimulation of enzyme synthesis in the presence of lactose

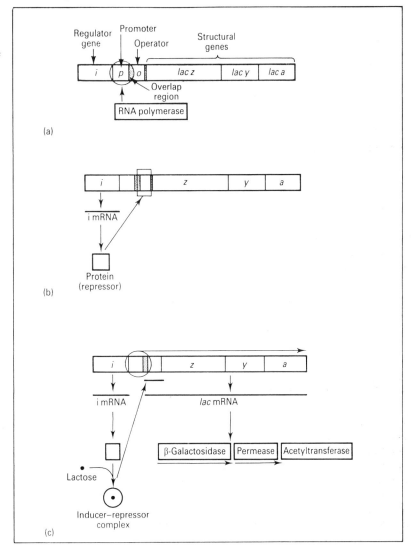

the glycolytic pathway, and the carrier (Section 9.3) usually called lactose permease which enables lactose to enter the cell. On the addition of lactose to the culture medium, both enzymes plus a third called acetyltransferase not involved in lactose utilization but in the catabolism of certain other β-galactosides are synthesized. Analyses of cellular mRNAs demonstrate the presence of *lac* mRNAs only after the supplementation of the medium. Thus the addition of lactose has induced transcription.

In the absence of lactose (Figure 17.9b), the regulator gene produces an mRNA molecule which gives rise to a protein which has an affinity for the operator site. Since the promoter and operator sites overlap, the operator-bound protein prevents the attachment of RNA polymerase. Transcription of the structural genes denoted as *lacZ*, *lac Y* and *lacA* is inhibited, i.e. repressed, therefore the protein product of the regulator gene is termed a

repressor. On the addition of lactose (Figure 17.9c), disaccharide binds to the repressor molecule causing a conformational change in the protein which results in the loss of its DNA-binding site. The operator site remains protein-free and RNA polymerase may attach to the promoter site. Lactose is called an inducer and since it inactivates the repressor molecule, the process is called derepression. The transcription of the structural genes produces the required enzymes.

If glucose is present in the culture medium, the activity of the *lac* operon is not required as glucose can satisfy the organism's energy requirements. No *lac* mRNA is produced because of the activity of the repressor molecule and another factor, cAMP (Section 10.7). The intracellular concentrations of cAMP reflect those of glucose. Glucose lowers the concentration of cAMP and conversely increased cAMP concentrations alleviate glucose-mediated repression. In the absence of glucose, cAMP forms

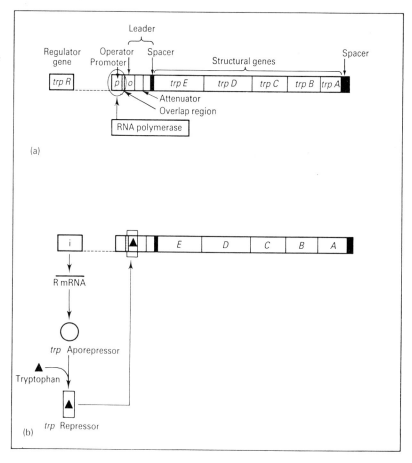

FIGURE 17.10   The *trp* operon of *E. coli*. (a) Organization of the *trp* operon showing bound RNA polymerase. (b) Inhibition of enzyme synthesis in the presence of tryptophan

a complex with CRP (cAMP-receptor protein, also called CAP or catabolite activator protein). cAMP induces a conformational change in CRP which enables the complex to bind to promoter sites and thereby stimulate transcription. In the *lac* operon, the cAMP–CRP complex must be bound to a base sequence in the promoter site to initiate transcription. In the absence of the cAMP–CRP complex, RNA polymerase–promoter binding is weak and unstable but in its presence, stronger binding occurs to enhance transcription. Therefore in the presence of glucose, transcription is inhibited by a lack of the cAMP–CRP complex resulting from low cAMP levels.

The *trp* operon governs the production of enzymes responsible for the synthesis of the amino acid, tryptophan, and operates when an adequate supply is not available from the culture medium. Therefore, tryptophan acts to inhibit the transcription of synthetic enzymes. In addition to structural genes, *trpA* to *trpE*, and promoter and operator sites (Figure 17.10a), there are two regions called the leader (*trpL*) and the attenuator (*trpa*). The regulator gene (*trpR*) is located at a distance from the operon. The regulator gene produces a protein called the *trp* aporepressor which cannot bind to the operator in the absence of tryptophan. In culture medium lacking tryptophan, the operon is active and the synthetic enzymes are manufactured. On the addition of tryptophan, the amino acid binds to the *trp* aporepressor to form an active *trp* repressor which binds to the operator and thereby inhibits gene expression (Figure 17.10b). Since the *trp* operon regulates a biosynthetic process, cAMP–CRP complexes are not involved. Also, tryptophan may be present at intracellular concentrations incapable of supporting normal growth and supplementary tryptophan synthesis is necessary. In this case, an on–off system is incompetent to meet cellular demands. The *trp* operon therefore is more complex than the *lac* operon with *trpL* and *trpa* which modulate synthesis against a background of deviating tryptophan levels by a mechanism called attenuation.

Suggested further reading

ALBERTS, B., BRAY, D., LEWIS, J., RAFF, M., ROBERTS, K. and WATSON, J. D. (1983) *Molecular Biology of the Cell*, Garland, New York

Hunt, T., Prentis, S. and TOOZE, J. (eds) (1983) *DNA Makes RNA Makes Protein*, Elsevier, Amsterdam

Spirin, A. S. (1986) *Ribosome Structure and Protein Biosynthesis*, Benjamin/Cummings, Menlo Park

CHAPTER 18

The replication of deoxyribonucleic acid

18.1 Semiconservative replication

Just prior to cell division, the DNA contained within the parental cell replicates so that each daughter cell may receive a high-fidelity copy of the genetic instructions which direct the synthesis of their proteins (Chapter 17). Three mechanisms of replication were proposed: conservative, semi-conservative or dispersive mechanisms. The conservative mechanism requires the synthesis of a complete DNA duplex molecule so that each first-generation daughter cell would contain either the parental DNA molecule or an entire newly synthesized molecule. Second-generation daughter cells would contain either the DNA present in the first generation or newly synthesized molecules. The semiconservative mechanism, postulated by Watson and Crick on the basis of their duplex model (Section 7.3), involves strand separation, whereby each strand may be employed as a template for the production of two new strands through hydrogen bond-directed complementary base-pairing. Each daughter molecule would be identical to the parental molecule and contain one of the parental strands together with one complementary newly synthesized strand. The dispersive mechanism proposed that each daughter molecule would consist of two strands in which short parental segments are spliced to short new segments. The mechanism employed *in vivo* was resolved in 1957 by Meselson and Stahl.

By growing *E. coli* for 14 generations on a medium containing, as sole nitrogen source, ammonium chloride in which the nitrogen atom was isotopically labelled, i.e. $^{15}NH_4Cl$, all cellular nitrogenous components including DNA become extensively labelled. DNA so labelled is marginally heavier than the common ^{14}N-containing DNA and sediments further on isopycnic centrifugation. Isolated DNA is mixed with a concentrated solution of CsCl in a centrifuge tube and subjected to centrifugation at 140 000 g for 20 h. During the centrifugation, the gravitational force draws the caesium ions towards the bottom of the tube until an equilibrium is achieved due to the sedimentation of the ions being opposed by their diffusion. The gradient is continuous between the highest CsCl concentration at the bottom of the tube and the lowest concentration at the top of the tube. During gradient formation, individual DNA molecules migrate downwards or upwards in the salt solution until their sedimentation/buoyancy is counterbalanced by the density of the gradient. Like molecules experience like forces to form a narrow band of molecules across the tube. The heavier ^{15}N-labelled DNA migrates to an equilibrium position lower in the CsCl gradient than ^{14}N-DNA.

In the Meselson–Stahl experiment (Figure 18.1), parental DNA molecules contain the heavy ^{15}N isotope. The organisms were transferred to fresh medium containing the common isotope and sampled at various time intervals. The DNA was isolated from the collected samples (the isolation procedure causing the fragmentation of the nucleic acid) and its sedimentation characteristics assessed by isopycnic centrifugation. At exactly one generation, i.e. a doubling in the number of organisms, a single band was identified on centrifugation equidistant from the positions of marker extracts of heavy and light DNAs. When the experiment was continued until a further doubling in cell

FIGURE 18.1   The Meselson–Stahl
experiment. (a) Isopycnic
centrifugation of DNA. (b) Results
of the experiment

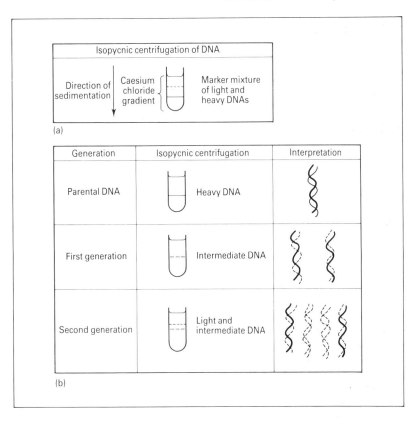

numbers, i.e. a second generation, the isolated
DNA exhibited two bands, one at the same intermediate position and the other at a position corresponding to that of marker light DNA. These results were interpreted as a demonstration of
semiconservative replication.

The structure of first-generation DNA was
ascertained by a second experiment in which the
isolated DNA was heat denatured (Section 7.5)
and subjected to CsCl gradient centrifugation. The
treated DNA demonstrated two bands, one corresponding to single-stranded ^{14}N-DNA and the
other to single-stranded ^{15}N-DNA. Therefore, the
intermediate DNA of first-generation bacteria con-
sisted of one light and one heavy strand. The semi-
conservative mechanism of replication had been
confirmed and the other potential mechanisms
were rejected. Similar experiments on eukaryotic
cells demonstrated the universality of the semiconservative mechanism in the replication of DNA *in
vivo*.

18.2 An overview of DNA replication

DNA replication has been extensively studied in
prokaryotes, especially in *E. coli* to which this text
is restricted. In overview the mechanism is relatively simple although the enzymology is rather
complex and attracts much research activity. DNA
replication like transcription (Section 17.2) can be
divided into three phases: initiation, elongation
and termination.

In *E. coli*, replication is initiated at a specific site
in a 245-base-pair region called *oriC* in which there
are highly conserved nucleotides to which DNA
initiation proteins, e.g. DNA-directed RNA

polymerase, protein A and DNA topoisomerase II, bind. From this single origin, replication of the circular chromosome proceeds bidirectionally as opposed to unidirectionally (Figure 18.2). As the replicating molecules resemble the Greek letter θ (theta), bidirectional replication of circular DNA duplexes is termed θ replication.

Elongation necessitates two replication forks at which the DNA helix undergoes local unwinding prior to the selection of apposite deoxyribonucleotides by hydrogen bonding to the bases of the two DNA templates and polymerization into two growing polynucleotide chains catalysed by a DNA-directed DNA polymerase. Since DNA-directed DNA polymerases, unlike DNA-directed RNA polymerases in transcription (Section 17.2), cannot initiate local unwinding of the DNA helix, these processes also involve DNA topoisomerases and helix-destabilizing proteins, e.g. single-strand binding protein.

Because of the antiparallel nature of the DNA duplex (Section 7.3), the two templates run in the $3' \rightarrow 5'$ and $5' \rightarrow 3'$ directions. Bidirectional replication requires simultaneous synthesis of two new complementary strands of the opposite polarity, i.e. $5' \rightarrow 3'$ and $3' \rightarrow 5'$ respectively. However, all known DNA polymerases polymerize only in the $5' \rightarrow 3'$ direction, i.e. the free 3'-OH group of a polynucleotide chain reacts with the 5'-triphosphate group of the next template-bound deoxyribonucleotide. The problem was resolved by Okazaki who demonstrated that the $3' \rightarrow 5'$ strand is firstly synthesized as small segments of about 1000–2000 deoxyribonucleotides in length. The segments, called Okazaki fragments, are then ligated by polydeoxyribonucleotide synthase (also called DNA ligase) to form a single $3' \rightarrow 5'$ strand. Therefore, during DNA replication the $3' \rightarrow 5'$ template is complemented by a $5' \rightarrow 3'$ strand in a continuous process whereas the $5' \rightarrow 3'$ template is complemented by a $3' \rightarrow 5'$ strand synthesized as fragments which are linked together, a process called discontinuous synthesis (Figure 18.3). The different modes of synthesis result in a time differential between the completion of the new strands. The strand completed by the continuous mode is called the leading strand whereas the discontinuously synthesized strand is termed the lagging strand.

Close examination of the Okazaki fragments revealed that the 5'-ends of the polydeoxyribonucleotide segments are covalently bonded to short lengths of RNA which is complementary to the DNA template. Subsequently it was discovered

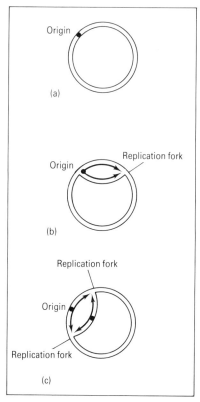

FIGURE 18.2   Schematic diagram of two models of DNA replication in a circular chromosome. (a) Initial organization. (b) Unidirectional model. (c) Bidirectional model

that synthesis of the leading strand also requires an RNA primer (Section 18.3). In contrast to transcription, termination of replication does not require a special base sequence to signal that the synthetic process should cease. In *E. coli*, replication is normally terminated at a site diametrically opposed to the origin of replication. In the lagging strand, the growing end of the nascent fragment progresses to the 5'-end of the primer of the preceding fragment and fragment synthesis is interrupted. In the leading strand, synthesis is terminated only on completion of the strand. The template strands and their new complementary strands spontaneously wind to form two daughter DNA duplexes each of which contains one parental and one newly synthesized strand. The resultant molecules are catenated, i.e. the two circular molecules are interlinked. Decatenation is achieved by a DNA topoisomerase which nicks, opens and reseals the chains (Section 18.3) so that replication produces two separate circular duplexes.

FIGURE 18.3 Summary of enzymes involved in the replication of an *E. coli* chromosome

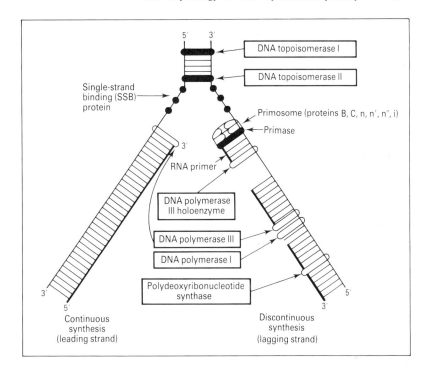

18.3 The enzymology of DNA replication in prokaryotes

Replication of the chromosome of *E. coli* is initiated by the local unwinding of the DNA at an A–T-rich site in the *oriC* region to form a replication bubble. To the single strands of the replication bubble bind the DNA initiation proteins: single-strand binding (SSB) protein, DNA-directed RNA polymerase, the primase enzyme and at least seven prepriming proteins of which A, B, C, n, n′, n″ and i are known (Figure 18.3). SSB protein coats the separated region to prevent duplex reformation through hydrogen bonding. The two RNA primer molecules are produced by different enzymes. DNA-directed RNA polymerase, which is also employed in transcription (Section 17.2), synthesizes the leading strand primer whereas lagging strand primers are the product of the primase enzyme. The function of protein A is unknown. Proteins B, C, n, n′, n″, i and the primase interact to form a unit called a primosome. The primosome migrates along the lagging strand in a 5′→3′ direction, driven by the hydrolysis of ATP bound to the n′ protein, to locate sites at which the primase should commence the synthesis of primer mol-

ecules for Okazaki fragments. At these sites which are not defined by any specific sequence, protein C promotes the binding of protein B to the DNA. Protein B induces a conformational change in the DNA which permits the primase to start primer production.

The capability to elongate nucleotide chains necessitates the exposure of template nucleotide sequences. Therefore the polymerase activity must be preceded by the continuous unwinding of the DNA duplex. The circular chromosome of *E. coli* exists as a left-handed supercoil (Section 7.3). Initially, the left-handed coils counterbalance the right-handed twists generated by the advancement of the replication fork. However, after approximately 5% of the DNA has been replicated, right-handed supercoils may be produced and replication would cease because movement of the fork is impaired.

Strand separation is catalysed by DNA topoisomerases. Type I DNA topoisomerases, either DNA topoisomerase I or III, prevents the unwinding process in one section of the circular molecule from producing a highly twisted structure in another region by introducing transient nicks into one strand. This relaxes the twisting structure by permitting free rotation of the strand by passing the intact strand through the break. On alleviation of the supercoiling, the enzyme reseals the strand. The DNA topoisomerase I reaction has no energy requirement since the enzyme binds to the 3'-end of the nicked strand to harness the energy of the phosphodiester bond which is utilized during bond re-formation in the rejoining process. This activity is regularly repeated to maintain the native structure of the DNA duplex. In *E. coli*, type II DNA topoisomerase acts to advance the replication fork by unwinding the duplex. This is achieved by nicking both strands and passing another double-stranded segment through the severed strands and resealing both strands. DNA topoisomerase II has an energy requirement which is satisfied by the hydrolysis of ATP. The biological role of DNA topoisomerase III requires further clarification.

The polymerization of deoxyribonucleotides into DNA is catalysed by enzymes called DNA-directed DNA polymerases which are capable of a high rate of catalytic activity. The 4.6 million base-pairs of *E. coli* are replicated in 40 min, i.e. at an approximate rate of 1700 nucleotides per s. There are three DNA polymerases in *E. coli*, designated DNA polymerase I, II and III. The first of these, DNA polymerase I, was discovered in 1956 by Kornberg and its investigation laid the foundation for the current understanding of DNA replication. DNA polymerase I is capable of the synthesis of DNA only in the presence of all four precursor ˙ nucleoside 5'-triphosphates, i.e. dATP, dGTP, dCTP, dTTP and existent DNA. If the reaction mixture lacks any one of the dNTPs, synthesis of DNA is inhibited. In addition, the enzyme requires 5'-triphosphates and does not polymerize dNDPs, dNMPs or ribonucleotides. The two nucleotides undergo a condensation reaction in which the terminal 3'-OH group of the chain reacts with the 5'-triphosphate group of the adjacent template-bound nucleotide. The energy for the condensation is provided by the cleavage of the pyrophosphate group from the nucleotide.

The enzyme requires existent double-stranded DNA to act as a primer and as a template. A primer is a nucleic acid molecule which has a free 3'-OH group to which a nucleotide may be added by a condensation reaction. This means that DNA polymerase I cannot act in synthesis *de novo*, only

in an elongation process. Although the original study utilized DNA as a primer molecule, RNA fulfils the primer function *in vivo*. In the template role, each strand of DNA determines the correct order for insertion of the deoxyribonucleotide bases through hydrogen-bonding arrangements in which adenine forms two hydrogen bonds with thymine and guanine forms three hydrogen bonds with cytosine (Figure 7.5). Therefore, whenever adenine appears in the template it specifies the positioning of thymine into the daughter strand and vice versa. Similarly, template cytosine and guanine determine the position of each other in new strands. For DNA replication a template of DNA is usually a prerequisite.

In 1971, Cairns and DeLucia discovered that some mutants of *E. coli* contained little DNA polymerase I activity and were sensitive to ultraviolet light. These properties indicated that DNA polymerase I did not have a major role in replication but was more likely to have an important function in the repair of damaged DNA. Subsequently two additional DNA polymerizing enzymes were identified and called DNA polymerase II and III. A distinct role for DNA polymerase II in replication has not been elucidated. DNA polymerase III is regarded as the major replicative enzyme. Although polymerase I is present in *E. coli* in the largest quantity, i.e. 400 molecules per organism, with polymerase II and III amounting to about 40 and 10 molecules respectively, the specific activity (Section 6.1) of polymerase III is much higher than that of the other enzymes.

The holoenzyme of DNA polymerase III consists of at least seven distinct polypeptides which are synthesized by different genes (Table 18.1). The β-subunit of polymerase III is required to recognize and bind to the primer. Upon the positioning of the holoenzyme at the initiation site, the β-subunit dissociates from the holoenzyme to permit the core of the enzyme to bind tightly with the primed DNA template to form a competent initiation complex. This process is ATP dependent and involves the γ-, δ- and τ-subunits. The core enzyme consists of three polypeptides, α, ε and θ. The α-subunit is responsible for polymerization and demonstrates a 3'→5' exonuclease activity which is involved in proofreading the newly attached nucleotide. The ε-subunit functions in the regulation of the proofreading. The genetic locus and the function of the θ subunit remains unresolved. The γ, δ and τ polypeptides contribute to the highly

TABLE 18.1   The subunit structure of DNA polymerase III holoenzyme of *E. coli*

Polypeptide chain	Molecular mass (kDa)	Genetic locus
α	140	*dnaE*
β	37	*dnaN*
γ	52	*dnaZ*
δ	32	*dnaX*
ε	25	*dnaQ*
θ	10	N.A.
τ	78	*dnaX–dnaZ*

N.A., not available

efficient operation of the core enzyme. It is postulated that the τ-subunit functions in the creation of a dimeric form of the polymerase in which this subunit interconnects two core enzymes. The dimeric structure can then polymerize both continuous and discontinuous strands in a coordinated fashion whereby one monomeric unit produces the continuous strand and the other synthesizes the Okazaki fragments of the lagging strand. As each nucleotide is polymerized to its respective chain, the enzyme moves the distance of one nucleotide along the template.

The duplication of the genetic message necessitates a high level of accuracy in the copying process. Normal base-pairing arrangements, i.e. A with T and C with G, may be compromised, e.g. by tautomerism (Section 7.5) so that C may align with A. To maintain the fidelity of DNA replication, a mechanism of detection and correction of such errors is necessary. The proofreading mechanism is a function of the DNA polymerases. In addition to their polymerizing activities, all polymerases also exhibit exonuclease activities (Table 18.2). The distortion created by an inappropriately placed nucleotide may prevent its 3′-OH group from participation in the condensation reaction. The polymerizing activity of the enzyme ceases and a separate $3' \rightarrow 5'$ exonuclease activity is stimulated to remove the unpaired base from the growing end

of the daughter chain. Following the cleavage of this base, the exonuclease activity is inhibited and the enzyme reverts to its polymerizing function. The $5' \rightarrow 3'$ exonuclease activity is not involved with proofreading but is important in the repair of DNA which has sustained damage by physical or chemical agents (Section 18.4).

Discontinuous synthesis of the lagging strand requires the removal of the primer, the resultant gap filled and the linking of the newly synthesized segments. DNA polymerase I activity accomplishes the first two tasks. Ligation of the segments to form a single $3' \rightarrow 5'$ strand may be catalysed by polydeoxyribonucleotide synthase since only phosphodiester bond formation, and not the insertion of nucleotides, is involved. Because the 5′-end of a segment consists of a monophosphate group rather than the triphosphate group of an inserted nucleotide, the energy for the formation of a phosphodiester bond must be supplied in contrast to the polymerase-catalysed reaction. The organism-dependent source of the energy for polydeoxyribonucleotide synthases is either ATP or NAD^+. In *E. coli*, the enzyme utilizes NAD^+ in a reaction in which NAD^+ is cleaved into AMP and nicotinamide mononucleotide (NMN). In addition to this important role, polydeoxyribonucleotide synthases function in DNA repair (Section 18.4).

TABLE 18.2   The catalytic activities of the DNA-directed DNA polymerases of *E. coli*

Activity	DNA polymerase		
	I	II	III
$5' \rightarrow 3'$ Polymerizing activity	+	+	+
$3' \rightarrow 5'$ Polymerizing activity	−	−	−
$3' \rightarrow 5'$ Exonuclease activity	+	+	+
$5' \rightarrow 3'$ Exonuclease activity	+	−	+

18.4 DNA repair

Potential damage to the genetic information may occur by inaccuracy in replication but this is circumvented by the proofreading capacities of the DNA polymerases (Section 18.3). However, a number of physical and chemical agents may interact with the DNA with profound consequences, e.g. the cell may become cancerous. Variously damaged DNA may demonstrate the loss or modification of bases including base dimerization, strand breakages or covalent crosslinkages.

The absorption of ultraviolet radiation may cause the dimerization of adjacent pyrimidine bases, e.g. thymine (Figure 18.4). Pyrimidine dimers distort the helical conformation of the DNA. The integrity of the DNA may be restored by either the process of excision repair or enzymic photoreactivation. In excision repair (Figure 18.5), the deformity is detected by a specific deoxyribonuclease (EC 3.1.25.1) which nicks the strand on the 5′-side of the damaged site. Since the distortion reduces hydrogen bonding, this region of the strand becomes loose. DNA polymerase I utilizes the free 3′-OH end, created by the deoxyribonuclease, as a primer and the intact strand as the template to elongate the DNA to fill the gap. The pyrimidine dimer region is excised by the $5′ \rightarrow 3′$ exonuclease activity of DNA polymerase I. This newly synthesized section of DNA is ligated to the 5′-end of the nicked strand by polydeoxyribonucleotide synthase. The alternative process of enzymic photoreactivation involves photochemical reversal of the dimerization reaction. The enzyme, deoxyribodipyrimidine photo-lyase binds to the damaged region of the DNA strand and uses the energy of visible light to disunite the thymine residues.

Whereas thymine dimerization is the most important reaction promoted by the UV irradiation of cells, loss of purine bases (depurination) is the most common chemical damage to the DNA. This occurs through the spontaneous hydrolysis of the glycosidic linkage between the base and the deoxyribose moieties. Repair is again effected by excision repair but in this case, the lesion is detected by another deoxyribonuclease (EC 3.1.25.2) which nicks the strand at the 5′-side of the damaged site before DNA polymerase I and polydeoxyribonucleotide synthase restore the DNA. The bases of the DNA may suffer chemical damage, e.g. deamination, alkylation, ring opening and reduction of double bonds. These modified bases may be detected by a specific member of a family of enzymes called DNA glycosylases which removes the offending base by hydrolytic cleavage of the glycosidic linkage. Excision repair then operates to reconstruct the DNA at the lesion.

FIGURE 18.4   Thymine dimer formation

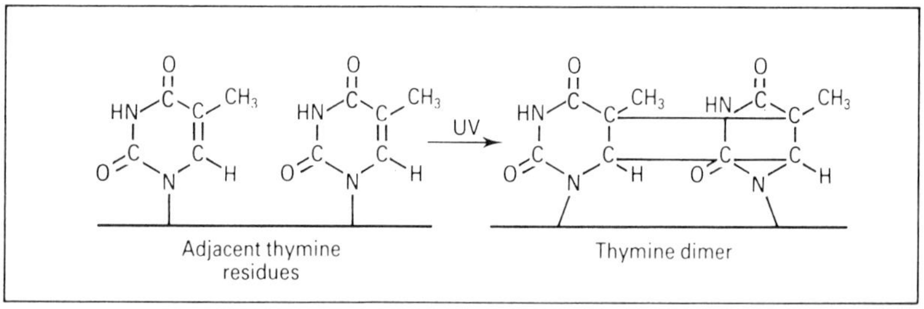

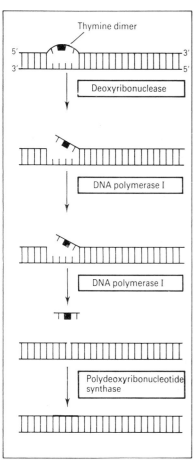

FIGURE 18.5   Excision repair mechanism for the correction of pyrimidine dimerization

---

Suggested further reading

FREIFELDER, D. (1987) *Molecular Biology*, 2nd edn, Jones and Bartlett, Portola Valley
LEWIN, B. (1987) *Genes III*, Wiley, New York

CHAPTER 19

Gene cloning

19.1 Applications of gene cloning

Gene cloning involves the production *in vitro* of new DNA molecules which contain novel combinations of genes or oligonucleotides and the propagation of such recombinant DNA molecules by the exploitation *in vivo* of the replicative mechanisms of bacteria (Section 18.3) and other organisms. The developments of genetic engineering techniques have permitted the alteration of the genome of microorganisms so that it produces substances of little intrinsic value but of great medical or economic value to mankind.

Foreign genes have been implanted into the DNA of *E. coli* to enable the production of useful proteins. Members of the antiviral family of proteins called interferons have been produced by these methods, and clinical trials to ascertain their efficacy in the treatment of certain cancers have been conducted. Human hormones such as insulin, somatostatin and somatotropin have been synthesized in *E. coli*. Insulin controls the level of glucose in the blood and its deficiency may result in a variety of serious diabetic conditions. To overcome problems associated with the production of insulin from pig and cow pancreases, the increasing demand for insulin and the immunological sensitization of the patient by continued injection of an animal protein, human insulin has been successfully synthesized from artificial genes on a commercial scale. The first human polypeptide hormone synthesized in *E. coli* was somatostatin which, containing 14-amino acid residues, was used to develop techniques for insulin production. Somatostatin is employed in the treatment of numerous disorders characterized by excessive growth. The hormone antagonistic to somatostatin

is somatotropin (human growth hormone) which is employed in the treatment of dwarfism.

Gene cloning could potentially provide contaminant-free blood products of high purity. A coagulation factor, Factor VIII, is required by certain haemophiliacs. The risk of hepatitis and acquired immune deficiency syndrome (AIDS) due to the unintentional collection of blood from virus carriers identified this factor as a candidate for production by DNA recombinant techniques.

In agriculture, techniques have been developed which permit the transfer of the characteristics of one plant to another through bacterial infection. Such techniques may create new varieties of plants with desirable characteristics, e.g. resistance to infection, the ability to withstand adverse weather conditions or the capability of nitrogen fixation.

Non-protein products may be synthesized by recombinant methods. Numerous important pharmaceuticals are small molecules, the biosyntheses of which require the sequential involvement of different enzymes. The cloning of all the relevant genes on to a single plasmid (Section 9.1) offers a means of enhanced production of the substances. The antibiotic, actinorhodin, has been synthesized in *Streptomyces* by such methods. Experimental vaccines against certain viral diseases have also been produced by recombinant DNA technology.

Gene cloning has played an important role in fundamental biological research. Its value lies in the preparation of DNA fragments containing a specific gene and has resulted in advances in knowledge of the structure, function, expression and the control of the activity of that gene. Recombinant DNA techniques have been applied to the study of the regulation of metabolism. The ascribed role of citrate synthase in metabolic regulation has resulted from the interpretation of data obtained by studies *in vitro*. However, through cloning of the *E. coli* citrate synthase gene, the intracellular level of citrate synthase can be manipulated through the regulatory unit of its gene (Section 17.8) by the non-metabolizable inducer, isopropyl β-D-thiogalactopyranoside, to permit the calculation of metabolic flux rates.

To understand fully the regulation of any metabolic pathway, the properties of the regulatory enzymes must be resolved (Section 10.6). The manipulation of cloned genes has provided significant quantities of enzymes for their purification. Further investigation of their structure/organization including the determination of their primary structures, structure–function relationships and the analysis of the roles and expression of multigene families, e.g. protein kinase C-related genes, have expanded our knowledge of metabolic regulation. Indeed, gene technology promises enormous benefits in a wide variety of biological pursuits.

19.2 Outline of gene cloning methodology

The strategy for gene cloning is outlined in Figure 19.1. A fragment of DNA containing the gene of interest is inserted into a host DNA molecule which is normally capable of promoting its own replication within the host cell. These host DNA molecules are called vectors. The insertion of the foreign gene into the vector is accomplished by the use of a class of enzymes called restriction endonucleases. The DNA of interest is cleaved into numerous fragments by a restriction endonuclease which results in a staggered cleavage (Section 19.4). The vector is separately cleaved with the same enzyme to produce 'sticky' ends (or cohesive ends). Upon mixing the fragments and the treated vector, hybridization (Section 7.5) yields a selection of recombinants which are ligated by polydeoxy-ribonucleotide synthase to produce vectors each carrying a different passenger DNA (Figure 19.2). Depending upon the nature of the vector, techniques are available for the transportation of the recombinants into the host cell.

The replicative machinery of the host cell is exploited by the vector to produce numerous identical copies of itself each containing the implanted gene. When the host cell replicates, copies of this gene appear in each daughter cell. Further vector replication occurs. After numerous cell divisions, a clone of identical host cells results. Each cell in the clone contains copies of the recombinant DNA molecule. The clone containing the DNA fragment of interest must be identified before the harvesting of an abundance of the desired gene.

FIGURE 19.1 Strategy for gene cloning in bacteria

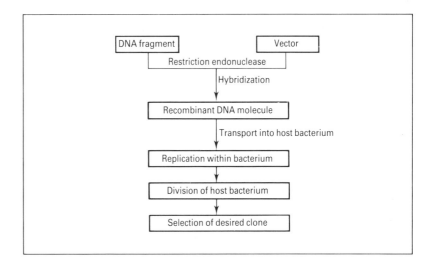

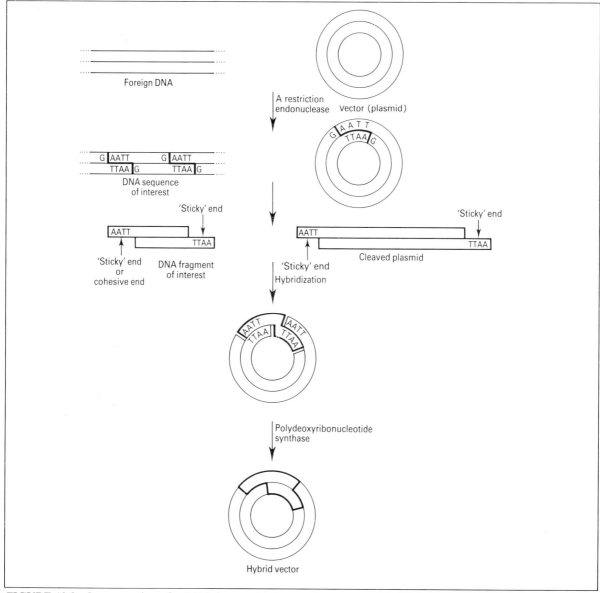

FIGURE 19.2 Incorporation of a DNA fragment into a vector

19.3 Vectors employed in *E. coli*

Vectors are DNA molecules, capable of replication in the host organism, into which a gene may be implanted to construct a recombinant DNA molecule. To be a successful vector, there are two requisites for the DNA molecule:

1. It must be capable of replication within the host cell to produce numerous copies of the inserted gene.
2. It should be relatively small.

Molecules of less than 10 000 nucleotides are more amenable to manipulation *in vitro* as larger molecules tend to shear during purification. Suitable vectors for use in bacterial systems are small plasmids and bacteriophage chromosomes. Bacteriophages are a group of viruses which specifically infect bacteria.

Plasmids are circular molecules of DNA located outside the nuclear region of prokaryotes. They usually contain one or more genes frequently responsible for the conferment of a useful property to the microorganism, e.g. antibiotic resistance (R-plasmid), promotion of sexual conjugation between bacterial cells (F-plasmid). The plasmid DNA contains a nucleotide sequence which can act as an origin of replication (Section 18.2) to permit the independent multiplication of the plasmid. Smaller plasmids utilize exclusively the replicative enzymes of the host (Section 18.3) whereas larger plasmids (approximately 250 kilobases) may contain genes which encode enzymes specific for plasmid replication. However, some plasmids integrate with the bacterial chromosomal DNA and are replicated along with the bacterial genome. The term episome is employed to refer to these integrative plasmids.

For efficient genetic engineering, the plasmid DNA should be obtainable at high levels. Some plasmids are found only as three or four copies per cell. More useful are plasmids which have a high cellular copy number, e.g. 25–50 copies per cell. Techniques are available to amplify the copy number further. If an inhibitor of protein synthesis, e.g. chloramphenicol, is added to a culture of plasmid-containing bacteria, chromosomal, but not plasmid, DNA replication stops. The number of plasmids per cell thereby may increase to over one thousand.

Although plasmids are common features of bacterial cells, they are relatively rare in other organisms. Many strains of the yeast *Saccharomyces cerevisiae* contain a well-characterized and useful large plasmid called, because of its length, the 2 μm plasmid. Because of this plasmid this yeast is regarded as a potential host organism for exploitation by the pharmaceutical industry.

Bacteriophages, like all viruses, contain only a single nucleic acid molecule (usually DNA but occasionally RNA) which carries a relatively small number of genes enclosed by a protective protein coat called the capsid. The two main types of phage which infect *E. coli* are the head-with-tail phages, e.g. phage λ, or filamentous phages, e.g.

M13 (Figure 19.3). The head component of the head-with-tail phages is frequently an eicosahedron (having 20 triangular faces and 12 corners) which encompasses single- or double-stranded linear or circular DNA (or single-stranded linear RNA). The tail is a complex multicomponent structure which often ends in tail fibres. In filamentous phages, the nucleic acid, which is in an extended helical form, is contained within the capsid.

The life cycles of all phages are essentially the same although many variations in the detail of the general pattern are recorded. The phage attaches to receptors on the bacterial surface. These receptors are varied and have other roles for the benefit of the bacterium. The phage injects its DNA through the bacterial cell wall. The bacterium loses its ability to either replicate or transcribe (or both) its own DNA. The phage DNA molecule is replicated usually by a phage-specific DNA polymerase encoded by phage genes. Other phage genes provide for the synthesis of protein components. The transcription of phage mRNA is usually initiated by bacterial RNA polymerase but thereafter either the bacterial enzyme is modified to recognize phage promoters or a phage-specific RNA polymerase is manufactured. New phage particles are assembled and are discharged as infective agents from the bacterium into the surrounding medium by the enzyme-catalysed (endolysin) lysis of the cell wall. A few filamentous phages including M13

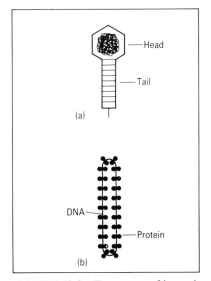

FIGURE 19.3 Two types of bacteriophage infecting *E. coli*. (a) Head-with-tail phages. (b) Filamentous phages

utilize the process of budding in which phage particles are released through swellings in the cell wall. Since major damage to the bacterium is avoided, filamentous phage particles can be produced and released over substantial periods of time.

The life cycle processes (Figure 19.4) may be rapid (of less than 20 min duration) in which case it is called a lytic cycle. The major characteristic of a lytic cycle is that phage DNA replication is sequentially followed by the synthesis of phage proteins and packaging. The phage DNA does not exist free for any length of time in the host cell. Alternatively, the phage DNA may be implanted into the host DNA (similar to episomal insertion) and may be retained through thousands of cell

divisions. However, the integrated form of the phage DNA called the prophage lies dormant until it is eventually released from the host genome. The phage DNA then directs the production of new phage particles which are released through cell lysis. This form of life cycle is described as a lysogenic infection cycle. The mechanism by which the lytic cycle or the lysogenic cycle is selected remains to be verified.

Of the many varieties of bacteriophage, only phage λ and filamentous M13 have been confirmed as major cloning vectors in *E. coli*. Phage λ has a 48.5 kb DNA molecule which has been sequenced and mapped so that the positions and functions of its genes are known. Related genes, e.g. those

FIGURE 19.4   Infection of a bacterium by a bacteriophage

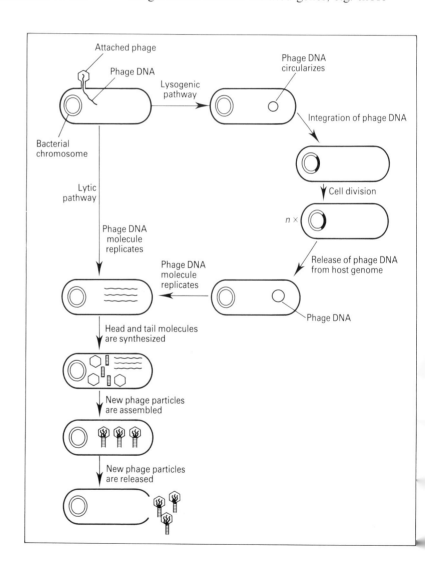

encoding capsid proteins or those governing integration into the host genome, are clustered so that each group may be regulated collectively. The λ DNA molecule is a double-stranded linear molecule conforming to the Watson–Crick model (Figure 7.4) with the exception of a 12-nucleotide single-stranded region at both ends. These complementary regions are called 'sticky' or cohesive ends because they may hydrogen-bond with one another to circularize into an entirely double-stranded molecule (Figure 19.4) or with the ends of two different DNA molecules. The λ DNA cohesive ends are called cos sites and provide a single-stranded region to which a foreign DNA fragment, produced by a restriction endonuclease, may attach to form a recombinant molecule. Cosmid vectors will be considered in Section 19.5.

Like all filamentous phages, M13 gains entry to the bacterium following binding to the tip of the pilus, a hairlike structure on the surface of F-plasmid-containing *E. coli*. M13 has a single-stranded genome of only 6.4 kb which severely limits its number of genes. This is possible because

(i) its capsid consists of only three proteins and (ii) the phage DNA remains separate from the bacterial chromosome thus gene products involved in insertion are not required. On entry of M13 DNA into the host cell, the single-stranded viral DNA acts as a template for the production of a complementary strand with which it hydrogen-bonds to form a double-stranded molecule. This replicative molecule remains separate from the host genome and produces over 100 copies of itself before cell division proceeds. Each resultant daughter cell receives some copies of the phage DNA which continue to replicate. For the production of new phage particles, linear single-stranded DNA molecules are manufactured from the double-stranded molecules. New viruses are periodically released through budding.

The small size of the M13 genome makes it convenient to use as a vector. The single-stranded cloned genes thereby obtained are ideal for DNA sequencing (Section 19.7) and certain other procedures.

19.4 Restriction endonucleases

The insertion of a foreign gene into the vector is achieved by the use of restriction endonucleases. These enzymes *in vivo* protect certain strains of microorganisms from bacteriophage infection by the destruction of foreign DNA molecules. Since this phenomenon is called host-controlled restriction, the enzymes are referred to as restriction endonucleases. Hundreds of restriction endonucleases have been purified from a wide variety of microorganisms. Since the destruction of bacterial DNA would be lethal, the corresponding sequences in the microbial genome are protected by the methylation of adenine or cytosine residues.

These enzymes have been classified into three types (Type I, Type II and Type III), according to differences in their modes of action. For example, Type I enzymes recognize a specific nucleotide sequence but cleave variable sequences over 1000 base-pairs from the recognition site. Type II enzymes have cleavage sites which are within or close to their recognition sites whereas the cleavage sites of Type III enzymes lie 24–26 base-pairs

downstream (towards the 3′-end) of their recognition sites. In addition to their nucleolytic cleavage, Type I and Type III endonucleases catalyse the methylation of DNA. Type II enzymes demonstrate only endonucleolytic cleavage; other enzymes which recognize the same sequences catalyse the methylation reactions. Restriction endonucleases are known by an acronym consisting of an abbreviation for the source organism and strain and a specific enzyme number in Roman numerals (Table 19.1).

Type II enzymes cleave their substrates in a very precise manner, a feature of major importance in gene cloning. These enzymes recognize specific short (four to six base-pairs long) palindromic sequences only in DNA and nick at least one strand. A palindrome is a word or sentence which reads alike backward and forward as exemplified in the British place-names of Glenelg and Notton. The cleavage sites are symmetrical and produce either linear (blunt-end) or staggered (cohesive-end) incisions. Since cohesive ends are valuable in the insertion of a foreign DNA through complementary hydrogen-bonding arrangements prior to ligation, blunt-end cleavages may have a single-stranded region introduced by several methods, e.g. the attachment of linkers, adaptors and homopolymer tails.

TABLE 19.1   Some examples of cleavage sites of Type II restriction endonucleases

Source	Enzyme	Recognition site
Haemophilus parainfluenzae	HpaI	5' G − T − T ↑ A − A − C 3' 3' C − A − A ↓ T − T − G 5'
Haemophilus aegyptius	HaeIII	5' G − G ↑ C − C 3' 3' C − C ↓ G − G 5'
Escherichia coli RY13	EcoRI	5' G ↑ A − A − T − T − C 3' 3' C − T − T − A − A ↓ G 5'
Nocardia corallina	NcoI	5' C ↑ C − A − T − G − G 3' 3' G − G − T − A − C ↓ C 5'

▶ indicates cleavage site.

19.5 The transport of recombinant DNA molecules into a host bacterium

The mode of entry of recombinant DNA molecules into the host cell is dependent upon the nature of the vector. The introduction of a DNA molecule into a bacterium or any other living cell is termed transformation. Certain species of bacteria, e.g. *Bacillus*, can easily acquire DNA molecules from a surrounding medium since they have developed pertinent mechanisms. However, most species, e.g. *E. coli*, can take up only small quantities of DNA. With plasmid vectors, a population of *E. coli* is bathed in cold calcium chloride (50 mmol dm^{-3}) solution containing the hybrid plasmid. This treatment enhances the DNA binding to the bacterial surface. Raising the temperature to 42°C expedites the transport of the DNA into the cell. Although this technique allows the incorporation of plasmids into the bacterium, the uptake is poor (maximum achievable uptake is approximately 1%).

Phage vectors may be introduced into a bacterial cell by two processes: transfection and packaging *in vitro*. The process of transfection is similar to transformation but the term is employed to signify the involvement of phage DNA. Transfection produces even poorer yields than plasmid transformation. The technique of packaging *in vitro* involves the preparation of two cultures of bacteria, each of which has been infected by a different defective λ strain. The strains are selected so that each carries a mutant gene for a different capsid protein. Infected bacteria synthesize and accumulate the other phage components but the lack of one protein prevents the assembly of phage particles. Upon mixing lysates from both bacterial cultures, all the necessary components are provided for the packaging of added recombinant DNA molecules into mature phage particles. These particles may infect a bacterial culture in the normal manner (Section 19.3).

Contrived vectors called cosmids which combine some of the advantages of plasmids and phages have been constructed. A cosmid is in essence a plasmid to which the *cos* sites of the phage λ genome (Section 19.3) are attached. These sites permit the introduction of plasmid DNA into a bacterium by the *in vitro* packaging technique as long as the *cos* sites are separated by 37–52 kb of DNA. Recombinant molecules constructed using cosmids may therefore be introduced into *E. coli* with higher efficiency. A major advantage of cosmids is their capacity for cloning DNA fragments which are too large for other vectors. The recombinant DNA fragment carried by a cosmid is selected by the techniques developed for plasmid vectors.

19.6 Selection of recombinant DNA

Low levels of DNA incorporation demand methods of detecting which bacterium contains foreign DNA. Also, since a variety of foreign DNA fragments, produced by the action of a restriction endonuclease, have been introduced into a culture of *E. coli* (Section 19.2), some bacteria will carry DNA fragments which do not contain the gene of interest and only a few bacteria will have the appropriate fragment. A number of methods of gene detection are available, e.g. vectorial marker, hybridization and immunological detection.

To identify bacteria which have taken up the vector, a common ploy is to utilize a characteristic of the vector, i.e. a vectorial marker. Plasmids possessing an antibiotic-resistance marker will enable a microorganism to grow in culture medium containing that antibiotic. Bacteria lacking the plasmid fail to develop colonies. For example, the plasmid pBR 322 contains antibiotic-resistance markers for tetracycline and ampicillin. Therefore, bacteria transformed by this plasmid are capable of colony formation in tetracycline- and/or ampicillin-containing medium and are easily selected.

Hybridization and immunological detection permit the identification of bacteria which carry the desired gene. The hybridization technique involves the growing of the organism on a plate of solid nutrient medium and the analysis of the DNA extracted from each resultant colony for the DNA of interest. The search is conducted through the ability of this DNA to hybridize with a complementary radioactive (^{32}P) probe. Commonly employed probes include single-stranded DNA synthesized from isolated mRNA by RNA-directed DNA polymerase (reverse transcriptase). To reduce the enormity of the task, bacterial colonies are replica-plated from the solid medium on to a filter paper which is then treated with NaOH to rupture the cells and denature the DNA. The paper is flooded with the radioactive probe and DNA–DNA hybridization occurs with a complementary sequence. Autoradiography, in which radioactive emissions blacken the emulsion of an exposed X-ray film, is employed to locate the desired colony (Figure 19.5).

Immunological methods may be employed to detect the products of the foreign gene. After transformation, growth and replica-plating, the

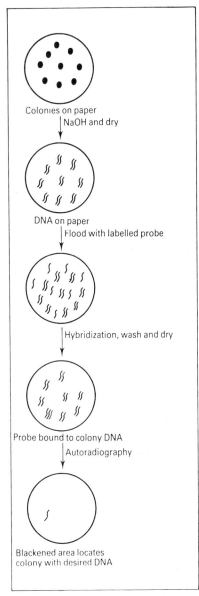

Colonies on paper
   NaOH and dry

DNA on paper
   Flood with labelled probe

   Hybridization, wash and dry

Probe bound to colony DNA
   Autoradiography

Blackened area locates
colony with desired DNA

FIGURE 19.5   Colony hybridization

replica colonies are lysed to release their protein contents on to a cellulose nitrate membrane pre-coated with a specific antibody (Section 4.7) which interacts with the protein. Other proteins do not bind specifically to the antibody. The membrane is washed to eliminate non-specific binding of proteins and flooded with ^{125}I-labelled specific antibody or fluorescein-labelled antibody. Following further washing, the desired colony is detected by autoradiography or immunofluorescence respectively.

Upon selection of the appropriate colony, large-scale cultivation of the microorganism increases enormously the number of recombinant DNA-containing cells which may be exploited for our benefit.

19.7 DNA-sequencing techniques

Gene cloning has made available sufficient quantities of genes to permit their primary structures to be determined. Before the advent of rapid techniques, sequence analysis was restricted to very short nucleotide sequences. Nowadays, DNA sequencing can be performed faster than protein sequencing (Section 4.4). Rapid DNA sequencing is frequently performed by either the dideoxy method of Sanger and Coulson or the Maxam–Gilbert method.

The dideoxy sequencing method utilizes *in vitro* the polymerase activity of *E. coli* DNA polymerase I contained within the Klenow fragment of the enzyme to synthesize a collection of radioactively

labelled fragments through the controlled inhibition of the replication process by the addition of dideoxyribonucleotides (containing 2,3-dideoxyribose) to the growing strand. Since a 3'-OH group is not available, the elongation process is halted (Figure 19.6). The template is a single-strand copy of the DNA to be sequenced to which a single-strand primer complementary to the preceding template bases is hybridized (Section 7.5). For each determination (Figure 19.7) four reaction mixtures are employed, each containing all four dNTPs one of which is labelled, e.g. dGTP, dCTP, dTTP, and [α-^{32}P]dATP plus one different dideoxyribonucleotide (ddNTP). In each reaction mixture, oligonuc-

FIGURE 19.6   Dideoxyribonucleotide-induced termination of DNA synthesis

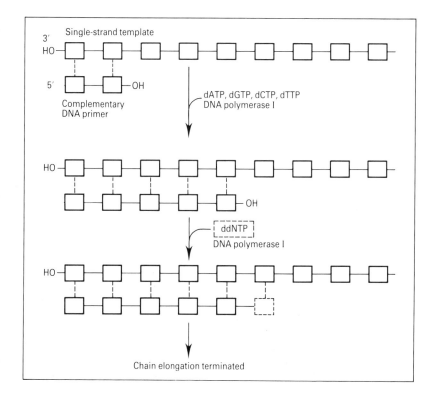

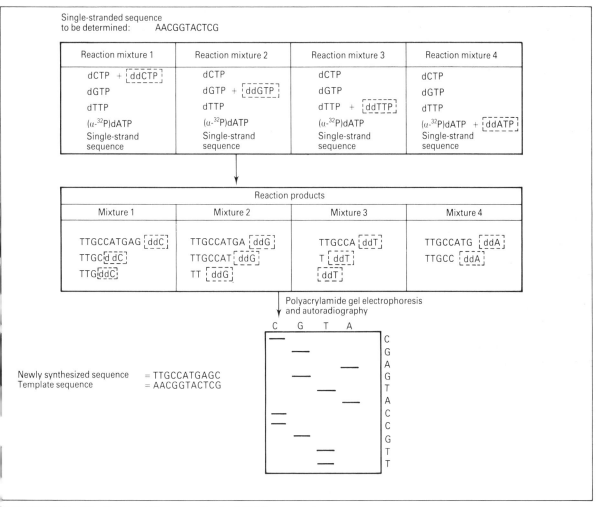

FIGURE 19.7   The Sanger dideoxy method of DNA sequencing

eotide chains of varying length but all terminated with the same base are generated. The chains may be separated according to size by polyacrylamide gel electrophoresis. Because a radioactively labelled dNTP was present in the four reaction mixtures, all oligonucleotide chains may be detected by autoradiography (Section 19.6). Since all four reaction mixtures are adjacently electrophoresed in the same gel, the DNA sequence can be read directly from the autoradiogram (X-ray film) starting at the fastest (smallest) fragment located nearest to the bottom of the film. A DNA segment containing 200 nucleotides may be sequenced in one experiment by this method.

The Maxam–Gilbert technique provides not only

an alternative to the dideoxy method but permits the sequencing of a double-stranded DNA and the identification of DNA–protein-binding sites. A specific segment of double-stranded DNA is selected by the use of an appropriate restriction endonuclease (Figure 19.8). This segment is labelled at both 5′-ends with ^{32}P using the enzyme, polynucleotide 5′-hydroxyl-kinase. A different restriction enzyme is used to divide the segment into two fragments. Each fragment is separately processed. The complementary strands are then separated. Each labelled single-strand fragment is treated with a specific chemical reagent which reacts with one (sometimes two) of the four bases, e.g. guanosine is methylated at the N-7 position by

FIGURE 19.8 The Maxam–Gilbert method of DNA sequencing

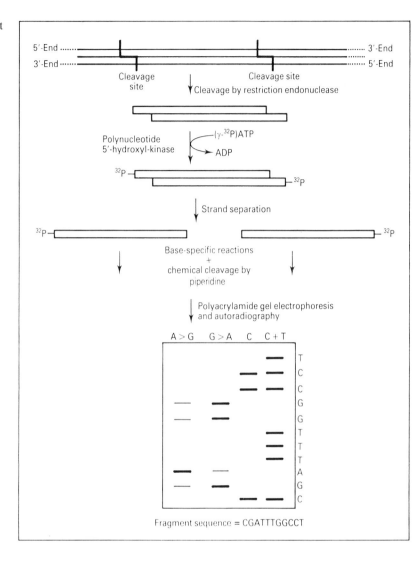

dimethyl sulphate. The modified base renders the fragment susceptible to subsequent chemical cleavage. Piperidine at 90°C breaks firstly the glycosidic linkage between the modified base and the deoxyribose and secondly the sugar–phosphate backbone at the former position of the removed base. A pertinent reaction time permits the modification of one randomly located base per DNA molecule. A series of radioactive fragments are produced which extend from the ^{32}P-labelled end to the position of a modified base. Four specific chemical reactions allow the cleavage by piperidine preferentially at guanines (G > A), or at adenine (A > G) depending upon precise conditions, at

cytosine alone (C) and equally at cytosine and thymine (C + T). By performing polyacrylamide gel electrophoresis and autoradiography as per the dideoxy method, the sequence of the DNA can be deduced from the pattern of bands on the autoradiogram. Protein-binding sites may be located through the masking of base-modification reactions by DNA-bound protein.

Rapid DNA-sequencing techniques have been applied to the sequencing of RNA molecules. Through the employment of the retroviral enzyme, RNA-directed DNA polymerase, RNA may serve as a template for the synthesis of a complementary DNA (cDNA) copy which may then be sequenced.

The derived sequence may be interpreted in terms of the sequence of the original RNA molecule.

DNA-sequencing techniques have advanced our knowledge of the storage and expression of genetic information through the discoveries that eukaryotic DNA contains introns (Section 17.3), that the genetic code is quasi-universal (Section 17.5), that different codons for the same amino acid are used preferentially, that functionally related genes are often physically located in the same region of the chromosome, that viral genes may be translated in different-reading frames to produce different proteins and that transcriptional promoters contain a consensus sequence (Section 17.1).

Suggested further reading

BROWN, T. A. (1987) *Gene Cloning: An Introduction*, Van Nostrand Reinhold, Wokingham

GLOVER, D. M. (1984) *Gene Cloning: The Mechanics of DNA Manipulation*, Chapman and Hall, London

Index